# UNDERSTANDING
# SUSTAINABLE CITIES
## Concepts, Cases, and Solutions

K. David Pijawka

Martin A. Gromulat

**Kendall Hunt**
publishing company

Cover image created by authors.

**Kendall Hunt**
publishing company

www.kendallhunt.com
*Send all inquiries to*:
4050 Westmark Drive
Dubuque, IA 52004-1840

ISBN 978-1-4652-0344-1

Printed in the United States of America
10  9  8  7  6  5  4  3  2

# TABLE OF CONTENTS

# FOREWORD

We find ourselves at a crossroads where our conceptions of individual freedoms and the political and economic systems derived from the framers of the Constitution of the United States collide with the natural systems of the Earth, to the ruinous long-term detriment of us all. Neither political nor economic models have ever factored in the natural limits of the planet, and that seminal document outlines neither aspirations nor objectives relative to our relationship with the natural world. Our political and economic designs are at once too limited and too simplistic to address the complex issues intrinsic to the emerging discourse of sustainability—challenges such as intergenerational equity, adaptive management, industrial ecology, and natural capital conservation, which offer new principles for organizing knowledge production and application. These inherent limitations are a consequence of not only the relative immaturity of our conceptual tools but also, and more fundamentally, the implicit "aspiration of self" that the Constitution endorses. As a consequence, the individual perspective has inevitably outweighed the collective, with the result that adequate protection for the collective has lost out.

As dynamic, hardworking, and productive as our society has been from the outset, one would expect our nation to have exerted an impact on the environment. Yet in only 250 years we have contributed significantly to an alteration of the natural patterns of the atmosphere and both land and ocean ecosystems to the extent that future natural capital assets for our long-term wellbeing are actually at risk. While we have pursued our aspirations, roughly 20 percent of the planet's bird species have been driven into extinction, 50 percent of all freshwater runoff has come to be consumed, seventy thousand synthetic chemicals have been introduced into the environment, the sediment load of rivers has increased fivefold, and more than two-thirds of the major marine fisheries on the planet have been fully exploited or depleted. Through our pursuits we have in effect eliminated the fishing stock of the oceans for generations, altered the atmosphere of the planet, and condemned future generations to the impact of human induced sea-level rise.

Building the capacity of our colleges and universities to respond to the challenges of sustainable development requires that we rethink these institutions and recalibrate their structures and practices. As president of Arizona State University (ASU), I have led an effort to reconceptualize the youngest of the roughly one hundred major research institutions in the United States through a comprehensive "design process." This reconceptualization represents an effort to pioneer the foundational model for what we term the "New American University"—an egalitarian institution committed to academic excellence, inclusiveness to a broad demographic, and maximum societal impact. Sustainability is at the core of this conception, not simply because interdisciplinary research on human-dominated environmental systems has long been one of the strengths of the university, but because we have explicitly deemed it an institutional commitment.

With the establishment of the Global Institute of Sustainability (GIOS) in 2004 and the first-of-its-kind School of Sustainability three years later, ASU has positioned itself in the vanguard of interdisciplinary research on environmental, economic, and social sustainability. The institute brings scientists and engineers together with government policymakers and industry leaders to share knowledge and develop solutions to pressing real-world problems. With research in areas as diverse as agriculture, air quality, marine ecology, materials design, nanotechnology, policy and governance, renewable energy, risk assessment, transportation, and urban infrastructure, faculty members affiliated with GIOS are addressing some of the most critical challenges of our time, as well as training future generations of scientists, policymakers, and practitioners.

ASU is educating a new generation of leaders through collaborative, transdisciplinary, and problem-oriented training that addresses environmental, economic, and social challenges. Teaching and research seek adaptive solutions to such issues as rapid urbanization; water quality; habitat transformation; the loss of biodiversity; and the development of sustainable energy, materials, and technologies. A further objective is to engage the community in supporting sustainability initiatives, including widespread reductions in greenhouse gas emissions.

Along with guiding principles of modern societies such as human rights, sustainability is an epochal issue that must be addressed by the citizens of a planet whose population already exceeds 6 billion and that is projected to approach 10 billion. Organizing research and teaching efforts to seek solutions to the grand challenges associated with sustainability represents an important dimension of such an imperative. Through research and teaching associated with sustainability, ASU has sought to design a prototype both for deliberate institutional evolution and large-scale academic reorganization to tackle some of the most intractable challenges of our era.

From the outset of the American republic, the thoughtless and unmitigated exploitation of natural resources has contributed to a way of life that we have come to realize is unsustainable. Only recently have we begun to rethink and revise our flawed model. Fifty years ago, Rachel Carson's *Silent Spring* helped set the stage for the environmental movement. She alerted us to the fact that through the use of synthetic chemicals we had altered and contaminated our food supply and ecosystems, though what she articulated was a type of self-defeating decision-making. The same lack of foresight that led to the degradation of the environment is reflected in the design and structure of our cities. Much of our designed world is not only unsustainable, but is actually inimical to our long-term interests.

In an effort to redeem ourselves, however belatedly, let us at last add one more value to the conception of the self as formulated by the Constitution. To provide for the common good, we cannot consider justice only for those of us present; we must also conceptualize and enact into law provisions for justice for future generations. To ensure the equitable pursuit of happiness we cannot look only at the decades immediately ahead of or behind us; individually, we must come to terms with the realization that decisions made during the past 250 years have put humanity during the next several thousand years at potential risk. In the twenty-first century, we must at last declare sustainability a core aspirational value of the American people, on the same level as liberty, justice, and equality.

Today's college students comprise the first generation that perceives sustainability as a core value and regards nature as our guide. We are entering a new epoch in which we are capable of conceptualizing, building, and advancing sustainable cities designed to be adaptive, resilient, and able to take advantage of the benefits of the environment. Better integrating the built environment with natural systems will enable us as a society to get on a sustainable path. This book, and the class that it is based on, strives to give students and others the necessary information to help lead us into a sustainable future.

*Michael M. Crow, president of Arizona State University*

# ACKNOWLEDGMENTS

Understanding Sustainable Cities: Concepts, Cases, and Solutions developed out of an undergraduate course at Arizona State University (ASU), *Sustainable Cities*, which has been delivered every semester for the past six years. Over time, the course changed to reflect the rapid evolution of sustainability ideas in academia, global policies (mostly from the United Nations), urban based practices, and the growth of a new field of study—sustainability education. In 2004, ASU and its President Michael Crow established the Global Institute of Sustainability (GIOS) as a means of achieving the university's vision for sustainability. Dr. Crow—who was deeply committed to sustainability long before the concept became ubiquitous—worked with a group of world-renowned advisors to design a structure for the Institute that makes it the hub and agent for ASU's comprehensive sustainability effort. GIOS spans and supports all colleges and units at ASU (including the authors' department, the School of Geographical Sciences and Urban Planning) to infuse sustainability across the university's curriculum, research, and campus operations. Going beyond the campus, it also imparts its knowledge and practices to local, national, and global agencies, policymakers, and business leaders. Thanks to Dr. Crow's vision, determination for innovation, and commitment to interdisciplinary education, GIOS has become a place for students and faculty to communicate, to exchange views with the top world thinkers on sustainability, and to engage various policy organizations across the country. President Crow deserves many thanks for establishing such an open, engaging, and creative place in which the *Sustainable Cities* course was launched and flourished.

We also thank President Crow for writing the Foreword. The book contains several chapters authored by faculty who are nationally recognized experts in various fields of sustainability and have given presentations in the *Sustainable Cities* course over the years. Before writing their chapters, the contributors' presentations were each discussed with them, as were the content, tone, and cases they planned to write about, so as to deliver a thorough piece written for undergraduate and graduate students to understand the specific topic, see the importance of sustainability connections, and contemplate real-world solutions. We thank each of the contributors for their chapters and thoughtful consideration of the educational role of their pieces: Rimjhim Aggarwal, Anthony J. Brazel, Winston T. L. Chow, Edward (Ted) Cook, Aaron Golub, Subhrajit Guhathakurta, Bjoern Hagen, John C. Meunier, Charles L. Redman, Darren M. Ruddell, Carissa Taylor, and Ray Quay. Additional thanks to Bjoern Hagen who helped develop the Timeline and also developed the case study of Freiburg, Germany. We discussed the book with Christopher Boone, Judith Dworkin, Subhro Guhathakurta, James Buizer, Luc Anselin, and Kevin McHugh, who gave us excellent advice. Years back, when Bob Kates, Presidential Professor of Sustainability Science at the University of Maine, visited ASU as an advisor to GIOS, he mentioned the importance of a textbook on sustainability based on classroom experience and we took his advice. Trained as a geographer, Dr. Kates has led interdisciplinary programs addressing hazards, climate, and adaptation, and has been an influential force in the development of sustainability and continues to be a mentor and friend to one of the coauthors. Also, much thanks to Professor Chris Boone for reviewing the History of Sustainability Chapter and providing insightful comments on interpreting sustainability history. Deborah Koshinsky also helped edit several chapters and provided valuable advice. Special thanks to ASU Clinical Professor of Law Susan M. Chesler who not only edited several chapters, but also added important detail and clarity to the contents, thus enhancing the book's richness. We owe a great debt to Kendall Hunt's National Acquisition Editor, Angela Lampe and her team. Angela helped with the design layout, and worked with the chapter contributors and with us on every aspect of structure and images. She saw the importance of sustainability in higher education and was committed to seeing this book realized. Finally, we would like to thank Ceirra Smith, an ASU undergraduate student studying English Literature, who helped out with the references.

*K. David Pijawka and Martin A. Gromulat*

# INTRODUCTION

This book is a direct byproduct of an undergraduate course given every fall, spring, and summer at Arizona State University. The course, *Sustainable Cities*, is the basis for this book and its coverage of urban sustainability. I developed and first delivered the course in 2006 at the university in conjunction with the opening of its School of Sustainability, which offers five degrees in sustainability. This broad-based and transdisciplinary course likely has the largest enrollment of any sustainability course, with an approximate annual enrollment of 1,000 students, and I have taught it every year since its inception.

The text contains the following chapters: An Introduction to Sustainability Concepts and Principles; History of Sustainability; Earliest Urbanism; Environmental and Social Justice; Managing Water Resources: The Central Issue for Sustaining Life; Making Desert Cities Sustainable; Sustainable Transportation; Coping with Global Climate Change; The Urban Heat Island Effect and Sustainability Science: Causes, Impacts, and Solutions; Sustainable Agricultural Systems for Cities; Urban Ecology and Green Networks; Examining Sustainability through Urban Models; and, finally, Course Assignments: Learning Outcomes in Sustainability Education. As a result, it provides students with a plethora of subject matters in urban sustainability. In similar fashion as the course itself, this book also provides both the instructor and students with in-depth knowledge about crosscutting issues, concepts, and solutions inherent in modern sustainability thinking. But, just as importantly, it illustrates how cities can and have applied these concepts into their programs, policies, and urban planning and design. Such concepts include the Ecological Footprint, modeling urban sustainability, sustainability indicators, urban adaptation, climate action planning, resiliency building, remaking suburbia, urban ecological planning, and collaborative visioning processes for sustainable urban futures.

Like the course, the book is not directed at any specific technical field or audience, such as engineering or biology, although students from these fields often take the course. It is interdisciplinary and broad-based, reflective of "sustainability science" itself:

> Meeting fundamental human needs while preserving the life support systems of planet Earth will require a world-wide acceleration of today's halting progress in a transition toward sustainability. A significant response to this challenge from the scientific community has begun to emerge from various global and regional programs of environmental research.[1]

That was written 10 years ago; we have a lot of catching up to do. This book is aimed at furthering that discussion and meeting the challenges of a transition toward sustainability, to meet the needs of future generations and our environment.

This book also discusses values and ethics (philosophy), perceptions and behavior (social sciences), green infrastructure (urban ecology and green networks), restoration of cities and place-making (urban planning), green design (urban design and architecture), urban policies and programs (public policy and public administration), and learning from the earliest cities (anthropology and archeology).

Students taking the *Sustainable Cities* course tend to be eclectic; they are generally either looking for a general course in sustainability or needing to meet a sustainability course requirement from various programs. Moreover, the course is a core requirement for several majors, including planning, sustainability science, and business. The textbook also considered the fact that students may need to take a *Sustainable Cities*-type course to satisfy a university's general education requirements. As such, this textbook was designed with a sustainability framework and sensibility in mind to deliver basic educational goals in these broader areas. Accordingly, this book is geared toward undergraduate or graduate students, specifically students who require or seek a foundational, introductory course in sustainability or urban sustainability; it's also geared toward those students in programs requiring an interdisciplinary, broad–based learning experience that provides and explains sustainability concepts, cases, and solutions, and also explores what cities have done and are doing in terms of developing sustainability solutions to pressing urban problems.

Additionally, the book can be used as a supplement in other environmental, sustainability, geology, anthropology, and social sciences classes in which the professor wishes to cover selected issues in sustainable cities or sustainability. Because the text was written, to the extent possible, in accessible plain language, the book also can serve as a reference for practitioners, policymakers, researchers, and engaged citizens who are interested in urban sustainability and wish to learn more about how best to make our cities sustainable.

Why a course and a book on sustainable cities? In great part, it is because, for the first time in history, the majority of the world's population resides in cities, and it is estimated that by 2030, the number of urban dwellers will reach 60 percent of the world's population. Cities are now responsible for consuming 75 percent of the world's energy and emitting 80 percent of the world's greenhouse gases. Cities are rapidly growing globally at an average of 2 percent per year. We are fast approaching the point where the majority of the population will be living in urban areas. The projection is that in approximately 50 years' time, two-thirds of the world's population will live in cities.

As a result, climate and other changes will have the greatest effect on people living in cities. It is clear that this generation of students, the first who are directly studying the concepts of sustainability, will unfortunately inherit and be responsible for solving our unsustainability binge, and for fixing our planet. Accordingly, a comprehensive text on sustainable cities is needed now more than ever.

This text is unlike other sustainability books, which are typically edited volumes of various sustainability topics where authors were invited to address a specific research topic that fits into a larger theme, or an assembly of previously written papers that ostensibly fall within a sustainability-based theme. Based on the interdisciplinary nature of the *Sustainable Cities* course, contributors to the text are primarily faculty from different disciplines throughout the university who have a recognized expertise in an area of sustainability. They were first invited to develop and provide a lecture on their area of specialty for the course. The nature and goal of each of their lectures was not only to teach the fundamentals of that particular area without being overly research orientated, but also to be consistent with the goals of sustainable education and learning outcomes, integrate that particular lecture's content with the other material covered in the course, and provide important examples of real-world solutions to urban problems.

The *Sustainable Cities* course, and the accompanying text that grew out of the class, is specifically designed to provide students with a comprehensive introduction to the concepts surrounding urban sustainability, whether or not they have prior background in this field. We have included the following sections in each topical chapter in an effort to help guide the reader along and stimulate critical thinking: *Why this Chapter Is Important for Understanding Sustainability*, the definitions of *Key Concepts and Terms, Lessons Learned for Achieving Sustainability, Supplemental Readings*, and *Discussion Questions*. The book is designed for use in a single semester course, and each of the 13 chapters, 14 if you include this "chapter," which we suggest that you have your students read, roughly corresponds to one week's worth of reading and course coverage.

Like any other casebook of its kind, this book does not address all of the possible sustainability examples and solutions. There is much more information available regarding all of the topics discussed herein that can readily be found in our supplemental reading suggestions or with a quick Internet search. A primary goal of this book is to examine the concepts and complexities presented by sustainability, while exploring the potential that exists for solutions within the current system to advance sustainable cities forward.

The textbook covers the basic sectors and elements of cities such as transportation, the built environment, and water systems, from the perspective of urban structure, processes, and form. It does this dynamically by using a twofold approach: first, each topic is examined from an historical approach, and second, it is discussed through an exploration of the need for sustainability solutions for each sector. Once these sections are covered in their respective chapters, the chapter provides illustrations of how the sustainability programs, plans, and projects were implemented in various cities. Therefore, each of the topical chapters addresses the subtitle of the book—concepts, cases, and solutions. For example, the built environment consists of various building sectors such as housing, industrial buildings, and commercial property. The "structure" refers to how these are allocated over city space, where they are located, their age, and conditions, while "form" refers to such factors as density, distances from a central business district, if applicable, and spatial relationships to each other and other land uses. Each of these factors has an impact on measures of urban sustainability. For instance, a large, regional shopping center at the periphery of a city would likely result in large-scale automobile traffic between places of residences and the shopping center, decreasing air quality and increasing carbon dioxide emissions. This, coupled with the likely use of large quantities of asphalt to build the necessary parking structures for the new shopping center, and a lack of shade structures, increases surrounding temperatures and, because of the "urban heat island" effect, ultimately results in an indirect increase in water usage, among other negative environmental consequences (see Chapter 9). Additionally, these "islands" negatively affect communities by also increasing energy demand, air conditioning costs, greenhouse gas emissions and resultant air pollution, and heat-related illness and death.

Our textbook treats the topic of sustainable cities from the following educational perspectives:

- Urban subject matter is covered in all of the chapters; additionally, each chapter provides information, insight, and perspective, thereby imparting knowledge regarding how best to transform conventional cities into sustainable cities.

- Furthermore, the topical chapters discuss the underlying concepts and goals of sustainability for that subject, provide cases and illustrations of their applications, and demonstrate what can be achieved by employing sustainable solutions to transform present-day cities into truly sustainable ones.

- The topical chapters are "specialized" in the sense that they deal with a particular sustainability issue, and they are also broad-based because they cover three important sustainability learning outcomes: an education in transdisciplinary thinking; an understanding of the connections between theory, concept, and real-world applications; and, an understanding of how to appreciate the differing impacts suffered by conventional cities versus sustainable ones.

The three chapters that are not specifically singular elements of cities include chapters on "An Introduction to Sustainability Concepts and Principles," "History of Sustainability," and "Course Assignments: Learning Outcomes in Sustainability Education." These chapters are unique to an urban sustainability textbook and will assist the student and instructor alike in facilitating an understanding of the foundational ideas of sustainability, and their connections to cities. For example, the chapter "An Introduction to Sustainability Concepts and Principles" includes discussions on the definitional issues of sustainability, sustainability science, sustainable development, and the three pillars or E's of sustainability: social equity, environmental protection, and economic development. We propose a fourth E, education, and are hopeful that this text helps further that objective. This chapter also explores important sustainability principles, an exploration of ethics and values, sustainable design principles and indicators, and place making.

Chapter 2, the "History of Sustainability," is a provocative look back at the "recent" history of sustainability beginning in 1898 with the release of Ebenezer Howard's utopian eco-city book, *Garden Cities of To-morrow,* right up until the present day as sustainability-minded cities prepare climate action plans in an effort to reduce "rarely" experienced weather phenomena we currently witness, which scientists believe are exacerbated because of global climate change. To name just two that have far-reaching effects, first, there is Colorado's biggest wildfire in the state's history that destroyed hundreds of homes and forced the evacuation of at least 35,000 residents in and around the state's second-largest city; and, second, the increased frequency and number of "Excessive Heat Warnings" issued by the National Weather Service because of an early-summer 2012 heat wave that is wreaking havoc across a large swath of the country and that brought with it several all-time record highs, including 109 degrees at both Nashville, Tennessee and Columbia, South Carolina, while Fort Wayne, Indiana tied its all-time record high from 1988 and the "Dust Bowl" years of 1934 and 1936!

Our "History" chapter is unlike typical history write-ups of what happened when, because accompanying the chapter is a detailed timeline separated out from the text that contains the description and significance of major events and natural disasters; legislation; books and reports; and movements and responses. This historical approach is foundational for sustainability education. The underlying intellectual currents that presently influence public concern and legislative action demonstrate the compelling connections between global concerns and local efficacy and action, and help us separate out the principal factors influencing the somewhat complex history of sustainability since before even the 1987 Brundtland definition gave meaning to the term.

Additionally, our "Course Assignments" chapter provides a brief, but important segment on learning outcomes in sustainability education and includes eight thought-provoking assignments that challenge students to think critically about current pressing issues in sustainability. Each assignment contains a discussion regarding the learning outcomes and objectives in the context of sustainability education. The assignments correspond to specific chapters in the book as an added educational value. For example, Chapter 1 covers the Ecological Footprint concept, which measures humanity's demand on nature by calculating the amount of land required for a particular level of natural capital consumption plus the assimilation of pollutants and waste. In the corresponding assignment (Number 4: The Ecological Footprint), students are asked to develop their own footprint, analyze its implications, and evaluate what they could do to lower their impact. The goal is for students to understand the consequences of the over-consumption of resources to meet society's "needs," and the corresponding reality of our behavior in relation to the earth's resources and resulting global biocapacity deficit. In terms of educational outcomes, knowledge about larger sustainability issues is gained by starting from a personal, value-based level. The material on sustainability competencies calls for ethics based evaluation and critical thinking about changes in behavior, both at the individual and societal levels. To achieve these competencies, the footprint assignment exposes students to the reality of our individual consumption behaviors and resultant costs to the planet. Additionally, we have found that the assignment has inspired students to think about individual ethics, especially when they begin to recognize the importance of their own consumption in local to global transformations, particularly in terms of the volume of waste products, life cycle cost, carbon dioxide emissions, and possible injustice issues. According to end-of-the-semester surveys, students were highly motivated by this assignment with over 80 percent indicating that it resulted in personal behavioral changes.

Lastly, we have paid close attention to the scholarship in sustainability education, the necessary learning outcomes, as well as what a broad-based undergraduate or graduate course in sustainability should cover. As a result, the text evolved, took shape, and is informed by several publications and presentations on the specifics of what students require in an introductory sustainability course and, accordingly, that information is reflected in this textbook. These important learning outcomes include:

- *Interdisciplinarity.* By definition, sustainability is interdisciplinary and requires that the substance and science of numerous disciplines converge to better understand the complex nature of modern urban sustainability problems and to achieve successful and forward-thinking outcomes and solutions. The textbook does this in a number of ways: first, we endeavored to ensure that no one dominant discipline or science is the focus or is overly emphasized; as such, it is not a textbook on economic sustainability, although economic issues and development weave their way throughout nearly every chapter. The textbook does not specifically focus on physical, ecological, and natural sciences as a text in sustainable or environmental science might. Rather, physical, ecological, and natural sciences are brought into the readings to help explain such topics as global climate change, urban heat islands, socio-ecological systems and their vulnerabilities, and to show how adaptation and mitigation strategies can successfully work and reduce adverse impacts. The content of the chapters intentionally embrace a holistic perspective, and the reader will learn that the solutions to our urban problems are both multifaceted and require transformative learning and interdisciplinary approaches.

- *Developing a New Vocabulary.* The textbook strives to impart an understanding of basic sustainability concepts and principles so that the reader gains an appreciation for comprehending and effectively communicating this new vocabulary, as well as insight into methods and programs used by cities in confronting their challenges. Some key terms that students will become familiar with include: Ecological Footprint; megacities; food miles; life cycle assessments; LEED-ND (Leadership in Energy and Environmental Design for Neighborhood Development) rating systems; ecosystem assets, adaptation responses, scenario-based planning, overshoot, natural capital, collaborative efficacy, urban density, greenhouse gas, and more! To this end, each topical chapter identifies key concepts and knowledge terms at the start of the chapter and defines the terms in the margins where they first appear. We anticipate that this structure will facilitate students' familiarity with the vocabulary of sustainability.

- *Connecting Theory to the Real World.* Our aim is to provide students with a better understanding of the connections between theory and applications, to become immersed in urban communities to glimpse their places, people, cultures, and problems, and to discern the positive impacts that sustainable actions and programs achieve and how best to measure those changes. The textbook directly makes these connections, and the chapters demonstrate how sustainability solutions and policies are working successfully by way of case studies and illustrations, both domestic and international. Additionally, we seek to inspire and foster the necessary critical thinking that present-day sustainability issues demand.

- *Connecting Sustainability Science to Urban Solutions.* As discussed above, the textbook utilizes a sustainable science framework that examines the scientific causes of urban problems such as global climate change, healthcare, urban heat island effects, and disturbed hydrological cycles and depleting groundwater supplies, among others. In addition to providing a scientific context to understand the problems and possible solutions, there is also an emphasis on how to tackle multifaceted solutions. For example, we explore some of the various ways that cities are confronting global climate change at the local level, through various adaptation and mitigation efforts, as well as how resiliency thinking can be applied to restructure and strengthen cities, especially those located in hazardous locales. For the first time, in Chapter 12, the textbook illustrates how to use urban simulation modeling for examining possible sustainable futures. Many chapters discuss the connections inherent between urban problems and the necessary capacity to enable sound decision-making in situations fraught with high levels of uncertainty—an emerging area in sustainability.

- ***The Role of Values and Ethics.*** Sustainability education literature emphasizes the importance of including ethics and values in sustainability courses, and yet it is a competency area that is often ignored. In this book, the importance of values and ethics are interwoven throughout the chapters, and are discussed within numerous contexts such as the Ecological Footprint, environmental justice, and the history of environmental catastrophes.

Sustainability has now become a concern of virtually every sector of human society. It provides a framework and a positive vision for the future of our families, cities, and global community in conjunction with preserving our fragile, and ever-diminishing, natural resources.

I am thankful to my coauthor, colleague, and friend, Marty Gromulat, without whose assistance this text may not have become a reality.

*K. David Pijawka*

# An Introduction to Sustainability Concepts and Principles

*K. David Pijawka*
*Martin A. Gromulat*

## ▰▰ WHY THIS CHAPTER IS IMPORTANT FOR UNDERSTANDING SUSTAINABILITY

Some of the salient concepts in urban sustainability are identified and discussed in this introductory chapter, although the ideas of sustainability are woven throughout all of the chapters in this text-book. For example, the idea of "adaptation" is found in Chapter 8, and the need for "anticipatory governance" is found in Chapter 5. This chapter first argues that it is at the city level that sustainability solutions have to be found and that the international conferences hosted by the United Nations (UN) over the last 20 years have moved stridently and quickly toward sustainability actions for cities (see Chapter 2). While climate change models and their physical attributes are mostly discussed at the global level of consideration, it is within cities that climate action planning is prevalently taking hold and that "adaptation" strategies are being developed and implemented. Moreover, this chapter argues that it is due to the changing nature of cities that sustainable solutions and action are urgent given that urban problems are compelling, large scale, and likely to worsen over time.

According to the UN, the world's population reached six billion at the end of 1999. In just 12 years, the global population reached seven billion in October 2011. Between 2011 and 2050, the world population is expected to increase to 9.3 billion. The urban areas of the world are projected to absorb all the population growth over the next four decades—while at the same time drawing in some of the rural population. By 2050, the urban population is expected to account for 86 percent of the population in the more developed regions and 64 percent of that in the less developed regions. Overall, the world population is expected to be 67 percent urban in 2050. Accordingly, it is now more important than ever to incorporate sustainable planning for urban development as a modality for addressing the inadequate infrastructure and negative environmental impacts that are pervasive in urban areas. How to remake cities, build new ones, and apply sustainability concepts are approaches that comprise the heart of this book, and the present chapter introduces the rationale for this thinking.

Additionally, the chapter examines the definitions of sustainability, and specifically the background, meaning, and applications of the Brundtland Commission's definition of sustainability and how it can be applied to "sustainable community development." Each of the three domains of sustainability—economic development, equity or social capital, and the environment, are discussed in terms of their meaning and applications. Equity is discussed in Chapter 4; sustainability indicators, and the need for visioning, collaboration, and participatory approaches to decision-making and sustainable community development are discussed in this chapter. The "Ecological Footprint" is an important metric, now extensively used to demonstrate the comparison between consumer demand on natural resources and the carrying capacity of these resources and is discussed later in this chapter. The Ecological Footprint is a very useful tool at all levels—the individual, city, and national levels. This chapter introduces some basic concepts on how to reduce the Ecological Footprint, the related roles of life cycle cost accounting, and the importance of producing and purchasing goods locally. These concepts and principles, while introduced in this chapter, are also developed in individual chapters and woven throughout the book.

As a textbook on sustainable cities, the overarching question concerns: What do, and what should, sustainable cities look like? Therefore, this chapter introduces and discusses the various ideas of what many describe as an eco-city—Freiburg, Germany. We present Freiburg as a case study at the beginning of the book because it shows how sustainability elements and principles can come together in one city and can be applied elsewhere. The concepts and principles inherent in this sustainable city are then discussed and explained.

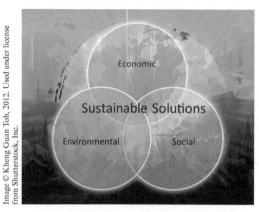

**The three pillars of sustainability: Environmental, Social, and Economic.**

# Changes to Cities and the Need for Sustainability

Despite the long history of environmental deterioration and debates over the most appropriate and effective approaches to prevent and ameliorate environmental problems, much of the focus on the problems themselves and their solutions has been in the context of cities. This is not said to overlook the importance of the world's loss of wetlands, natural flowing rivers, groundwater supplies, viability of marine life, and the world's replacement of large forested regions for agriculture. Moreover, one of the major debates of the last two decades has been related to a global level concern—to lower the amount of greenhouse gas (GHG) emissions in the atmosphere in order to abate catastrophic climate change. In fact, the main objective of the international Kyoto Protocol (adopted in December 1997 and entered into force in February 2005) was to decrease levels of carbon dioxide emissions by advanced industrial countries by approximately 5.2 percent annually to reach a global goal of below 1990 levels by 2012. In terms of sustainability, much of the discussion and recent developments of environmental degradation have centered on the problems and their sustainable solutions at the urban level. For example, it is now widely recognized that the impacts of global climate change, while occurring at regional levels, will be observable especially at urban levels. It is at the local level that we see the development of "adaptation" policies to prepare cities for threatening future events. Moreover, recent reports have examined how cities have begun to initiate climate action plans (see Chapter 8). More than 200 U.S. cities are also developing sustainability plans to help reduce carbon emissions and increase water efficiency.

This book argues that global problems, for which sustainable development is imperative, have as their bases the serious environmental and social conditions that must be resolved at the urban level (see the discussion of "Agenda 21" in Chapter 2). As singular entities, cities contribute substantially and exceedingly to the declining condition of global natural assets and ecosystems. Based on the concept of the Ecological Footprint, we now appreciate the fact that the total consumption needs of a city (in terms of fuel, foodstuffs, ores, water, clothes, and waste disposal) far exceed the land area of the city itself. In the early history of environmentalism, as discussed in Chapter 2, the first eco-city vision developed by Ebenezer Howard in 1898 was formulated in reaction to the severe congestion, pollution, overcrowding, and deteriorating health problems of an industrializing London, England. Howard's "Garden City" consisted of roughly 30,000 people living on 1,000 acres surrounded by greenbelts. Surprisingly, the plan (as conceived by Howard) contained many of the elements identified for a green city today: small human scale, open space in gardens and urban agriculture, employment based on local production, livable communities, and public transportation. The environmental and social problems in cities were viewed by early twentieth century transcendental writers like Ralph Waldo Emerson and Henry David Thoreau as anti-nature and devoid of spiritualism. One task incumbent upon urban sustainability today is to reintroduce indigenous nature back into cities a concept known as "biophilia," through the inclusion of wildlife corridors, reintroduction and restoration of indigenous vegetative species, enhancement of biodiversity and protection of fragile urban ecosystems, reestablishment of natural infrastructure systems, preservation of natural areas within cities, and restoration of regional green networks (see Chapter 11).

The global-to-local and local-to-global pathways are important concepts in urban sustainability. While climate change may already be impacting cities through greater frequency of flooding and long-term drought conditions, it is the extensive use of fossil fuels for automobiles and heating and cooling of a multitude of buildings that result in the most significant emissions of carbon dioxide that ultimately affects the global climate. Therefore, policies and plans related to reducing emissions of carbon dioxide in cities are essential; these policies are of two kinds (see Chapter 8). Notably, there are "mitigation" strategies or policies aimed at reducing carbon dioxide emissions through the use of alternative renewable energy technologies, such as solar power and wind power, and other sources. For example, several states are coordinating with utility providers to reach renewable energy benchmarks as part of the fuel mix. Second, there are "adaptation" strategies that are targeted at reducing the level of vulnerability to threats from natural hazards due to climate change impacts. The World Health Organization noted in 2008 that because over 50 percent of the world's population now lives in cities, it is expected that 75 percent of the world's energy is consumed in urban areas and cities are responsible for up to 80 percent of the GHG emissions. Therefore, much of the focus on sustainability and its solutions must be centered on cities.

Cities themselves are changing very rapidly and impacting global environmental conditions, but cities are also in desperate need of attention and sustainable development because urban conditions are generally worsening. Notably, the world is urbanizing very rapidly. In 1950, just over 60 years ago, less than 30 percent of the global population resided in cities. By 2000, it was estimated to be at 47 percent, and by 2008, a milestone was reached with over 50 percent of the world's population living in cities. This shift will likely continue, and by 2025, only 13 years from now, it is expected that the figure could be near 60 percent. As the world's population has shifted (and continues to shift), an interesting phenomenon is taking place: the developed, industrial countries have essentially stabilized the percentage of people living in their cities, while cities in developing countries, many of which are impoverished, are continuing to grow in population numbers and in geographical size. For example, Africa's rural population has declined rapidly since 1950, but it is projected that by 2050, its urban population will be approximately 60 percent. A similar trend is occurring in Asia and the Pacific Islands, and in the Latin American countries including the Caribbean. For these countries, urban population accounted for around 60 percent in 1970 and may increase to 80 percent by 2020 and remain steady until 2050. Likewise, the rural population will also remain steady at approximately 20 percent of the population of these regions.

In contrast, in Europe, it is estimated that there we will be few shifts in population between the rural and urban population over the next several decades. In North America today, we have almost reached the 80/20 percent ratio between urban and rural populations. UN statistics reveal that by 2025, Asia will have 55 percent of its population living in cities and for South America, that estimate is 88 percent. With the shift of rural to urban populations, there is also a corresponding move to larger cities. In 1990, there were 369 cities in the world with populations over 750,000, with the majority (154) located in Asia. In 2011, 468 cities had populations over 1 million persons. The change in city size has resulted in the creation of megacities; these are metropolitan areas that have populations of over 10 million persons. In 1970, the world had only two megacities: Tokyo and New York. Since then, their number has increased markedly and most new megacities have arisen in developing countries. By 2025, the number of megacities is expected to reach 37. Today, five cities have populations over 20 million. The cause of the growth of these cities is two-fold. First, it is due to the significant increase in the global population from 1960 to the present global population of over seven billion, mostly in developing and industrializing countries. Second, it is caused by the migration from rural areas to cities, which we expect to continue in developing countries for the foreseeable future. One projection of the global population may take us to 16 billion people by 2100. What does this mean for cities in the developing world where most of this growth will take place? What does this mean for sustainable community development?

This rate of growth is unprecedented in our history, and it raises serious concerns about poverty and grim health conditions in these large cities in developing countries. In many of the megacities, air pollution levels are staggeringly high, and dangerously unhealthy. Many of the largest cities have expanding slums that have by now become permanent features on the landscape, along with corresponding problems in health conditions, lack of infrastructure, and severe water scarcity. The World Health Organization reports that most of the countries in Africa have only 25 to 50 percent of their population served by treated water. Population growth in urban areas of developing countries has also raised issues for sustainability in the area of food security, namely that migration to cities impacts food production as urban regions face water scarcity, soil erosion, and land degradation. Due to their high concentrations of people, megacities are particularly prone to supply crises, social disorganization, political conflicts, and the impacts of natural disasters. The 2004 book, "Limits to Growth: The 30 – Year Update," supports the notion that there is a grave global situation due to the exponential population growth exceeding the earth's capacity to produce and replenish. These urban problems have been identified in several recent UN conferences on sustainable development, especially "Agenda 21" (see Chapter 2). Megacities are the ultimate examples of urbanization, and thus may provide valuable insights for urban geographers and planners who try to understand the impact and implications of urbanization processes and to help contribute to finding urban sustainability solutions.

Sustainable solutions for the poorest cities in the world require immediate and global attention: there is a looming failure to support their exploding populations because the bare necessities in food production and potable water are declining at dramatic rates. In 2010, the Food and Agriculture Organization of the UN estimated that approximately 600 million people in developing countries were experiencing chronic under-nutrition and of those, 27 countries had low or critical food security indices.

Busy Indian Street Market in New Delhi, India. In 2011, New Delhi's population surpassed 11 million people.

The information provided above is supported by some shocking data on food production discussed in Walker and Salt's 2006 book, "Resiliency Thinking: Sustaining Ecosystems and People in a Changing World." For example, global grain production must be increased by 40 percent from the 2004 baseline in order to meet demands by 2020, due to increased population growth, declining cereal production, and diminishing water supplies for agriculture. The world's farmers produced more grain in 2011 than ever before, yet global grain production has fallen short of consumption needs in seven of the past 12 years. Freshwater use may also exceed available limits, demonstrating the decline in ecosystem services for this vital resource. Moreover, it is quite worrisome that our global Ecological Footprint has been increasing to the point where it now surpasses its carrying capacity. The Ecological Footprint is the amount of bioproductive land that is equivalent to the total consumption of people for food, fuel, clothing, and consumer products plus land utilized for waste and assimilation of pollution (see "Our Ecological Footprint: Reducing Human Impact on the Earth" written by Wackernagel and Rees in 1998). In 2007, the total global Ecological Footprint worldwide was 18.0 billion global hectares and the average person's Footprint was 2.7 global hectares. However, land availability based on global estimates of biologically active land was only 1.8 global hectares per person. This overshoot of approximately 50 percent means that in 2007, we used the equivalent of 1.5 earths to support our consumption.

In 2004, when the 30-year update of the well-known study "Limits to Growth" was published, it presented a global computer model showing continuous and projected exponential population growth, along with diminishing availability of nonrenewable fuels, food production, and bio-productive land as well as increased air and water pollution. Its argument is that at the global level, we are exceeding the earth's carrying capacity in natural resources because of huge and unabated consumer demand. While technology can help in increasing our capacity for production as illustrated by the Green Revolution, or as a nation we can find other sources of nonrenewable oil, such as in the tar sands region in Canada, the limits to continuous, unmanaged growth based on natural capital is being reached. In the next section of this chapter, we examine the data from urban regions in developing countries that indicate growing deficits especially in fresh water, expanding slum areas, and land degradation.

The central issue in sustainable development is that the Ecological Footprint has been expanding over the last few decades as an aggregate measure due to population growth and on a per capita consumption basis. If we divide the global bio-productive land by the world's population, there are only 1.8 global hectares of land to consume per person; consuming more than our carrying capacity is known as "overshoot." The updated "Limits to Growth" report in 2004 indicated that we are over consuming the globe's productive resource base to the equivalent of 1.2 planets. This overshoot and its ramifications can be observed in the deleterious conditions of the largest cities in developing countries.

An application of the Ecological Footprint concept is compelling as a crude indicator, as it informs us of the current level of our "ecological debt" that needs to be restored or regenerated in order to return to our one earth biocapacity. The growth in our Ecological Footprint is fascinating: in 1960, we were only utilizing about 0.5 of the globe in consumption and land equivalency, and we reached the global carrying capacity in the period around 1985–1990. If we continue to consume natural resources at the same rate as we have been consuming them over the last 50 years, our ecological deficit will reach the equivalent of 2.0 planets by 2040. When students are asked to discern their own individual footprints using one of the many Ecological Footprint models available on the Internet and convert that to a global footprint (see Assignment Number 4 in Chapter 13), most students are surprised by the results: if all people in the world lived like they do in terms of consumption, it would likely result in a footprint equivalent to eight earths. While, fortunately, across the globe, people do not consume at levels equal to United States students, this exercise does raise important questions on ethics and values concerning land capital, natural resources, and equity.

Understanding the condition of many of the groundwater aquifers in the United States can help explain the need for sustainability. As population and urban development increase in regions dependent on groundwater supplies, more groundwater is removed for agriculture, manufacturing, domestic uses, and drinking water. As the rate of water taken out of the groundwater aquifer continues to increase, the carrying

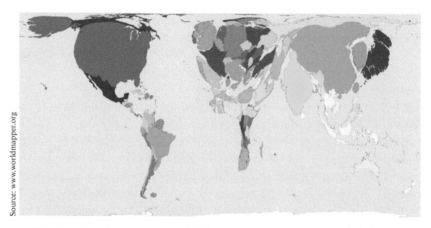

Source: www.worldmapper.org

**Map showing the proportion of all biocapacity in the world, which includes cropland, pasture, forests, and fisheries. Sixteen percent of the world's biocapacity is in Brazil and this is being lost very rapidly due to growth and agricultural development.**

capacity starts to diminish. At some point in time, the demand of water will start to exceed the carrying capacity level, leading to overshoot. More groundwater can still be removed until the aquifer starts to fail. Of course, groundwater aquifers can be replenished through efficient rainwater catchment and wastewater recharge into the aquifer, where natural systems will help restore the groundwater. This is referred to as ecosystem services that provide important benefits to the human-ecological system. Ecosystem services are discussed in Chapter 11.

For example, in Arizona, the 1980 Groundwater Code recognized the need to manage the state's finite groundwater resources aggressively in order to support the growing economy. The Code established management goals for five designated urban areas with the heaviest reliance on mined groundwater. Programs were created to address the problem of limited groundwater supplies when new development is created in an effort to preserve groundwater resources and promote long-term water supply planning; the regulations were based on demonstration of a 100-year water supply that was developed on the basis of current and committed demand, as well as growth projections. On the supply side, municipalities can purchase land outside of their jurisdictions in order to own the rights to use groundwater under the land—a form of land banking. On the demand side, municipalities can enforce conservation policies and promulgate price structures for withdrawing water. Sustainable management implies addressing all of the potential adaptation mechanisms to assure long-term and permanency of the groundwater resource.

## Defining Sustainability

Sustainability requires an examination of human values and behavior and the long-term adverse impacts to ecosystems and diminishing natural capital to establish a framework that will eliminate ecological deficit while building communities that are safe, just, healthy, and inspired by nature. The following provides the most widely accepted definition of sustainability from the Brundtland Commission (1987):

> *Sustainable development is development that meets the needs of the present without compromising the ability of future generations to meet their own needs.*

There has been significant debate over the meaning of the terms used in the Brundtland definition, particularly about meeting the needs of the present and meeting the needs of future generations. The idea of sustainable development comes out of two earlier international UN conferences. The first was the 1972 UN Conference on the Human Environment, also known as the Stockholm Conference. It focused on the need for a common outlook on the environment and human conditions. While developed countries' concerns focused on environmental quality and diminishing natural capital, developing countries' concerns were primarily about poverty, water shortages, land degradation, living conditions, and pollution. The goal was to reach a compromise among the nations about the needs of the "human environment." The notion of meeting present needs and assuring future needs was developed, thus establishing the sustainability framework.

The idea of development that meets the needs of the present considers poverty, homelessness, ecosystem degradation, disappearing species, and reduction of our natural capital, as well as social equity. This definition also addresses the need to provide for the future by meeting our needs "without compromising the ability of future generations to meet their own needs." To have the ability to meet future needs implies a need for intergenerational equity, and thus society cannot permit the continuous increases in ecological deficits in natural capital through consumption. This idea is rooted in the limited and dated concept of "sustainable yield," which suggests that the consumption of forests, fisheries, and land must have limits in order to continue the generation of the yield without diminishing returns.

There are a number of principles that guide how we can conceptualize sustainability. As discussed in Chapter 2, sustainability consists of three overlapping spheres or domains (known as the three E's: equity, environment, and economy). Sustainability implies an integrated balance between managing resources or economy, achieving social equity, and protecting the environment. Some scholars have argued that it is not necessary to deal with all three spheres simultaneously; however, the idea in the book "Resiliency Thinking" is to at least consider environmental issues within a framework of a socio-ecological or human–ecological coupled system.

# Social Dimensions of Sustainability

Cities are beginning to think about sustainability in terms of its social dimensions as well as a means of protecting environmental resources. The following sections explain briefly key aspects of sustainability that relate to social justice, sustainability indicators, and public participation.

## Social Justice

The concept of social justice encompasses the principle of the equal distribution of the resources in a city. Thus, cities are exploring methods to increase public accessibility to mass transit, develop affordable housing, expand access to jobs especially as employment centers relocate away from central cities, and promote broad access to open spaces and parks. There is strong evidence that minority populations in some cities have to travel farther to enjoy open space and that there is less park space per capita in minority neighborhoods. Social equity is encapsulated within the framework of the Environmental Justice Movement, which focuses on the disproportional risk suffered by minority and low-income populations resulting from environmental risks and hazards (see Chapter 4). While these issues deal with intragenerational equity, the Brundtland definition is concerned with intergenerational equity; that is, we have a "stewardship" responsibility to assure future generations that we will not leave the world any "deficits" in terms of overshooting the carrying capacity of the earth's ecosystems. Interestingly, given that there already is an ongoing global deficit, the role of current urban sustainability is to find approaches to stabilize these socio-ecological systems from further degradation and then to restore or regenerate the loss in "biologically active land." The Six Nations Iroquois Confederacy is known for their seven generations philosophy: for every decision you make, one should consider that the decision will impact the next seven generations.

## Sustainability Indicators

During the last 15 years, many cities have begun implementing sustainability indicator programs that measure how well the community is doing along different dimensions. The indicator programs vary among cities because they often reflect the specific characteristics of the community and concerns of the local residents. Regardless of the differences among the various indicator programs, three common types of indictors exist: 1) economic indicators that examine such things as employment levels, poverty rates, and home ownership rates; 2) social indicators that measure such things as high school graduation rates, crime rates, physician availability per capita, political efficacy, and level and quality of public services; and 3) environmental indicators, that typically address air quality, water pollution, safety of drinking water, and the number of contaminated sites. When combined, many of these indicator programs are referred to as "quality of life" indicators, aimed at providing data to determine whether municipal efforts are meeting their stated goals. Data for most indicator programs are collected from annual governmental reports, and public surveys seeking information on individuals' level of satisfaction with city services, public access, and other subjective factors such as feelings of safety, livability, sense of community, and happiness levels, which are typically not found in governmental reports.

Indicators are measures that explore the degree to which municipalities are reaching their articulated goals; therefore, sustainability goals are often somewhat different than the more conventional goals of cities. Sustainability indicators are exemplified by how well cities are performing in terms of such issues as public transit mileage and usage, amount of recycled materials, availability of public open space, number of LEED (Leadership in Energy and Environmental Design) certified buildings, city fleet vehicles using reduced-emissions fuels, amount of renewable energy used, and number of green jobs, among other factors. In 1992, the UN released its "Agenda 21" report that stated, "indicators of sustainable development need to be developed to provide solid bases for decision-making at all levels and to contribute to a self-regulating sustainability of integrated environment and development systems." (See Chapter 2.) Sustainability indicators are multidimensional and necessarily recognize the connections among the three domains of social equity, economy, and the environment. The indicator program for Seattle, Washington was one of the first sustainability indicator systems and most well-known. It received recognition by the United Nations Centre for Human Settlements with an "Excellence in Indicators Best Performance" Award in 1996.

## Visioning, Collaboration, and Participation

The socio-political dimension is integral in developing sustainable solutions. As discussed in Chapter 2, the UN's "Agenda 21" report promoted actions and policies for advancing sustainability through recommendations for participatory forms of governance. Transparency is requisite in decision-making that necessitates the public's participation in the political processes and is inherent in developing and implementing policies to achieve urban sustainability. Many of the sustainability indicator programs are products of collaborative decision-making at community levels. Citizen participatory processes including visioning sessions with community members are fundamental in evaluating the future direction of a community in terms of sustainability and in identifying strategies to achieve sustainability goals. Sustainable community development also requires transformational governance to make informed decisions about complex ideas under a level of uncertainty, as well as new approaches to governance through the use of adaptation strategies, advanced scenario planning, and anticipatory governance covered in Chapter 5.

# Sustainable Community Development

Sustainable community development also implies consideration of supporting the local economy while simultaneously protecting and restoring local ecological services. Two key aspects entail consuming and producing locally and making decisions using "life cycle accounting."

## Produce and Consume Locally

The concept of "food miles" refers to the average number of miles that food must travel from where it is produced and warehoused to points where it is ultimately sold. The average miles that food travels to U.S. cities is approximately 1,200–1,500 miles, and present-day food consumption is often not based on seasonality as it was previously. Because food and other consumption products are often imported from outside local areas, the number of smaller neighborhood businesses are diminishing and being replaced by larger national outlets, thus altering the character and sense of place of cities and leading to the decline of many areas as the local economy loses its resiliency and even viability. It is a serious problem when foods are imported largely only to supermarkets outside of inner cities, leaving "food deserts"—areas without supermarkets or grocery stores mostly in low-income, minority neighborhoods where residents frequently do not have access to cars (see Chapter 4). In addition, these communities often have low employment levels, a lack of medical clinics, few parks, and pollution from nearby highway traffic; it is thus not surprising that childhood diseases like obesity, diabetes, and asthma are increasing, especially in inner cities.

Sustainable community development aims to find solutions for these problems through community planning. For example, some cities are expanding light rail systems to help increase ridership from inner city areas to employment centers; the problem of food deserts is receiving much needed public attention; and neighborhood revitalization based on sustainability solutions is being supported in cities through grants from the federal government's Department of Housing and Urban Development.

## Life Cycle Accounting

Consuming and producing goods locally will also help develop sustainable neighborhoods by establishing self-sufficiency and capital accumulation. Sustainability requires that decisions about consumption of products, whether it is the decision regarding which furniture to purchase for a university or a home, or whether to take public transit or a car to work, requires life cycle assessments. Life cycle analysis calculates the environmental costs of each phase of the product cycle, from attaining the materials (mining, lumbering), to transporting the materials for processing, to manufacturing, through packaging, to retail markets, and ultimately to a landfill or to be used as recycled material. Certainly, the expenditures are less if the life cycle costs are measured between "cradle to cradle" (because the cost of disposal of waste is eliminated) rather than "cradle to grave" because it assumes there is not a recycling component. Environmental costs are the direct and indirect costs of producing a product, such as the air pollution resulting from manufacturing and transportation to the health costs of people exposed to the pollution. The environmental costs for producing the basic materials are calculated on the basis of fuel consumed, utilization of natural materials and ores, water, and other factors. When students are asked to calculate the life cycle costs associated with consuming one meal consisting of hamburger, fries, and a large soda, they are at first surprised to learn that it may take up to 2,000 gallons of water to produce the meal, and that the actual direct and indirect costs are over $200, most of which are intangible environmental costs.

# Reducing the Ecological Footprint

This concept was briefly discussed above with respect to demonstrating that there are limits to growth because our global population is consuming natural capital greater than its carrying capacity, and thus actions must be taken to reduce the footprint of a global consumption level that now equals 1.5 earths. Steps that can be taken to reduce the global Ecological Footprint include:

- Preserving our natural capital and using technological substitutes;
- Incentivizing or lessening of the rate of consumption, through legislation or otherwise;
- Investing in expanding the natural capital through programs such as land banking for future groundwater supplies;
- Restoring and regenerating natural capital;
- Utilizing renewable energy sources;
- Practicing sustainable yield principles; and
- Applying economic tools and values to ecosystem services.

Based on the book "Our Ecological Footprint: Reducing Human Impact on the Earth" by Wackernagel and Rees, the Ecological Footprint measures the demands of a given population on nature. It is measured by equating the land area needed to sustain the resource consumption of a particular population, and it can be calculated for a person, a city, a country, and even a university. The amount of land in this equation is the biologically active land area required to produce the resources consumed – water, fuel, crops, and land needed for waste assimilation. Once the global land equivalency is calculated, we can estimate the biologically active land that exists as ecosystem services and compare population demand to the global biological capacity of the earth's ecosystems. A primary goal of sustainability is to avoid ecological deficits by either expanding the carrying capacity level to assure future assets and capital or by reducing consumer demand.

# The Concept of Resiliency

Resiliency is a key principle in helping define and frame urban sustainability. Both today and in the recent past, serious pressures have confronted cities and a few have experienced long-term problems and disruptions from major events that have put an urgent focus on developing resilient communities. We can identify the disaster caused in 2005 by Hurricane Katrina in New Orleans (and from which the city has still not fully recovered), the economic downfall of cities like Detroit that were based on a single manufacturing industry, and the 2010 BP (British Petroleum) oil spill that devastated the states bordering the Gulf of Mexico, to name just a few. Disasters, like urban resilience, take many forms, such as natural catastrophes, economic downturns, and human-caused incidents. The concept of resiliency is woven throughout this book (even if not explicitly stated), and it is vital to social-ecological systems, global climate change, anticipatory governance, community and place making, and energy alternatives and security, among other topics.

A resilient city is one that has developed the systems and capacities to be able to absorb shocks and stresses so as to still maintain essentially the same functions, structure, systems, and identity, while at also implementing strategies to mitigate future shocks and stresses. The concept of resiliency originated in the ecological sciences and was later utilized in managing social-ecological systems, and has since grown to encompass the idea of improving human and community capacities to bounce back from various types of shocks and stresses, including health and economic disruptions, building and infrastructure failures, natural disasters and the loss of ecosystems, and human-caused or intentional disruptions.[1] Cities should implement resiliency thinking and principles to directly confront present problems, and prevent or diminish future threats.

Resiliency measures should be applied as a fundamental building block to various urban conditions and at varying geographical scales: neighborhoods, communities, cities, and larger regions. To develop a city that is resilient, all of the functions within the city must also be resilient. For example, as a response to "peak oil" demand, a city should have a resilient energy system that uses renewable energy and is built on a more local scale to meet the needs of its residents. Petroleum is a finite natural resource subject to depletion; accordingly, peak oil refers to a point in time when we have extracted more than 50 percent of the available and readily extractable oil. Many experts agree that we are (or will soon be) reaching peak oil. Once this plateau is realized, it becomes more difficult to extract the remaining resources. As a result, there will no longer be enough available oil to meet our consumption needs. The built environment and crisis management policies of the city must also be resilient; for a coastal city, that may mean building break walls and developing emergency evacuation procedures to address the threats of rising sea-levels due to climate change. Similarly, cities should encourage transit-oriented development and strive to be more pedestrian and bicycle friendly, thus providing varied transportation options and lowering carbon dioxide emissions, traffic congestion, and pollution—thus leading to increased resilience.

Resiliency and sustainability are interrelated concepts and resiliency is often viewed as a cornerstone of sustainability. In fact, there is an argument that sustainability is a product of resiliency plus "anticipatory governance" (see Chapter 5). The sustainability of an ecosystem, a landscape, or a city requires resilience. By enhancing the resiliency of a city, not only will it become more sustainable, but it will also provide a higher quality of life to its residents.[2] In addition, strengthening resiliency is becoming increasingly important in coping with the effects caused by climate change and other environmental impacts. Sometimes, change or disruption is gradual and predictable, such as the diminishing availability of fossil fuels. On the other hand, sometimes the change or disruption is sudden, turbulent, and traumatic, such as the impact of a devastating earthquake or hurricane. The concept of resiliency demands that communities prepare for, and learn to adapt to, both kinds of disruptions. Some measures to combat climate change include building highly energy-efficient homes using mainly local materials, thereby also strengthening the local economy, and the advancement of community-supported agriculture and urban farms. These are physical measures to build resiliency, but non-physical measures can include reducing the root causes of social vulnerabilities to disasters, strengthening social networks, establishing adaptive governance, and making connections across varied geographic scales, specifically local-to-local and local-to-national political connections through organizations. Resilient communities after disasters are those that have prepared for and applied these and other measures of social capital.

## Attributes of Resilient Cities

We will next review the resiliency indicators that attempt to quantify and rank the most resilient cities in the United States. The most resilient cities will likely share some, or all, of the following attributes:

Rochester, Minnesota: ranked the most resilient city in the United States.

- **Adaptability**: the capacity of people and cities to manage and influence resilience; adaptability is crucial because when a community suffers a shock or crisis, it is important that the community adapt to avoid changing from a stable, healthy environment into an unstable, undesirable one. Adaptability can also assist a community become more resilient to future shocks or stresses by helping it develop into a more desirable, well-functioning community.

- **Diversity**: the promotion of biological, landscape, social, and economic diversity; cities must be more flexible because the more alternatives available to respond to a disruption, the greater the ability of a city to absorb that shock and continue to function normally.

- **Innovation:** an emphasis on learning, experimentation, locally developed rules, and embracing change as opposed to always doing things in the same way; for example, building flood resistant coastal communities instead of relying on the traditional provision of flood relief and hazard insurance, will foster adaptability leading to increased and continued resiliency.

- **Natural capital**: represents the natural assets of a community, including: non-renewable resources like fossil fuels and mineral deposits; renewable resources such as fish or timber; and ecosystem services, such as pollination or purification of air and water.

- **Social capital**: refers to social relationships among individuals and the norms and trust that they generate; it is essential to developing coordination and cooperation for the mutual benefit of a community when a disturbance strikes.

In order to increase their adaptability and resilience, urban communities should begin implementing planning strategies that will enable them to respond to crises more effectively and adapt to the economic, social, and physical stresses that will ultimately be brought about by climate change and other stressors. Resilience in social-ecological systems such as urban environments focuses on the development of strong communities, interconnected networks, and strong leadership.[3] Cities present prime opportunities to develop these principles due to the close proximity of their residents to each other; the fact that many residents work, live, and recreate within the same community; and the existence of a local governance structure. Cities have the benefit of having dedicated leaders through municipal government structure, as well as an overlap with state and federal governmental systems. Accordingly, understanding, anticipating, and managing resilience (as much as is possible) is vital to helping a city absorb, adapt, and prevail in relation to shocks and disturbances.

## Building Resiliency to Disasters

In March 2012, the UN published "How to Make Cities More Resilient: A Handbook for Local Government Leaders." The handbook addresses why building disaster resilience is beneficial; what kind of strategies and actions are required; and how to go about doing so. In order to achieve sustainable development, the concept of resilience and disaster risk reduction must be part of urban design and strategies. Cities face a growing number of issues that threaten to increase their risk of disaster, including growing urban populations, which put pressure on land and services; the decline of ecosystems due to human activities such as road construction, pollution, and unsustainable resource extraction; adverse effects of climate change that will likely increase the frequency, intensity, and location of floods and other climate-related disasters; and decaying infrastructure and unsafe buildings, which may lead to collapsed structures (which, for example, was seen in the "collapse" of Haiti after the catastrophic 2010 earthquake).

A resilient city minimizes the impacts of disasters by not only reducing GHG emissions, but also by having organized services and strong infrastructure; establishing an inclusive, competent and responsible local government that is committed to sustainable urbanization; empowering residents to participate in decision-making; and planning to anticipate and mitigate the impact of disasters, including the incorporation of monitoring and early warning technologies. The handbook provides ten essential factors for making cities disaster resilient: institutional and administrative framework; financing and resources; multi-hazard risk assessment; infrastructure protection; protection of vital facilities; building regulations and land use planning; training, education and public awareness; environmental protection and strengthening of ecosystems; effective preparedness, early warning and response; and recovery and rebuilding communities.

## Resiliency Indicators

The Building Resilient Regions network has developed a tool called the Resilience Capacity Index (RCI) that provides data and ranks 361 United States metropolitan areas in terms of their resiliency. They examine the ability of urban communities to respond to local and national challenges and discern what factors lead to a more resilient city. RCI is a single statistic summarizing a region's score on 12 equally weighted indicators based on three dimensions: 1) economic dimension (income equality, economic diversification, regional affordability, and business environment); 2) socio-demographic dimension (educational attainment, lack of disability and poverty, and high levels of health insurance); and 3) community connectivity (civic infrastructure, metropolitan stability, homeownership, and voter participation). As a gauge of a community's ability to respond effectively to a future stress, the RCI reveals strengths and weaknesses, and allows decision-makers and leaders to compare their resiliency to that of other metropolitan areas. There are some discernible patterns across the country. Areas in the Northeast and Midwest tend to have higher levels of resiliency, in contrast to the lower propensity for resilience capacity in the South and Southwest. Places that have experienced rapid population growth, such as many metropolitan areas of the South and West, often earn low resilience scores. RCI favors attributes, including metropolitan stability, regional affordability, homeownership, and income equality, which are most often found in slower-growing regions. The cities that have been ranked highest in terms of overall resilience are: 1) Rochester, MN; 2) Bismarck, ND; 3) Minneapolis-St. Paul, MN-WI; 4) Barnstable Town, MA; and, 5) Dubuque, IA.[3]

All cities must strive toward building their resiliency to the various types of shocks and stresses that are likely to occur with increasing frequency, such as extreme weather events, natural disasters, and environmental changes. There are a growing number of experts in the field that believe that "resilience is the key to sustainability."[4]

## What does a Sustainable City Look Like?

To answer this question, we begin by examining one of three urban settings that are best known to be the most sustainable: Civano in Tucson, Arizona; Curitiba, in Brazil; and Freiburg, Germany. The Curitiba case study is covered in Chapter 7 Sustainable Transportation because that city is recognized primarily for its public transportation system and policies providing for open space. Civano is a neighborhood designed based on New Urbanism principles and sustainable home building, including solar technologies, and is addressed in Chapter 6. A case study of Freiburg, Germany and its urban form, policies, and use of sustainable energy sources follows, and can serve as an exemplification of a sustainable city. Following the case study, we will examine each of the characteristics that support its claim of being a sustainable city.

### ECO-CITY FREIBURG: Germany's center for renewable energy

*Bjoern Hagen*

#### Background

The city of Freiburg is located in the southwest corner of Germany, at the edge of the Black Forest, and very close to the borders of Switzerland and France. Founded in the year 1122, the city was strategically located at a junction of trade routes between the Mediterranean Sea and the North Sea. Freiburg was heavily bombed during World War II and

Image © Rom, 2012. Used under license from Shutterstock, Inc.

**City Center of Freiburg.**

*Continued*

carefully reconstructed based on the city's medieval plan that includes a unique system of small waterways throughout the historic center.

**Pedestrian Zone with Historic Waterway.**

Today, the purpose of the small canals/waterways is no longer to channel fresh water into the city, but instead, they add to the pleasant and comforting atmosphere of the city's pedestrian environment.

The city's population of approximately 220,000 people is a hub for regional eco-tourism and center for academia and research. The Albert Ludwig University in Freiburg is one of the oldest universities in Germany and has been the largest employer since the end of World War II.

### Green Movement

Because of the large academic community, Freiburg became a center of the country's **"green" movement**, which started in the 1970s. The movement led in 1979 to the founding of the Green Party,[1] whose political agenda contains numerous environmental goals such as the nuclear energy phase-out and stricter environmental protection laws. An important event that led to the Freiburg of today was a successful citizen protest against the plans to build a nearby nuclear power plant in 1975. Many protest leaders and other people involved in Freiburg's green movement remained in the area and became involved in local and regional politics, often involved in the city administration and found employment in educational or research activities, or founded environmentally based companies. As a result, the mayor and more than 25% of the council are currently members of Germany's Green Party.[2]

### Eco-City Freiburg

Over the last few decades, Freiburg focused heavily on becoming a recognized green and sustainable city. The city has won various national and international environmental awards for its policies and developments. Freiburg is especially well

**Green movement** - green movements are often grass-roots movements advocating social reforms and the protection of the natural environment and resources.

known as a green or **eco-city** for its efforts in transportation, alternative energy systems, and sustainable place-making.[3] Other sectors the city administration focuses on to make the city more sustainable include waste management, land conservation, and promoting a green economy.[4]

## Transportation

Transportation plays an important role in Freiburg's urban development policy. Since 1969, the city has established its **Global Transport Concept (GTC)**, which is a traffic management plan that is updated every 10 years. The main goals are to reduce total automobile traffic volume in the city and support the advancement of public transit, cyclists, and pedestrians. Furthermore, the GTC focuses on creating a rational balance between all modes of transportation. In 1969, the first GTC policy implemented was the creation of a bicycle path network. This network was quickly followed by a considerable expansion of the tramway network (light rail) and the conservation of the city center into a pedestrian zone in 1972. More than 300 miles of bike paths and bike-friendly streets exist throughout the city, as well as 8,000 public bike parking spaces. The tramway network is now the most used transit system in the city. Almost 75% of all public transit users rely on the tram for their daily travel. Furthermore, 70% of the population lives within 550 yards of a tram stop. This distance promotes walking to a tram station and the creation of transit oriented development around stations or higher density development. During peak hours, the tram runs every 7.5 minutes. All stations have park-and-ride as well as bike-and-ride facilities. What makes Freiburg's public tram system truly sustainable, however, is the fact that it is powered by **renewable energy** sources. Approximately 80% of the energy used to power the tram system is generated by hydropower, and the remaining 20% is provided by solar and wind energy.

Besides aiming to make public transit convenient, fast, reliable, and comfortable, the city administration tries to make it as affordable as possible. A monthly transit pass costs about 50 Euros and gives unlimited access to more than 1,800 miles of routes from numerous transportation companies throughout the entire region. This is much cheaper than the monthly costs of owning and operating a private car. Because of Freiburg's transportation policies, the vehicle-miles traveled by car fell significantly, and as a result, greenhouse gas emissions declined as well. Between 1982 and 1999, the contribution of bicycling to the city's total volume of traffic increased from 15% to 28%. The number of people using public transit also increased in this period, from 11% to 18%.

Image © ArTono, 2012. Used under license from Shutterstock, Inc.

**Train in Freiburg's Pedestrian Zone.**

*Continued*

**Eco-Cities** - eco-cities, or sustainable cities, consider environmental impacts in their design and policy decisions. In addition, eco-cities strongly support the use of renewable energy sources, public transit, and compact and walkable neighborhood design.

**Global Transport Concept (GTC)** - the Global Transport Concept is a traffic management plan that is updated every 10 years. The main goals are to reduce traffic in the city and support public transit, cyclists, and pedestrians. Furthermore, the plan focuses on creating a rational balance between all modes of transportation.

**Renewable energy** - energy sources which are natural, such as sunlight, wind, and geothermal heat. Due to peak oil and growing environmental concerns, more governments support the use of renewable energy sources.

Among university students, nearly 90% use public transit or bike. Simultaneously, only 30% of the entire traffic volume is generated by private automobiles.

### Green Energy

In addition to the GTC, Freiburg is characterized by a progressive energy policy. The city's energy policy is based the three pillars: energy saving, efficient technologies, and renewable energy sources. Since 1992, the city has enforced strict building design standards for new houses. These standards have reduced heating oil consumption from about 12–15 liters to 6.5 liters per square meter. To improve energy efficiency in existing buildings, Freiburg instituted a comprehensive support program for home insulation and energy retrofits. Due to the expenditures for this program, which cost around 1,2 million Euros in subsidies and 14 million Euros of investments, energy consumption declined by around 38% per building.

In terms of efficient energy technology, Freiburg relies heavily on a system of **"combined heat and power plants" (CHP)**. These power plants reuse the waste heat from electricity production to generate electricity and useful heat for buildings. The city relies on more than 100 of these plants. The majority of the CHPs are small scale and located directly in the neighborhoods they serve. In addition, 14 large, combined heat and power plants are located at the city's outskirts. CHP plants are powered by natural gas, **biogas**, landfill gas, **geothermal** energy, wood chips, and heating oil. The steady increase in the number of these power plants has allowed Freiburg to decrease its reliance on nuclear power from 60% to 30%.[5] Today, around 55% of the city's electricity is produced by CHP plants or other renewable energy sources. The remaining percentage is imported, 30% of which comes from external nuclear power plants. For the near future, Freiburg's goal is it to further increase the amount of renewable energy and reduce the reliance on nuclear power and fossil fuel.

Freiburg's renewable energy sources consist of solar, wind, hydropower, and biomass. And although all four sources are utilized, the city is most famous for its support of solar energy. Throughout the city, the use of **solar energy** is highly visible. More than 400 photovoltaic installations occur on both public and private buildings.

The 1.6 million square feet of photovoltaic cells produce more than 10 million **kWh/year**. However, solar still only provides a small fraction of the city's electricity needs. The total electricity demand is well over 1,000 million kWh/year. Nevertheless, solar energy also became an important element of Freiburg's sustainable economy. The highly visible solar installations attract eco-tourism, and the support of solar energy has attracted numerous scientific and educational organizations.[6] For example, nearly

Image © Peteri, 2012. Used under license from Shutterstock, Inc.

**Solar settlement and farm.**

**Combined Heat and Power Plant (CHP)** - these power plants reuse the waste heat from electricity production to generate more electricity and useful heat for buildings. CHP plants can be powered by natural gas, biogas, landfill gas, geothermal, wooden chips, and heating oil.

**Biogas** - a renewable energy source created by the biological breakdown of organic matter without oxygen. Common organic waste used for biogas production are dead plants, animal material, animal feces, and kitchen waste.

**Geothermal** - geothermal power stations generate electricity by extracting heat from the lower layers of the earth. This heat is used to power turbines, which in turn are linked to generators that produce electricity.

**Solar energy** - this technology allows generating energy by converting sunlight into electricity using solar panels. Solar panels use solar cells made up of photovoltaic material.

**kWh/year** - kWh stands for kilowatt hour and is used as a unit of energy.

Soccer stadium.                    Business Building with solar energy.

10,000 people are employed by 1,500 companies from the green economy sector. The green economy sector includes research facilities, environmental education programs for university students, as well as for solar technicians and installers, and manufacturing. Various companies produce solar cells and machinery to create the cells. In addition, these companies have attracted numerous suppliers and service providers in a green-supply-chain system. In the solar industry alone, more than 80 businesses employ 1,000 people or more.

## Sustainable Living and Place-making

One of the most sustainable neighborhoods in Freiburg also relies heavily on solar energy. This neighborhood, Vauban, is 38 hectares in area. Vauban is located in an area of a former French military base close to the city center.[7] The final development plan was approved in 1997; Vauban is now an attractive and family-friendly community of about 5,000 people. Due to carefully designed zoning regulations and policies, low-energy buildings are obligatory in this district and **zero-energy** or **energy-plus buildings** with solar technology are prominent. The 60-plus energy homes in this neighborhood create more energy than they consume. Their residents earn, on average, 6,000 Euros per year by selling the surplus energy back to the grid.

Based on the Vauban district master plan, the neighborhood is characterized by a dense pattern of primarily attached housing and multifamily housing. Green spaces between the housing clusters ensure good climatic conditions and provide play areas for children. The green corridors channel fresh air into the neighborhood, while vegetation filters the air and reduces the ambient air temperature during the summer. A set of U-shaped access roads limit access of cars to the neighborhood. Instead, the life of the community takes place in the interior pedestrian spaces where cars are not allowed. The extensive set of walkways and paths connects the different housing areas and makes the entire neighborhood very bicycle and pedestrian friendly. Furthermore, Vauban has its own CHP plant using wood chips from local forestry, which provides all residents and local businesses with power.

In addition to the efforts of implementing solar energy, promoting walkability, and creating a sense of community, the neighborhood has received much attention internationally for its efforts to promote car-free living. Before the construction of Vauban, the state zoning law required builders to provide parking space for every

*Continued*

**Zero-energy building** - zero-energy buildings use different technologies such as solar and wind to harvest energy on site. These type of buildings are very energy efficient and do not have to rely on the city's energy grid. Furthermore, zero-energy buildings and energy-plus buildings do not produce any carbon emissions.

**Energy-plus building** - due to good insulation, special design guidelines, and the use of renewable energy sources, energy-plus buildings create more energy than they consume. Residents can make extra money by selling the extra energy back to the grid.

Image © Daniel Schonen, 2012. Used under license from Shutterstock, Inc.

**Zero-Energy and Energy-Plus settlement structures in Vauban.**

housing unit. The law was changed due to organized lobbying by the so-called Forum Vauban, a group of people advocating for a car-free neighborhood. Nowadays, Freiburg can waive any parking requirements if the developer can prove that the future residents will not own a car and that extra land is available to create parking spaces if residents choose to own a car at a later date. In the case of Vauban, costs of housing and parking are separated, and if residents choose to own a car, they have to cover the costs of a garage parking space at the fringe of the neighborhood. The onetime charge is about $14,000 per car. This cost is a strong incentive for residents to find alternative ways of getting around, such as using the tram system or the bicycle. New residents are offered a special mobility package as an alternative to owning a car. The package includes membership in a car-sharing company, a one-year local transit pass, as well as a 50% reduction on train tickets. Official numbers report about 250 motor vehicles per 1,000 Vauban residents, which is much lower compared to the national average in Germany of 500 automobiles per 1,000 residents.

If we use Freiburg as an exemplar to help define a sustainable city, there are a number of discernible characteristics and principles that should be noted:

- *Low Ecological—Environmental Impact.* The use of extensive solar energy and homes that are carbon neutral and utilize passive design can reduce the emissions of carbon dioxide. The reduction of fossil fuel use for energy is the best strategy for mitigation of GHG emissions because it not only avoids these emissions in the first place, but it also avoids the need for remedial actions for climate change action planning after the fact.

- *Cluster Housing and Densification.* New areas in the city are zoned for cluster housing with higher densities ensuring special "green" zones within the city that combine solar-based housing, cluster development, open space, and use of public transit.

- *Green Employment.* As the city became known as a solar energy community, it utilized that recognition to generate green jobs in energy research at the university, employment through eco-tourism, and manufacturing of solar collectors and other technologies for local and external consumption. Thus, employment is locally generated through renewable energy economic activities.

- *Pedestrian Environment*. Community policies have supported and encouraged pedestrianism, such as extensive bicycle pathways, monetary incentives for not having a car, punitive action for requiring a garage, and the opening of a pedestrian public transit space in a new neighborhood. Numerous social benefits also emanate from this kind of sustainable planning and design, including viable areas for social space and interaction, community building, and an enhanced quality of life and satisfaction from a sense of wellbeing and community efficacy. Although these social attributes have not expressly been tested for in Freiburg, New Urbanism scholars have shown that increased walkability and more open space leads to an enhanced sense of neighborliness and a heightened sense of community.

- *Emphasis on Resiliency*. Sustainable cities can be distinguished by a diverse set of small energy systems located in neighborhoods. Freiburg's energy mix consists of wind energy systems, solar collectors, hydropower, and photovoltaic building systems. Such a system provides redundancy, but in terms of community resiliency, it provides security because these small technologies are not dependent on fossil fuel and its attendant political and economic constraints and fluctuations.

- *Place-Making*. Sustainable cities should be recognized for their interest in building or restoring special places of history, culture, and community. These elements are an important part of the social domain in sustainable development. In the case of Freiburg, the historic medieval city that was destroyed in World War II was rebuilt with a similar spatial organization, using open public spaces and compact development without suburban sprawl. Later, the small canals that used to bring water into the cities were reestablished as a means of visually reintroducing history to the community and enhancing aesthetics.

- *Political and Policy Support for Sustainable Development*. The policies supporting "sustainable urbanism" are deeply entrenched in governmental support for solar research and manufacturing, high-density living, and habitat protection within the city. Urban planning for sustainable development is central to governmental activity from solar housing requirements, housing design, pedestrian environments, and bike trails. The city also encourages citizen participation in all of its programs.

- *Interconnectivity of Economic, Ecological, and Social Dimensions*. Like the universal framework for sustainable development that was developed by the Brundtland Commission, the city encourages and advances sound ecological and environmental goals (such as the reduction of GHGs) and supports an agenda of green employment in universities, research centers, and solar industries. Social and community based objectives through urban planning are also advanced and supported.

## ▉ LESSONS LEARNED FOR ACHIEVING SUSTAINABILITY

As we have seen, the changing nature of cities means that sustainable solutions and action are urgent because their problems are compelling and at a large scale. One of the keys toward achieving sustainable cities is to reduce their Ecological Footprint. Furthermore, the social dimensions discussed above must be considered and enhanced within any sustainability framework to advance sustainability within its three domains. Additionally, resilience and the ability to adapt to ever-changing conditions is an important element of sustainability within urban settings. As the case study of Freiburg, Germany illustrates, sustainable cities are within our reach and it presents a model towards which all cities should strive.

## Supplemental Readings

Rees, W., & Wackernagel, M. (1996). Urban ecological footprints: Why cities cannot be sustainable—And why they are a key to sustainability. *Environmental Impact Assessment Review, 16*(4), 223–248.

Kates, Robert W., Parris, Thomas M., & Leiserowitz, Anthony A. (2005). What is sustainable development? *Environment, 47*(3), 8.

Walker, B., Holling, C. S., Carpenter, S. R., & A. Kinzig. (2004). Resilience, adaptability and transformability in social–ecological systems. *Ecology and Society, 9*(2), 5.

# DISCUSSION QUESTIONS

1. What are the key social dimensions of sustainability and why are they essential to developing sustainable cities?

2. What can cities do to become more resilient to the effects of climate change?

3. What is Freiburg's Global Transport Concept?

4. What makes the Vauban neighborhood in Freiberg, Germany sustainable and what could be transferred to your community?

# History of Sustainability

*K. David Pijawka*
*Martin A. Gromulat*

## ■ WHY THIS CHAPTER IS IMPORTANT FOR UNDERSTANDING SUSTAINABILITY

Sustainability is not a new framework or science; it has been over 25 years since the creation of its most widespread definition in the Brundtland Report. This chapter is significant because it provides an introduction and explanation of how key sustainability principles developed, and it explains why the advancement of sustainability was, and still is, compelling and indispensable. One of the many important aspects revealed in this history is that to achieve sustainable solutions, there has to be an integration of recognized events, public concern and interest, and legislation. Unless there is such integration, real-world transformation will likely be difficult to achieve. Additionally, this chapter demonstrates how sustainability theories and concepts progress from local to global levels and why the continued interactions between the differing scales are a key theme in sustainability solutions. For students and readers unfamiliar with the topic, this chapter also provides insight into the important vocabulary needed to comprehend and communicate effectively about sustainability.

## Thinking about History

Sustainability is often called a new science, framework, or ethic; it has at its core the idea of surviving—the provision of continuous life without endangering future generations by over consuming our present global resource base. Certainly, there is a plethora of definitions of sustainability, as demonstrated in Chapter 1, and any history of sustainability will usually follow the streams and threads of the definition or theme utilized in that particular definition. However, whichever definition is selected as a basis for establishing a history, common approaches to such a history will include major events and their impacts, identification of new discoveries in science, innovative legislation and policies, significant books and reports, and points of public discourse and concern. As of this writing in 2012, three seminal events influenced and guided the writing of the following sustainability history.

The first concerns the concept of sustainability as being "new." Modern sustainability received a jump-start in 1987 when The World Commission on Environment and Development, overseen by former Norwegian Prime Minister Gro Harlem Brundtland, brought to our attention the importance of striving for economic development that safeguards our natural resources. From this gathering came the Brundtland Report, drafted by an international group of politicians, civil servants, and experts on the environment and development. They crafted the "classic" definition of sustainable development: "development that meets the needs of the present without compromising the ability of future generations to meet their own needs."[1] This idea dramatically transformed our view of the environment and altered sustainable development from a narrow, physical notion grounded on the concept of sustainable yield in forestry and fisheries, to a much more comprehensive and integrated framework that connected economic and ecological policies.[2]

Prior to this Commission, the United Nations had struggled to find a way to address global environmental problems. The industrialized countries had proposed international treaties and action, but the developing nations had prioritized the need for economic development, with little interest in environmental regulation. The Commission provided the conceptual framework for coordinated action, proposing that all nations have a stake in fostering economic development, but of a new kind: sustainable. It proposed sustainability as an integral framework, in which economic development, social equity, and environmental protection are seen as inseparably related goals.

The Brundtland Commission advanced public understanding of the link between economic growth of the poorer nations and global environmental protection. The Commission argued that poorer countries must have the opportunity to develop economically, because if they are denied that opportunity, it will be much harder to convince all countries to support practices that can be sustained over time. At the same time, richer countries must foster policies to favor environmental conservation with economic development. The official United Nations definition of sustainability has three dimensions, or pillars, also known as the "Three Es" of sustainability: environmental protection, economic development, and social equity.

As helpful and groundbreaking as the Brundtland definition was, a potential difficulty of it is that it is now 25 years old. Accordingly, a helpful way of looking at sustainability's history is to develop a perspective on the trajectory of sustainability since the creation of the Brundtland definition of sustainable development. In this way, we can identify the various international protocols and conferences that continued to expand on the principles of sustainability (such as the 1992 Agenda 21 action plan developed by the United Nations for the purpose of local sustainable development, and the 2002 Melbourne Principles, which seek to create environmentally healthy, vibrant, and sustainable cities); to establish standards and international goals (such as the 1997 Kyoto Protocol, an international agreement with the goal of reducing greenhouse gas emissions to prevent further increases in the global temperature); to foster the emergence of new intellectual and planning movements (such as sustainable design including transit oriented development, walkability, health planning, and retrofitting suburbs); and, to permit resiliency building and adaptation planning to reduce climate change impacts on local areas.

The second factor influencing a sustainability history is the fact that over 50% of the global population now resides in urban areas and that urbanization is continuing to increase. Much of this growth in the size of cities is taking place in developing countries where the movement of people from rural areas to cities has created a growing number of global megacities, each with over 10 million people. The top three megacities and their estimated populations are: 1) Tokyo-Yokohama, Japan (37.1 million); 2) Jakarta, Indonesia (26 million); and 3) Seoul-Incheon, South Korea (22.6 million).[3] Unfortunately, the migration of rural people to large cities generates significant social, economic, and environmental problems for which sustainability solutions are pressing and compelling. As discussed in Chapter 1, it is within these growing urban areas, which have large, complex land uses and spatial systems, that such sustainability problems become more complex and difficult to solve, and where institutional capacities for positive change are largely lacking in many cases.

The problems confronting each megacity, especially ones in developing countries, demonstrate that although substantial similarities exist between the megacities, variability also exists due to differences in culture and traditions, geographical location, level of industrial development, and level of adaptive capacity. The adaptive capacity is the ability to generate changes to reduce adverse impacts through physical structural changes (such as infrastructure investment), reduce vulnerability (such as the relocation of coastal areas prone to flooding and other coastal disasters), and build social resiliency (such as developing responsive sociopolitical institutions and self-sufficiency).

Because of this new urban form, certain sustainability problems have arisen that require confrontation, especially if we are to meet present societal needs and provide the means to assure intergenerational security of natural resources to meet future needs. These problems tend to manifest themselves as follows:

- The rapid shift in urbanization with growing populations has resulted in the increased demand for more agricultural land to meet urban needs, which unfortunately has caused massive clear-cutting of forests, which in turn frequently results in associated detrimental effects on ecosystems.

- Substantial population growth in urban areas has resulted in the overuse of wetlands and other sensitive ecological areas, which help protect urban areas by improving water quality and helping control floods. Where substantial urban invasion has occurred, these ecological systems have often been disturbed and become imbalanced to the point that they are no longer functioning properly, thus resulting in long-term ecosystem degradation that adversely affects humans.

- Urban growth in megacities has resulted in greater sprawl rather than densification. For example, the continuing, rapid growth of the largest cities in China over the last 20 years has resulted in a new form of high-density suburbanization, while the increase in wealth among urban residents has resulted in increased car ownership along with its associated negative effects of carbon dioxide emissions, air pollution, and related health hazards.

- Environmental, educational, and medical infrastructure in less wealthy megacities have not kept pace with the needs of its new residents and, as a result, there are inadequate water and wastewater systems, increased air pollution, and an increase in the number of untreated waste streams. Currently, approximately two-thirds of the world's population is without adequate water supplies. Furthermore, results from spatial geographical information systems and remote sensing studies indicate that in Southeast Asian and Latin American cities, increased rural immigration has resulted in population growth and an increase in the permanence of major slum areas.

The third event influencing the development of a sustainability history is the recent devastating and catastrophic January 2010 earthquake in Haiti, which is located on the island of Hispaniola. Hispaniola is an island that has within its borders two countries: Haiti and the Dominican Republic. In the not-too-distant past, the island was predominantly forested. The image below shows a compelling, bifurcated land mass separated by a winding river that cuts through the island. What is profoundly and clearly visible today is that the landscapes are totally different on both sides of the river. On the left side, Haiti is mostly brown and barren, and devoid of trees and vegetation. Haiti also lacks large-scale agriculture and industrial zones, and most of its residents live in its capital city, Port-au-Prince. In contrast, the Dominican Republic is green and not brown like its neighbor to the west; it is rich in vegetated cover, agriculture, and has a large tourist industry. Although 28% of the Dominican Republic remains forested, only 1% of Haiti still has woodlands. Like the satellite image, the socioeconomic statistics also reflect major differences between the two; for example, the median income in the Dominican Republic is over seven times greater than that in Haiti.

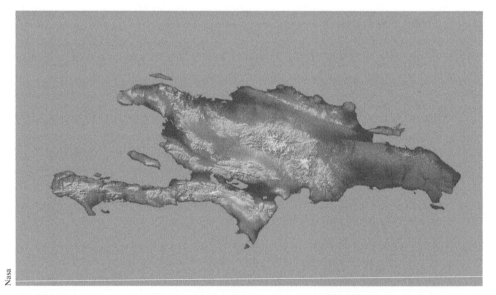

Nasa

**Map showing the topography of Hispaniola with severe deforestation evident in Haiti (approximately left one-third) and more forested Dominican Republic (right two-thirds).**

From an historical perspective, Haiti's earthquake proved devastating; damages were large, with substantial numbers dead and injured and property destroyed. There were approximately 222,650 deaths; an additional 310,930 injured; 2.3 million people displaced; and 403,176 buildings were damaged or destroyed.[4] In addition to the casualties and property damage, the earthquake also uncovered some of the country's underlying social and physical vulnerabilities that, unfortunately, amplified an already catastrophic natural disaster into a full-blown long-term humanitarian crisis. The barren and denuded countryside long ago lost its physical stability, with much of its topsoil for agriculture nonproductive or depleted due to a long history of deforestation. These problems are a direct result of the extensive deforestation: a loss of lumber and other building supplies; a severe deficiency in forest-derived charcoal, the main fuel for cooking; soil erosion; detrimental levels of sediment in the rivers; and reduced rainfall. The lack of agricultural development, protection of its natural resources, massive poverty and disease, and political corruption and outmigration have created vulnerabilities that diminish Haiti's capacity to respond effectively to natural disasters, and also frustrate recovery responses. Many months after the earthquake, relief distribution efforts were still difficult to undertake, temporary tent shelters were prone to seasonal floods (as of April 30, 2012, approximately 420,500 internally displaced persons were still living in "temporary" camps), and a large-scale cholera outbreak added to the misery following the earthquake, sickening approximately 544,044 people and causing 7,150 deaths since October 2010.[5] It became abundantly clear that needed infrastructure was not in place; the population was exposed to multiple hazards, adaptive planning to help reduce the size and scope of the impacts was nonexistent, and indigenous capacity for building resilient systems after the earthquake was lacking. The earthquake reflected perhaps a "tipping point" of a society that was close to what Jared Diamond characterizes as a collapsed state.[6]

What is clear from an historical perspective is that Haiti represents a land and people with a long history of unsustainable practices and an inability or lack of capacity to contend and deal with its growing societal vulnerabilities along social, economic, and ecological dimensions. The inadequate response to the earthquake and its devastating aftermath, along with Haiti's ever-expanding vulnerabilities, are products of a complex and difficult legacy where the capacity for applying sustainability principles is essentially nonexistent. We can learn a substantial amount from Haiti's history. The following are three such lessons to be learned:

1. Although it is very difficult to forecast natural disasters, major accidents, catastrophes, and similar problems, we do know that they will occur. When they do occur, they often reveal serious weaknesses in societies' ability to utilize adaptive decisions and policies and build resiliency through understanding a community's institutions, organizations, culture, and innate abilities. Sustainability can provide answers to how to best build anticipatory systems of governance over the long term to better respond and recover from such crises.

2. Oftentimes, a devastating event has two major impacts: 1) the exposure to that specific event, and 2) the manifestation of underlying social, economic, and ecological vulnerabilities or policies that inevitably amplify the event. This is true whether the event is the 2010 earthquake in Haiti; Hurricane Katrina, which struck New Orleans in 2005; the deforestation, desertification, depleted biodiversity, and social chaos in Sudan, Africa, after more than 20 years of devastating civil war, despite the signing of a peace agreement in 2005; or the 2010 British Petroleum (BP) oil spill disaster in the Gulf of New Mexico. Sustainability requires a deeper examination into such catastrophic events and seeks an understanding of their root causes to facilitate more robust and resilient social-ecological communities.

3. Sustainability is a forward–looking and aspirational discipline that often employs measures and indicators to measure progress and improve the world in which we live (such as the theme of the recent June 2012 Rio+20

Conference of "The Future We Want"); some of its goals are determining how best to improve a community, landscape, or part of an urban system such as transportation. For instance, how do we best make decisions to reduce carbon dioxide levels? How do we design neighborhoods to increase their walkability? What building materials should be used to reduce the effects of urban heat islands? To best answer these and similar inquiries, sustainability history compels that we also examine past failures and inadequacies to help understand the causes of current problems; seek to ascertain what has succeeded, what has failed, and why; and to think holistically to see how social, health, economic, urban design, and ecological dimensions can be the basis for integrative thinking about "legacy" problems. While many U.S. cities are moving forward with sustainable planning, new form-based design codes, sustainability indicators, smart city development and smart growth principles, and adaptation planning for global climate change, many legacy problems often remain overlooked or ignored by current sustainability efforts. Such problems include segregated central cities, high rates of urban food deserts, the slow pace of revitalizing industrial brownfields, the prevalence of Superfund hazardous waste sites, dilapidated housing, and failing automobile-intensive, isolated suburbs.

## The Structure of Sustainability History

This chapter takes a brief tour of 150 years of sustainability and environmental history with distinct phases identified and characterized. The Brundtland Report's 1987 definition of sustainable development continued the historical emphasis on conserving environmental and natural resources, but certainly went further in several ways. During the debates over policy and focus throughout the development of the Brundtland Report, developing countries expressed concern that environmental quality would be emphasized at the expense of development, and argued that many affluent countries had already achieved highly developed societies. Accordingly, this would have resulted in unfairly

Image © Caitlin Mirra, 2012. Used under license from Shutterstock, Inc.

**New Orleans skyline and areas flooded by Hurricane Katrina.**

penalizing developing countries; therefore, to alleviate this issue, developed countries compromised and agreed to incorporate the protection of environmental resources within the larger context of meeting future needs. As a result, the definition of sustainable development includes "development that meets the needs of the present" as well as future needs. Moreover, meeting both present and future needs of societies encapsulates the three pillars of sustainability: social,

**Workers attempt to remove thick globs of oil from the seashore of the resort area of Perdido Pass, Alabama due to BP's Deepwater Horizon drill rig explosion.**

economic, and environmental. The concept of integrating environmental or natural capital with societal and economic goals marks an historic departure from the singular concept of environmentalism or environmental protection and into a holistic sustainability framework.

Moving forward, sustainability would imply management within an interdisciplinary context: local to global considerations instead of environmental management at the regional scale; assessment of the health of the environment as a holistic system, and not just responsiveness to individual environmental problems; establishment of new monitoring systems based on publically determined indicators; and multifaceted policies and rules instead of business as usual "end of pipe" regulations. Another major departure that characterized the pathway to sustainability was the development of approaches to mitigate pollutants such as carbon dioxide that scientists now see as a global concern, because climate change effects are worldwide and not only limited to local areas. Conventional regulations to reduce carbon dioxide emissions have given way to other reduction measures such as changes and improvements in urban form, public transportation systems, neighborhood design, and other local adaptation measures. After generations of separating humans and nature, sustainability thinking connects the two in sometimes complex, but always important, socio-ecological systems.

As the principal concepts of sustainability and its applications are discussed in this book, it is important to consider the past ideas and concepts that paved the way for sustainability today. When considering the history of environmentalism in the last 150 years, three strands of thinking should be recognized to understand its evolution. First are the policies and legislation that have been promulgated; these are the controls, environmental quality standards, and responses by society to mitigate environmental harms and enhance the benefits of environmental management. In addition to this legislative history, the role of the sciences is especially significant because scientific findings have directly influenced and informed a great deal of the evolution of thinking about the environment and its management. For example, as science evolved, it enabled the identification of hazards that went undetected for many years, and the application of scientific thinking to the field of risk assessment in technology and ecosystems.

Second is the importance of climate science and modeling that enabled an understanding of, for example, the role of carbon dioxide emissions in our changing climate and projections of its effects. Chapter 12 discusses the evolution of urban spatial models and their importance in decision-making and planning for sustainable cities. Unfortunately, many societies most often develop new policies only after "unexpected" calamitous events. While the implementation of precautionary principles before a crisis threshold is reached is preferable, societies unfortunately generally only react after a crisis develops, and not before. At least "[c]risis has a wonderful way of galvanizing action."[7] We see this notion clearly in the environmental area as new federal flood relief legislation was developed following catastrophic flooding in the 1930s. The enactment of brownfields regulations and the 1980 Comprehensive Environmental Response, Compensation, and Liability Act, commonly known as Superfund, was promulgated in response to releases of hazardous substances that endangered public health and the environment. Extensive development took place and an elementary school and numerous homes were constructed in the Love Canal neighborhood of Niagara Falls, New York, on top of a former 16-acre hazardous waste landfill; this incident shook the consciousness of the nation when in 1978 it was reported that suspected carcinogens were leaching into homes, backyards, and the school.[8] Another environmental incident was the 1979 accident at the Three Mile Island nuclear power plant in Middletown, Pennsylvania, that caused a partial meltdown of a reactor core leading to offsite releases of radioactivity; the meltdown and its effects led to a long-term halt to the construction of new nuclear power facilities and to comprehensive changes to numerous areas of nuclear power plant operations, including emergency response planning, radiation protection, and increased regulatory oversight.[9]

Finally, the development and establishment of the Environmental Justice movement changed the way in which society viewed sustainability, in fact becoming one of the three main pillars of sustainability (namely, social equity). In 1971, The Second Annual Report of the Council on Environmental Quality cited evidence that urban residents in low-income and African-American neighborhoods were disproportionately exposed to

## TIMELINE OF THE MODERN SUSTAINABILITY MOVEMENT

**1898—*Garden Cities of To-morrow*, by Ebenezer Howard**
- **DESCRIPTION**—In this book, the author describes his vision of towns free of slums in which the residents experience the benefits of urban opportunities and the advantages of nature. The advocated settlement structure tries to achieve a balance between the needs of an individual and the community as a whole. According to the author, the ideal city would have 32,000 residents spread out over 2,400 hectares on a concentric pattern with open spaces and public parks.
- **SIGNIFICANCE**—This book marks the starting point of the garden city movement. This planning concept aims to create cities that are self-contained surrounded by greenbelts. Two cities in England were built using the methods and designs described by Howard: Letchworth Garden City and Welwyn Garden City.

**1949—*A Sand County Almanac*, by Aldo Leopold**
- **DESCRIPTION**—In a chapter titled "The Land Ethic," Leopold expands the concept of ethics from individuals to include the environment. Central to Leopold's philosophy is the notion that the land is to be respected and not to be thought of solely as an economic commodity.
- **SIGNIFICANCE**—The idea behind the "Land Ethic" reinforced the importance of preservation later embedded in national laws to protect wilderness areas. It also presented ideas that land by itself has intrinsic benefits that need to be valued. This idea evolved into the benefits of ecosystem services such as the air pollution filtering of vegetation or the absorption of $CO_2$ by trees.

**1961—*The Death and Life of Great American Cities*, by Jane Jacobs**
- **DESCRIPTION**—In this book, the author critiques the urban planning policies of the time. She argues that inner-city communities are destroyed by modernist planning principles. Moreover, the book provides detailed observations on how cities work and points out the importance of the "four generators of diversity" as the key conditions for a healthy and well-functioning urban community.
- **SIGNIFICANCE**—Jane Jacobs's ideas still have significant impact on today's urban planning approaches. This book in particular has greatly influenced new planning strategies such as New Urbanism, Smart Growth, and Traditional Neighborhood Design, which all acknowledge her "four generators of diversity." The generators are mixed use, short blocks, diverse building types, and density.

**1962—*Silent Spring*, by Rachel Carson**
- **DESCRIPTION**—This book made the public aware of chronic and toxic chemicals that accumulate and effect human health. It led to significant legislative changes in how to make decisions about the use of chemicals, especially pesticides.
- **SIGNIFICANCE**—Many credit this book as launching the modern environmental movement and for facilitating the ban on the insecticide DDT in the United States. The book led to the beginning of legislative investigations concerning the use of pesticides resulting in substantial changes in the Federal Insecticide, Fungicide, and Rodenticide Act (FIFRA) regulations and processes of suspending hazardous chemicals. It led the way for developing guidelines in the United States on regulating chronic hazards and was the first time the public began to understand the serious environmental and health threats of pesticide use.

higher rates of pollution.[10] Other findings substantiated this premise and determined that these populations are at a greater risk because hazardous waste sites and disposal areas were located predominantly in their neighborhoods. Thereafter, Presidential Executive Orders were given to federal agencies, directing them to implement policies to prevent and remedy these types of environmental inequities and injustices (see Chapter 4).

Image © Dobresum, 2012. Used under license from Shutterstock, Inc.

**Three Mile Island, Middletown, Pennsylvania.**

This chapter, and the accompanying timeline, describes many of the groundbreaking events related to sustainability. Additionally, the timeline identifies important natural disasters, legislation, books and reports, and movements and responses that informed the public and advanced sustainability thinking.

## Early Sustainability Thinking: Malthus, Thoreau, Howard, and Muir

This history section traverses from the 1800s to the early 1900s. Many students in my Sustainable Cities course ask: Why do we study people and events from over 100 years ago to better understand sustainability today? Part of the answer is that we must go back, to better prepare for the future. Additionally, various concepts and ideas that formed in the late 1800s helped refine and improve upon some of the theories and concepts that influence our current ideas on sustainability. We begin with the Malthusian

**1968—*The Population Bomb*, by Paul R. Ehrlich**
- **DESCRIPTION**—This best-selling book warned about mass starvation repeating the old Malthusian theory about the reduction of resources due to overpopulation and recommended swift action to slow population growth.
- **SIGNIFICANCE**—During the 1950s and 1960s, there was concern over a population explosion, and this book, along with others of its time, helped to bring this warning message to a wider audience and spark a worldwide debate on population control. It led to later thinking about impacts of environmental deficits from population, and not on overconsumption, which came later under modern sustainability.

**1968—UNESCO (United Nations Educational, Scientific and Cultural Organization) Biosphere Conference**
- **DESCRIPTION**—This event brought together representatives of government and non-governmental organizations to determine what must be done about what United Nations Member States perceived as threats to the biosphere. Those threats included the loss of biodiversity, climate change, and urbanization.

- **SIGNIFICANCE**—This was one of the earliest collaborative efforts at the global level that predates all the later sustainability conferences. It had a strong underlying theme of educating countries on the issues, but little on global action plans.

**1969—National Environmental Policy Act (NEPA)**
- **DESCRIPTION**—Federal law that requires all federal, state, or local agency projects that involve federal funds to prepare reports that detail the amount of environmental impact.
- **SIGNIFICANCE**—Gathering information on the environmental impact of a proposed project allows the agencies to introduce this new information into the decision-making process and reduce the amount of environmental damage. Many say that NEPA is America's environmental policy legislation and introduced the concept of Environmental Impact Statements (EIS) to address the nature and magnitude of impacts from federal related projects and potential mitigation. NEPA also introduced a very important role of citizen involvement into the EIS process.

**1969—*Design with Nature*, by Ian McHarg**
- **DESCRIPTION**—One of the first books to provide an approach for evaluating developments from a perspective of the most suitable developments based on environmental resources

and physical character of the land. It helped establish the use of Geographic Information Systems (GIS) in land use decisions.
- **SIGNIFICANCE**—This book influenced the NEPA approach to suitability analysis. McHarg's great contribution was to give us a philosophy and an approach to studying and making decisions on the suitability of land for various developmental purposes. It helped us understand the limits of development related to the physical aspects of the land and introduced ideas such as bio-capacity, threatened landscapes, land vulnerability, and carrying capacity.

**1970—Clean Air Act**
- **DESCRIPTION**—This federal law requires the Environmental Protection Agency to protect the public from harmful airborne pollution.
- **SIGNIFICANCE**—It set up standards for all cities and jurisdictions to achieve to reduce air emissions with sanctions against "non-attainment" areas.

**1972—United Nations Conference on the Human Environment**
- **DESCRIPTION**—Also called the Stockholm Conference, this conference focused on the need for a common outlook

theory and briefly discuss social Darwinism. The issues underlying the Progressive Era, and specifically the conservation and environmental movements in the late 1800s and early 1900s, pre-date our current concerns regarding urban health, food deserts, and the importance of preserving wilderness areas. For instance, as urban populations grew, pressures for reform mounted concerning issues such as sanitation and public health, the disappearance of open space, housing quality and overcrowding, and traffic congestion and inadequate transportation.[11]

During this time, as part of the reform movement to alleviate pollution and enhance living conditions, the world's first national park, Yellowstone, was established by the United States government in 1872, and New York City's Central Park, the nation's first landscaped public park, was designed by Frederick Law Olmsted and Calvin Vaux in 1857. The debate between keeping natural spaces preserved or intact, versus conserved through the planned management of natural resources to avoid wasteful or destructive use (environmental management), is deep-rooted in the United States and continues today, with debates such as whether to open the Arctic National Wildlife Refuge to oil exploration (which started in approximately 1977)[12] and, more recently, the

Image © nosefomane, 2012. Used under license from Shutterstock, Inc.

**Castle Geyser, Yellowstone National Park, California.**

and strategy to inspire and guide the peoples of the world in the preservation and enhancement of the human environment.
- **SIGNIFICANCE**—The conference was the first major conference organized by the United Nations that focused on environmental issues. Today, the conference is considered the beginning of international environmental politics and resulted in the creation of the United Nations Environment Programme (UNEP).

**1972—United Nations Environmental Programme (UNEP)**
- **DESCRIPTION**—UNEP is an international organization that focuses on protecting and improving the environment. The main goal is to support nations in their efforts to improve their citizens' quality of life in a sustainable manner that does not threaten the livelihood of future generations.
- **SIGNIFICANCE**—UNEP publishes many reports on different environmental issues. Important reports are related to the topic areas of climate change, disasters, and conflicts, ecosystem management, harmful substances, and resource efficiency.

**1972—Clean Water Act**
- **DESCRIPTION**—Federal law structured to stop the release of toxic substances into surface water.
- **SIGNIFICANCE**—Protections against water pollution in the United States have become more sophisticated over time beginning in the late 1800s. This Act went further than any before it had to heavily restrict uncontrolled water pollution and provided federal funds for secondary treatment facilities. It was the first federal water quality statute that provided federal responsibility for cleaning up surface water supplies.

**1972—*Limits to Growth*, by Club of Rome**
- **DESCRIPTION**—This book provides an important approach, using global modeling, to show the relationships between environmental resources, population, and demand. It forecasted a significant diminution in key environmental resources, particularly non-renewable resources and a projection of "collapse" around this time.
- **SIGNIFICANCE**—Although the publication of this book brought a great deal of scrutiny from the scientific community, it has had a significant impact on the conception of environmental issues.

**1973—Endangered Species Act**
- **DESCRIPTION**—Federal law designed to protect endangered species from extinction as a "consequence of economic growth and development untempered by adequate concern and conservation." As another one of the environmental protection laws enacted in the 1970s, this Act helps to protect critical habitat from development or natural resource extraction.
- **SIGNIFICANCE**—The success of this Act has been shown by the large numbers of species that have increased in population. Uncontrolled human development would certainly destroy the habitats and populations of many animal species.

**1973—*Small is Beautiful*, by E. F. Schumacher**
- **DESCRIPTION**—This book consists of different essays by the economist Schumacher in which he argues that the modern economy is unsustainable. He emphasizes that nature's capacity to handle human pollution is limited and argues for an alternative economy, which focuses on achieving the maximum of well-being with the minimum amount of consumption.

controversial Keystone XL Pipeline, a proposed $7 billion pipeline system stretching approximately 2,000 miles that would transport crude oil from the Athabasca oil sands in Alberta, Canada, to multiple destinations in the United States.[13] Similar to the recent interest in biophilic cities and humans' inherent need to interact with the natural world,[14] authors Ralph Waldo Emerson and Henry David Thoreau were important proponents of transcendentalism back in the 1800s. Transcendentalism is the American literary, philosophical, and spiritual movement that flourished in the early nineteenth century, and these authors argued for integrating nature and humans, and encouraged the view that nature has intrinsic values and should be respected and protected as part of individuals' spirituality. This section concludes with a discussion of Ebenezer Howard's utopian urban design of the late nineteenth century—perhaps the first "eco-city"—as a response to the unsustainability of a growing and industrializing London portrayed in his book *Garden Cities of To-Morrow*.

## Malthusian Theory

Today, sustainability thinking requires that we analyze demands for natural resources and their carrying capacity and the limits to growth resulting from increasing demands placed on ecosystems, resources, and natural capital. The discussion of the relationship between an increased population and the ability to produce resources to meet their growing demands is the topic of an essay by Malthus. The central focus

Image © Dle, 2012. Used under license from Shutterstock, Inc.

**The Lake at Central Park, New York City.**

- **SIGNIFICANCE**—This publication was one of the first to critique the use of the gross national product as the measure for human well-being.

**1976—U.N. Habitat Conference**
- **DESCRIPTION**—The conference, also called Habitat 1, took place in Vancouver, British Columbia, and was at that time the largest conference ever organized by the UN. The conference was a result of governments recognizing the potential threats of human activity to the environment. The conference was the first time that the world community discussed issues such as increasing urbanization, population growth, poverty, clean water security, or the need for sustainable urban design.
- **SIGNIFICANCE**—During the conference, the so-called "Vancouver Declaration on Human Settlements" was created. The declaration acknowledged the fact that many human settlements are in severe conditions, especially in developing countries, and that international cooperation needs to be improved in order to help them. The conference also led to the creation of the United Nation's agency UN-Habitat in 1978.

**1978—Love Canal Contamination**
- **DESCRIPTION**—Love Canal is a neighborhood located in Niagara Falls, New York. It became the subject of national attention when it was discovered that a school had been built on a toxic waste dump that had been disturbed by construction activity, thus leaking chemicals into the surrounding environment and ground water. A federal health emergency was declared when residents experienced an extremely high rate of miscarriages, birth defects, cancers, nervous disorders, and toxic milk from nursing mothers. Although the company that buried the waste properly disclosed the location of the toxic materials, it was blamed for improper disposal techniques.
- **SIGNIFICANCE**—This was the first time in U.S. history that emergency funds had been used other than for a natural disaster. This disaster led to the development of the nation's Superfund Act that legislated the identification of toxic sites, as well as the remediation and financial responsibility of the nation's 40,000 contaminated sites. It also led to other mandated cleanup efforts as well as new legislation aimed at pollution prevention and Brownfield cleanup in cities. While sustainability deals mostly with the present

and future, this disaster brings attention to our legacy problems as well.

**1979—Nuclear Accident at Three Mile Island**
- **DESCRIPTION**—During the early morning of March 28, 1979, the Three Mile Island nuclear power plant in Pennsylvania suffered a meltdown that released considerable amounts of radioactive gases into the atmosphere and led to the release of 40,000 gallons of radioactive waste into the Susquehanna River.
- **SIGNIFICANCE**—Noted as the worst accident in U.S. commercial nuclear power plant history, this disaster led to increased federal requirements and decreased public support for nuclear energy as an alternative to coal power plants. New regulations went into place halting the development of new nuclear plants until the nuclear waste problem is solved. Nuclear plants may be coming back because of concern over $CO_2$ from other energy production techniques.

**1980—*Global 2000 Report to the President***
- **DESCRIPTION**—This study commissioned by President Jimmy Carter utilized data from multiple sources to

of his essay, "An Essay on the Principle of Population," is the relationship between population, which Malthus argued grows exponentially, and food production, which only grows linearly. In time, as the population grows, it will reach a threshold so large that it will exhaust the ability to produce the required food. His essay was, in effect, about the concept of "carrying capacity," which demands that society either reduce population growth rates to meet food supply, or expand food production to meet population growth through technology, expansion of agricultural lands, or adjustments to food systems. This idea certainly pre-dates the book written by Paul R. Ehrlich, *The Population Bomb* (1968), predicting that the huge demand of our growing population would outstrip available resources, and *Limits to Growth*, by Donella H. Meadows, Dennis L. Meadows, Jørgen Randers, and William W. Behrens III written in 1974, which argued that unchecked consumption and economic growth was leading our planet toward "overshoot" of its carrying capacity, followed by inevitable disaster.

The central issue in the Malthusian concept is what sustainability is struggling with today; that is, the conundrum of increasing ecological footprints with a declining global resource base and carrying capacity. If population grows so fast and consumes resources at ever-increasing rates, we may not be able to replace or replenish the resources we are consuming, thus compromising our future needs. According to data from the United Nations, from approximately 1800 up until 1940, population has steadily increased, from 1 billion people to more than 2.5 billion. From approximately 1940 to 2011, the global population dramatically increased to more than 7 billion people. This explosion in population is occurring mostly in developing or rapidly industrializing countries, but this growth is also taking place in large cities as the global population is moving from rural communities to urban settings—a major revolution impacting the need for sustainability.

According to estimates by the United Nations, by 2100, the world's population will double from 7 billion to 14 billion. We must ask ourselves what effect that will have on natural resources and ecosystem health. According to calculations by the Global Footprint Network, in 2011, the world's ecological footprint was projected to

make predictions about future trends within the areas of population growth, global warming, energy demand, and resource scarcity.
- SIGNIFICANCE—In the tradition of the limits to growth mentality, this study was an early look at environmental predictions projected out to the year 2000. Far reaching, it was one of the first reports of its kind coming from the US government assessing the state of the environment including global climate change.

**1983— *Projecting Future Sea Level Rise*, by J. S. Hoffman, D. Keyes, and G. Titus**
- DESCRIPTION—Published by the U.S. Environmental Protection Agency (EPA), this report focused on estimating the range of future sea level rise. The purpose of the report was to support the decision-making process of planners, engineers, and policymakers in coastal regions.
- SIGNIFICANCE—The report states that climate change is real and that it could cause severe negative impacts. This was the first time the EPA acknowledged the existence of climate change and its potential threat to the population.

**1984—*State of the World*, by Worldwatch Institute**
- DESCRIPTION—Published annually since 1984 this book series examines current environmental changes. The most recent edition from 2012 focuses on how to move the global economy toward sustainable prosperity.
- SIGNIFICANCE—The publications from Worldwatch Institute are often used by policy makers to make better informed decisions. The institute was founded by Lester Brown, who is a very well-known and influential environmentalist.

**1984—Bhopal Disaster**
- DESCRIPTION—A toxic gas leak from a pesticide plant in Bhopal, India led to the immediate death of over 3,000 people living in the nearby shantytown. It is estimated that approximately 8,000 additional people died later from exposure and over half a million people reported suffering health issues from the incident. A number of employees went to jail because the company operating the plant was negligent about safety precautions and quality controls.
- SIGNIFICANCE—This disaster represented the concerns over global environmental equity issues. Advanced countries often use developing countries for manufacturing

chemicals using extreme ingredients exposing their population to hazards without adequate precautions. It created new concerns over emergency management and institutional capacity for safety and prevention.

**1986—Nuclear Accident at Chernobyl**
- DESCRIPTION—Prior to a routine shutdown on April 26, 1986, the reactor crew at the Chernobyl nuclear plant in present day Ukraine began preparations for an equipment test. Design flaws and operator error ultimately resulted in an explosion that sent radioactive material to cover a large part of Western Soviet Union and Europe. Hundreds of thousands of people were relocated from contaminated areas near the site.
- SIGNIFICANCE—This disaster brought significant attention to improving nuclear safety procedures and also considerably slowed the construction of new nuclear energy plants in every nation around the world. It helped to advance the concept that disasters are now global, moving the environmental debate from local to global and challenging the perceived level of institutional capacity for safety.

be 135 percent of the resources that the earth generated. Therefore, we are now using the earth's resources at a rate that would take between 1.3 and 1.5 planets to sustainably support the population. The research indicates that we are on track to require the resources of two earths well before the middle of the century. If everyone lived the lifestyle the average American lives today, we would need five planets.[15] This means that the land equivalency to the amount of natural resources and food consumed, plus land required for waste disposal, results in a global deficit in terms of being able to regenerate or restore the consumed resources. In 1960, the Ecological Footprint was only 41 percent of the earth's land base. What are the expectations if we have 14 billion people by 2100 with even larger individual consumption? Some estimates for this century predict a medium population projection that slows in 2040, and then a steady state with little population growth. This could be a result of diminishing returns, decreases in natural capital, but also could mean that people will have fewer children.

## The Reform Movement

From the late 1880s to the early 1900s, a reform movement was taking place, particularly in the larger U.S. cities of the Northeast, advancing professions such as Landscape Architecture, Public Administration, and Planning within urban settings. This movement was, in large part, a response to pressing urban issues of large-scale poverty, child labor, public health, overcrowded and low-quality housing, and the plight of immigration. At this time, photojournalists such as Jacob Riis increased public awareness of these poor urban conditions through his photographs depicting deplorable housing conditions, unhealthy living conditions, and poverty in overcrowded tenements. His image-laden book, *How the Other Half Lives*, (1890) propelled legislative reforms in zoning, building codes, child labor laws, and open space and urban parks. Because of these legislative reforms, the first professional organizations emerged to deal with urban blight and health. For example, New York adopted zoning regulations in 1916, which included the concept of the separation of land uses for the first

**1986—*Landscape Ecology*, by Richard Forman and Michel Godron**
- **DESCRIPTION**—This influential book laid out the importance of landscape ecology structures and processes. The book discusses important concepts such as landscape mosaics, natural buffer zones, connectivity and wildlife corridors, and deals with small ecological homogenies units known as "patches."
- **SIGNIFICANCE**—The research presented allows comparing different landscapes and identifying landscapes that are fragmented and need intervention. Furthermore, this concept of landscape ecology has been transferred to urban areas to analyze urban structures as well.

**1987—United Nation's World Commission on Environment and Development, The Brundtland Commission Report "Our Common Future"**
- **DESCRIPTION**—As an effort to bring environmental issues to the global political agenda, this report suggests that the environment and development are closely linked. It defines sustainable development as "development that meets the needs of the present without compromising the ability of future generations to meet their own needs."

- **SIGNIFICANCE**—This definition of sustainable development has been widely accepted by the sustainability movement. Furthermore, sustainability isn't seen anymore just as environmental management, but as the balancing of economics, social well-being, and ecology of an area.

**1988—Intergovernmental Panel on Climate Change (IPCC)**
- **DESCRIPTION**—The IPCC was cofounded by the World Meteorological Organization and the UNEP. The IPCC assesses on a regular basis the available scientific information relevant for improving the understanding of climate change and its possible environmental and socioeconomic impacts.
- **SIGNIFICANCE**—The Intergovernmental Panel on Climate Change is considered today as the leading institution for the assessment of climate change. Since 1988, the IPCC has released four Climate Change Assessment Reports. The fourth and latest report released in 2007 argues that enough scientific data are available to confirm that global climate change is mostly due to human activity and that greater environmental damages can be expected in the future. The fifth assessment report is currently underway and is scheduled to be released in 2014 or 2015.

**1989—Exxon Valdez Oil Spill**
- **DESCRIPTION**—The oil tanker Exxon Valdez ran aground near Alaska and spilled nearly 750,000 barrels of oil. The spill covered roughly 11,000 square miles and affected 1,300 miles of shoreline. Despite significant cleanup efforts, the affected area is expected to take a century or more to fully recover.
- **SIGNIFICANCE**—This oil spill killed wildlife in large amounts including seabirds, otters, seals, bald eagles, and billions of salmon and herring eggs. It brought attention to the destructive capacity of oil spills and this disaster increased public support for environmental protection and safety improvements.

**1989—The Natural Step**
- **DESCRIPTION**—This nonprofit organization was founded by Dr. Karl-Henrik Robert in Sweden with the aim of creating a sustainable society. The organization advises companies, municipalities, and academic institutions in their efforts to create sustainable products and neighborhoods, or conduct research.
- **SIGNIFICANCE**—This worldwide organization is considered one of the leaders in sustainability and has received multiple awards for their work. Today the Natural Step has

time. A new public health organization promulgated new regulations to prevent health epidemics and overcrowding. During this period, professionals who applied scientific approaches to decision-making were being introduced into city management. Large cities also began to develop urban parks in response to a concern over the lack of "breathing space" in cities, which pre-dated the current open space debate, the "urban livability" movement, and the concept of incorporating nature into urban areas through biophilic design. The reform movement of this era provided much momentum to addressing issues of health and open space in cities and the corresponding need for municipal reform.

**Small group of poor in Lower East Side, New York.**

## Preservation versus Conservation

Equally important was the ongoing discussion the historical literature often characterized as a debate between scientific conservation and environmental preservation. The individuals leading this debate about whether to build a dam in a wilderness area to supply water to the city of San Francisco were Gifford Pinchot and John Muir. Pinchot was the first chief of the United States Forest Service, and he argued for the conservation of the nation's reserves through planned use, applying "sustainable yield" principles. The sustainable yield principle focuses on the use and harvest of natural resources, such as timber, fisheries, coal, and agricultural land, but only up to a point where the harvest is able to be replenished, by protecting and placing limits on the annual yield.

---

offices in 11 countries and collaborates with many of the leading global brands.

**1992—*Towns and Town-Making Principles*, by A. Duany and E. Plater-Zyberk**
- **DESCRIPTION**—Well known urban designers Andres Duany and Elisabeth Plater-Zyberk advocate planning strategies that improve traffic conditions and increase the quality of residential life. The advocated principles and strategies comprise the mixing of land uses, the implementation of compact development patterns, the creation of walkable environments, and the allocation of transportation alternatives.
- **SIGNIFICANCE**—Today, these planning strategies are known as New Urbanism. Their proponents argue that land-use patterns have a significant impact on travel behavior and modal choice, and by implementing New Urbanism principles, Greenhouse gas (GHG) emissions can be reduced to mitigate the effects of climate change.

**1990—UN Human Development Index (HDI)**
- **DESCRIPTION**—Developed by the Pakistani economist Mahbub ul Haq, the index measures different factors that are important to determine the development of a country and their residents. Among the factors measured by the HDI

are poverty, literacy, education, and life expectancy. The Index ranges from 0 to 1. The higher the value, the more developed the country.
- **SIGNIFICANCE**—Since 1993, the HDI is used by the United Nations Development Programme for its annual report. Based on the index score, countries are classified into one of the three categories: low human development, medium human development, or high human development. Today, the HDI is considered the standard for measuring well-being.

**1992—Hannover Principles**
- **DESCRIPTION**—Developed by William McDonough and Michael Braungart, the Hannover Principles were among the first to comprehensively address the fundamental ideas of sustainability and the built environment, recognizing our interdependence with nature and proposing a new relationship that includes our responsibilities to protect it.
- **SIGNIFICANCE**—The Principles encourage linking long-term sustainable considerations with ethical responsibility, and reestablishing the integral relationship between natural processes and human activity.

**1992—Earth Summit in Rio de Janeiro, Brazil**
- **DESCRIPTION**—The Earth Summit, also known as the United Nations Conference on Environment and Development

(UNCED), was a major international conference with over 170 governments participating and about 17,000 people in attendance. The main topic areas were alternative sources of energy to replace the use of fossil fuels, public transportation systems, water security, and current and future patterns of production.
- **SIGNIFICANCE**—The summit laid the groundwork for the Kyoto Protocol and created the "Rio Declaration on Environment and Development," "Agenda 21," and the "Forest Principles." Furthermore, the "Convention on Biological Diversity" and the "Framework Convention on Climate Change" were established.

**1992—Agenda 21**
- **DESCRIPTION**—An action plan developed by the UN to be implemented locally for the purpose of sustainable development. It addresses social and economic issues related to poverty, consumption and health; conservation concerns including deforestation and biodiversity; and social justice, in terms of including decision-makers from underrepresented groups.
- **SIGNIFICANCE**—More than 178 governments have adopted Agenda 21.

The annual yield is the amount of natural resources that can be harvested each year without putting undue pressure on the carrying capacity of the resource, so that it cannot be replenished. This concept of protecting the natural capital up to the point where there are no diminishing returns is an underlying principle of sustainability.

On the other side of the debate was John Muir, the founder of the Sierra Club. He argued in favor of preserving certain wilderness areas of the country solely on the basis of intrinsic natural values. This debate continues today; we see it in controversies over protecting the environment versus growing the economy, and overprotecting small endangered species versus using areas for resource use and consumption.

In the context of debates between preservation, conservation management, and economic development, what role does sustainability as a science, an ethic, or framework play in resolving them? Inherent conflicts exist between the three articulated domains of sustainability—social equity, economic well-being, and the environment. Sustainability science requires that we examine all three of those areas to establish approaches on how to best deal with these inherent conflicts. One area of considerable conflict between the domains of sustainability is in the preservation or protection of endangered species versus the needs for community well-being and economic or employment opportunities. The answers are not obvious, and the science of decision-making is not exact, but recent strategies utilizing adaptive capacity, resiliency thinking with a focus on coupled human-ecological systems, and anticipatory governance may prove to be useful approaches at resolving conflicts between the three sustainability domains.

## Visioning the First Eco-City

This section dealing with the period from the 1800s to the early 1900s would be incomplete without a discussion of Ebenezer Howard, an urban visionary, and his book, *Garden Cities of To-morrow* written in 1898. Like the reformers discussed above, this book was a response to the serious urban problems of an industrializing London, such as smog and pollution, overcrowding, and public health issues. His idea was to build a series of small villages around London; these villages of about 30,000 residents

**1993—*The Environment as Hazard*, by I. Burton, R.W. Kates, and G.F. White**
- **DESCRIPTION**—The book explores how people worldwide experience and respond (adapt and cope) to numerous environmental hazards. The authors especially look at how experiences, research findings, and technology affect the development and implementation of environmental policies.
- **SIGNIFICANCE**—The book links hazards theory to risk analysis and shows how important it is to understand social systems while developing appropriate policies for environmental hazards. The book is an update of their earlier classic.

**1993—First Regional Sustainability Indicators**
- **DESCRIPTION**—In 1993, the organization Sustainable Seattle released the first set of regional sustainability indicators. The indicators address the areas of environment, population and resources, culture and society, and economy. Sustainable Seattle was founded in 1991. The organization works with communities to measure their efforts in becoming more sustainable and to improve social justice, shared decision making, and the conservation or restoration of natural environments

- **SIGNIFICANCE**—Since 1993, the list of indicators was expanded and improved. A second set of indicators was released in 1995 and a third set was presented in 1998. Today these indicators are used as a model for measuring urban sustainability.

**1993—U.S. Green Building Council (USGBC)**
- **DESCRIPTION**—A nonprofit organization formed to transform the way buildings and communities are designed, built, and operated, through the use of certification programs. They encourage lower energy and water consumption, reduced $CO_2$ emissions, and environmental preservation.
- **SIGNIFICANCE**—The USGBC has developed the Leadership in Energy and Environmental Design (LEED) rating system for different building types and entire neighborhoods. Today, the rating system is internationally recognized and provides a framework to implement sustainable design, construction, operation, and maintenance solutions.

**1994—*Earth in Mind*, by David W. Orr**
- **DESCRIPTION**—Orr argues that our ecological problems stem from a lack of appropriate education and suggests that

proper education, and not technological advancements, will lead to a more sustainable future.
- **SIGNIFICANCE**—This book illustrates how our education system is contributing to the destruction of the natural world and advocates for teaching students about the importance of considering the ecological implications of our industrialized society.

**1995—*Ecological Design*, by Sim Van Der Ryn and Stuart Cowen**
- **DESCRIPTION**—The book presents a new conceptualization of how to design by bringing together such issues as lifecycle assessment of materials, bio-mimicry, building with local resources and other sustainability factors.
- **SIGNIFICANCE**—The book was an enormous contributor to moving theory into practice through design.

**1996—Term Smart Growth coined by Maryland Governor Parris Glendening**
- **DESCRIPTION**—A national leader in the anti-sprawl movement, Glendening promoted the implementation of "Smart" Building Codes and mass transit options. He is generally credited for coining the phrase "Smart Growth" and it has been adopted by many other entities and organizations.

were to be self-sufficient and based on cooperative urban farming, with separated, smaller areas of industrial development. Additionally, each village would have centers for energy development, but essentially, the separation of land uses was critical so that people could live in relatively dense areas, thus providing opportunities for open space. Finally, in Howard's vision, the various villages would be connected through a mass transit rail line. It is quite astonishing that this concept of the ideal eco-city scenario was envisioned in the 1800s, and not in more recent times.

# The First Half of the Twentieth Century: Dustbowls, Sprawling Suburbs, and Urban Despair

This period reflects a history of cities that ultimately became antithetical to the goals of sustainability along all of its core dimensions—loss of local control, experimentation with technology and chemicals without a full understanding of their detrimental consequences, loss of a sense of place, spiraling growth of a suburban culture, and the emergence of severe social justice issues. We will begin with the first theme, the role of the federal government in environmental decisions and urban form.

## The Role of the Federal Government

The role of the federal government in the early 1900s in creating the dominant urban form of the United States today is fundamental in understanding the challenges confronting sustainability. The book *Cadillac Desert* by Mark Reisner (1986) was an important contribution to the history of sustainability. It documents the establishment of the American West through the significant influence of the federal government's dominant role in the nation's water resources development, achieved through dam building and other physical means to alter the natural flows of waterways to provide cities with potable water, large agricultural systems, and electric power. The development of the United States Southwest would likely not

- **SIGNIFICANCE**—Today, smart growth is a fixed planning principle with its own professional network called the "Smart Growth Network."

**1997—*The Ecology of Place*, by T. Beatley and K. Manning**
- **DESCRIPTION**—This publication provides an alternative to the current land development pattern causing urban sprawl, social isolation, and numerous economic problems. The authors do not only focus on the needed physical layout of a development, but also discuss a broad set of ways in which communities are organized and operate.
- **SIGNIFICANCE**—The book presents an approach to repairing and enhancing communities by introducing the vision of "sustainable places." The authors present a vision of an urban environment that reduces land consumption, strengthens local economies, and restores a sense of place and community among the residents.

**1997—Kyoto Protocol**
- **DESCRIPTION**—The Kyoto Protocol is an international treaty with the goal to reduce greenhouse gas emissions to prevent further increases in the global temperature. Today, more than 190 countries have signed the treaty.

- **SIGNIFICANCE**—The protocol is among the few international environmental treaties that are legally binding. As a result, the Kyoto Protocol can serve as a powerful legal instrument for mitigating climate change

**1999—*Natural Capitalism*, by P. Hawken, A. Lovins, and H. Lovins**
- **DESCRIPTION**—The book emphasizes how the current global economic system exploits natural resources and ecosystems. The book argues that the global economy does not value natural capital enough and without rethinking the relationships between human and natural capital, our current businesses and high quality of life cannot be sustained.
- **SIGNIFICANCE**—One of the first books that describes a sustainable economic model considering environmental limits and the planet's depleting natural resources.

**1999—Resilience Alliance Sweden**
- **DESCRIPTION**—The Swedish Resilience Alliance is an interdisciplinary research organization. Many different scientists and practitioners work together to improve the understanding of the dynamics behind social-ecological systems.

- **SIGNIFICANCE**—The published result from the Resilience Alliance includes key concepts in the fields of resiliency, adaptability, and transformability. The created body of knowledge presents important insights for sustainable policy and practice.

**2000—Millennium Summit**
- **DESCRIPTION**—For three days, many world leaders met in New York to discuss the future direction of the United Nations heading into the 21st century. The summit focused on global issues such as poverty, AIDS, globalization, and fair trade.
- **SIGNIFICANCE**—During the meeting, the Millennium Declaration was ratified. The Declaration provides a framework for the 189 member countries to help improve the quality of life of the population in the poorest countries.

**2000—*Earth Charter*, by the UN**
- **DESCRIPTION**—This declaration outlines a global roadmap for creating a just, sustainable, and peaceful society. The document addresses themes such as sustainable ways of living, sustainable development, and ecological integrity.
- **SIGNIFICANCE**—The drafting process was mostly driven by a global civil society initiative and over 45,000 organizations

have occurred without the water resources development of canals and irrigation systems, building of dams on rivers, and especially the control of the Colorado River through various investments in large-scale physical infrastructure. It is questionable, for example, whether cities such as Phoenix could have developed to become the sixth largest city in the country had it not been for the massive governmental investments and subsidies in water projects. In 1938, water from the Colorado River under the Colorado River Compact was allocated to the six basin states based on their population—Arizona, California, Nevada, Utah, New Mexico, and Colorado, and through three desert areas located in this region. At present, large infrastructure projects along the Colorado River enable this allocation of water distribution.

Image © timothy Oleary, 2012. Used under license from Shutterstock, Inc.

**Aerial view of a hydroelectric plant at Hoover Dam along the Colorado River.**

Federal planning at the scale undertaken by the United States Bureau of Reclamation was massive and reflected new thinking on the importance of investing in

and governments support the Earth Charter. Today, the Charter is often used for educational purposes in the field of sustainable development.

**2002—Melbourne Principles**
- **DESCRIPTION**—The Melbourne Principles are the result of an international charrette organized by the United Nations Environment Programme and the International Council for Local Environmental Initiatives. Altogether, ten statements were created on how cities can become more sustainable.
- **SIGNIFICANCE**—The principles were formulated in way that they could be easily understood by decision-makers to guide them in their efforts to make cities more sustainable. The principles were also adopted as part of the final communique of the World Summit on Sustainable Development 2002 in Johannesburg.

**2002—World Summit on Sustainable Development**
- **DESCRIPTION**—Taken place in Johannesburg, South Africa, the Summit occurred ten years after the first summit in Rio de Janeiro and focused on the challenge of sustainable development. Therefore, the summit addressed issues such

as corruption, armed conflicts, natural disasters, terrorism, chronic diseases, and many more.
- **SIGNIFICANCE**—Among several international agreements, the Johannesburg Declaration was the most significant outcome of the summit. The declaration focuses particularly on existing worldwide conditions that threaten the sustainable development of the world community.

**2002—*Cradle to Cradle*, by William McDonough and Michael Braungart**
- **DESCRIPTION**—Cradle to Cradle refers to a framework to create products of all kind that are waste free. The authors emphasize the benefits of an ecological intelligent design process, compared to the current industry standards in terms of creating products that can be recycled with the materials being used again. The book provides detailed descriptions of design principles and examples of products.
- **SIGNIFICANCE**—The book is acknowledged as one of the strongest arguments for a shift in how we think about producing goods. Furthermore, the book provides detailed descriptions of design principles and examples of products

**2004—*The Nature of Design*, by David W. Orr**
- **DESCRIPTION**—The book is an arrangement of several essays by the author, which are organized into thematic chapters. The book addresses the designer's responsibility to protect the environment and points out that most issues that the ecosystem faces today are a result of design failures of our modern time.
- **SIGNIFICANCE**—Throughout the book, the concept of ecological design is addressed from different directions providing a comprehensive overview of the topic. Orr advocates ecological design and urges educating college students about environmental awareness. He favors traditional processes, materials, and natural paradigms, but also acknowledges the need for modern approaches under certain circumstances. The book provides a sustainable mentality and attitude for the approach of future design.

**2005—*Native to Nowhere*, by Timothy Beatley**
- **DESCRIPTION**—The book critiques current development patterns for causing urban sprawl, the separation of uses, and the creation of anonymous communities.
- **SIGNIFICANCE**—Based on an extensive literature review, this book focuses on the role of the built environment in creating a sense of place and community.

integrated, regional projects that would entail employment, energy development, city growth, and agricultural production. These mega-stimulus projects had, as their foundation, development consistent with "multiple use strategies," regional development, and multi-phased planning. Multiple use strategies incorporated dams, water, and electric projects as a means for increasing employment opportunities and regional development.

Another example of this type of considerable federal government intervention is the Tennessee Valley Authority project of the 1930s. Again utilizing multiple-use strategies, the federal government invested in building major energy projects and dams for water supplies and agriculture uses in the region that included Tennessee, and parts of Mississippi and Alabama, a region fraught with underemployment and unemployment. The 1930s reflected the first time the government utilized multiple-use strategies for power and development that also addressed the goal of increasing employment and social transformations at a regional level. We should ask ourselves whether these were efforts at sustainable transformation. On one hand, the projects dealt with economic development, increasing employment during the Depression era, and created new forms of energy development; these efforts resulted in transformations of the social structure, education, and alleviation of poverty through a major federal stimulus—which can be thought to be "sustainable" development. On the other hand, however, these projects moved the federal government into a primary role in terms of energy development and social well-being, albeit in partnerships with local governments and the private sector, which represented a move away from local scale decision-making, one of the tenets of sustainability thinking.

## The Dust Bowl

In the 1930s, one of the most devastating disasters struck the United States, impacting nine states in the Central Plains, destroying farms and homes, and resulting in over 100,000 people migrating out of the region for jobs elsewhere. The victims of the Dust Bowl can be thought of as one of the first group of America's "ecological refugees." This disaster was slow in its beginning phases, and thus, it was difficult to

---

**2005—European Union Emission Trading Scheme (EU ETS)**
- **DESCRIPTION**—Launched in 2005, the EU ETS was designed to help support EU member states to meet the GHG emissions reduction targets set in the Kyoto Protocol. The EU ETS is a so-called cap-and-trade system that restricts the total amount of carbon dioxide that can be emitted from large industries. Companies that stay under the limit can sell their extra emission permits to companies that are not able to reduce their emissions.
- **SIGNIFICANCE**—The EU ETS was the first large emission-trading scheme in the world. After the three-year trial period, the trading program was fully implemented for the European Union in 2008. Although the program is not perfect, it is still considered a blueprint for many countries that are developing or have already launched their own cap-and-trade system.

**2006—Resilience Thinking, by Brian Walker and David Salt**
- **DESCRIPTION**—This book introduces the concept of resilience as a theoretical framework to challenge the current practices of resource management. It defines resilience as the capacity of a system to absorb disturbance and still retain its basic function and structure. This systems approach to sustainability encourages the consideration of less obvious effects from interaction between humans and the environment.
- **SIGNIFICANCE**—The book presents an alternative and more sustainable school of thought for resource use and management compared to the current paradigm that focuses on maximizing returns. The basis of sustainable thinking is to manage coupled socio-ecological systems.

**2006—An Inconvenient Truth**
- **DESCRIPTION**—Directed by Davis Guggenheim, this documentary aims to educate the public about the issue of global climate change. With the help of former U.S. Vice President Al Gore, the movie presents the science and impacts of climate change in a way that is easily understandable to the lay public.
- **SIGNIFICANCE**—This Oscar award-winning documentary is often credited with raising the public awareness regarding climate change and moving the topic up on the political agenda of many governments.

**2007—Fourth Assessment Report on Climate Change, by the IPCC**
- **DESCRIPTION**—The most current report by the IPPC on the existing body of knowledge regarding the science, causes, impact, and strategies of global climate change.
- **SIGNIFICANCE**—The Intergovernmental Panel on Climate Change (IPCC) estimated in their fourth assessment report in 2007 that the Earth's surface temperature increased by about one degree Fahrenheit in the last century. The report points out that the rapid change in global climate during the last several decades is mostly caused by human activity.

**2008—More than 50% of World Population Live in Urban Areas**
- **DESCRIPTION**—In 2008, the World Health Organization concluded that more than half of the world's population lives in an urban environment. As a result, cities and urban areas consume about 75% of the world's energy and are responsible for up to 75% of GHG emissions.
- **SIGNIFICANCE**—This statement emphasizes that a majority of the world's energy consumption either occurs in cities or as a direct result of the way cities function. Therefore,

recognize that an underlying environmental crisis was looming, yet the recovery process of restoring damaged ecosystems also was long term. Unlike an earthquake or hurricane, the effects of the Dust Bowl were not sudden, but rather characteristic of a slow onset hazard; however, similar to what happened after Hurricane Katrina struck New Orleans, the recovery created economic and social dislocations that lasted years. Years of highly inadvisable intensive agricultural practices, a long-term regional drought, and the resulting disappearance of nutrients in the soils contributed to the erosion of the topsoil that winds carried away. We have

Source: Library of Congress

**Son of farmer in dust bowl area. Cimarron County, Oklahoma**

historical records of the social effects on individuals and families in the music of Woody Guthrie and a record of the lives of the "ecological refugees" in John Steinbeck's infamous novel, *The Grapes of Wrath* (1939). In the Central Plains and elsewhere, the Dust Bowl was responsible for the resulting inability to farm the land, the loss of self-reliance, and the need to escape the environmental hazards. This disaster, however, ultimately led to an entire rethinking of how to stabilize soil, grow food sustainably, and develop means of protecting ecosystems. Seventy years later, we are looking at new approaches and methods in how we can more successfully manage socio-ecological systems through a concept called "Resilience Thinking," encapsulated in a book by Brian Walker and David Salt (2006).

## The Suburban Movement

The period from the 1940s through the 1960s represents an important era in terms of its long-term effects on issues surrounding the environment, culture, social justice, and

sustainability strategies and environmental policies cannot focus only on the natural environment, but must address the urban environment as the key area of consumption and pollution.

**2009—Copenhagen Accord**
- **DESCRIPTION**—This document was drafted during the 15th Conference of Parties to the United Nations Framework Convention on Climate Change. The document argues for the continuation of the Kyoto Protocol, which is set to expire in 2012. Furthermore, the Copenhagen Accord recognizes climate change as one of today's greatest challenges and emphasizes the importance of mitigation and adaptation strategies.
- **SIGNIFICANCE**—Compared to the Kyoto Protocol, countries were not able to agree on a legally binding agreement. Thus, the Copenhagen Accord is not a binding successor to the Kyoto Protocol. Instead, many countries pledge voluntarily to GHG emission reduction targets by the year 2020.

**2009—*Resilient Cities*, by P. Newman, T. Beatley, and H. Boyer**
- **DESCRIPTION**—The book discusses ways to make cities more resilient to the threats of peak oil and climate change.
- **SIGNIFICANCE**—Based on various case studies, the authors identify and examine seven key themes that are essential for a city to become more resilient and confront climate change on the local level.

**2010—BP Gulf Oil Spill**
- **DESCRIPTION**—An explosion on the Deepwater Horizon oil platform in the Gulf of Mexico on April 20, 2010 killed 11 workers and injured 17 others. The pipe connecting the platform to the well at the ocean floor broke, releasing nearly 5 million barrels of oil in the Gulf over a period of 3 months before it was capped.
- **SIGNIFICANCE**—Believed to be the worst environmental disaster in U.S. history, it was almost 20 times greater than the Exxon Valdez oil spill. The contaminated water killed wildlife, closed fisheries, and dramatically reduced tourism

along the Gulf Coast. Questions were raised as to the need for oil extraction that far off the coastline, the need for alternative energy sources, and the requirement for enhance institutional capacities to prevent and response to these types of disasters.

**2010—*Regenerative Cities*, by H. Girardet**
- **DESCRIPTION**—This report was developed by 30 experts on climate change, urban planning, and architecture from the HafenCity University Hamburg (Germany) and the World Future Council. The report targets policymakers on all levels who are interested in implementing policies to reduce cities' ecological footprint.
- **SIGNIFICANCE**—The report points out the important relationship between cities and its surrounding area in terms of making cities more self-sufficient. In total, 38 policy recommendations are presented. The policies focus on the areas of energy sufficiency, water security, waste management, solar energy, and local food, more nature in the city, green businesses, and restorative urbanization.

the disappearance of a sense of place. After World War II, people began moving out of central cities to suburbs with primarily new, single-family housing developments further away from the noise, pollution, traffic, and high-rises of cities. Suburbanization made it necessary for the separation of land uses among industrial, commercial, and residential uses, and the growth of massive shopping centers located in service areas of the residential dwellings. The federal government provided support and financial incentives to develop suburban homes, shopping centers, and new public transit systems through the creation of the national highway system, which resulted in the creation of a nation of widespread automobile dependency, and a proliferation of highly repetitive "cookie cutter" housing developments, and thus, caused the loss of meaningful place identity. The suburban movement of this period led to the formation of a new American dream based on individual home ownership and automobile dependency.

These new suburbs developed on what had previously been agricultural lands. Additionally, the movement away from cities required longer commutes to work and the construction of highway systems, resulting in increased vehicle miles traveled, traffic congestion, increased pollution emissions, and the destruction of old, stable urban neighborhoods to make room for the new highway construction, often through African-American minority communities, creating havoc and the destruction of neighborhoods that were previously stable and self-reliant. Although this may be a generalization, the 1940s and 1950s led to the outward movement of the white working-class members of the population and the inward movement of minorities into the central cities. These movements resulted in social and class segregation that became the concerns of the planners of the 1960s and 1970s.

The separated industrial land uses remained in central cities as centers of employment, but over time, these sites often became abandoned and contaminated with toxic chemicals. Now known as brownfields, these abandoned industrial sites in many U.S. cities were predominately located in near proximity to minority neighborhoods. The abundant presence of dangerous toxins in minority neighborhoods led to the Environmental Justice movement of the 1970s and 1980s, a social issue central to urban sustainability, as discussed in Chapter 4. It was also later that we began to understand the subtle and difficult problems that came with the suburban urban form. The automobile-dependent society supported by cheap nonrenewable energy brought with it accumulated carbon dioxide emissions that resulted in global climate change; the sense of neighborhoods and place identity declined, and along with it, childhood obesity increased; the prevalence of gated communities and the destruction of urban ecological networks; and the decline of the central cities. Sustainable Urbanism, with its current emphasis on urban design, placemaking, form-based zoning, and suburban repair, demonstrates the importance of alternative urban forms and the development of "livable communities."

Image ©Andy Dean Photography, 2012. Used under license from Shutterstock, Inc.

**Typical suburban neighborhood in the United States.**

# Pathways to Brundtland: Building the Foundation

With the separation of land uses starting in the 1940s and the proliferation of long distances of automobile travel from home to work and to school and entertainment, cities were beginning to be thought of as a societal problem in a manner similar to 60 years earlier when Ebenezer Howard envisioned more livable and sustainable communities. By the 1950s, new technologies such as nuclear power and outputs of industrial production such as pesticide chemicals were being utilized to fulfill the American dream alongside suburbanization. But the late 1950s and early 1960s also proved to be a period of the first public warnings that progress in technology and the suburban dream had unintended effects. Three major areas of concern began to stir the public consciousness: the emergence of nuclear technology; the massive expansion and use of pesticides; and the use of chemicals in the nation's food supply. These three societal issues changed the face of environmentalism from the beginning of its history for the reasons discussed below.

In all three cases, progress had been centrally defined by science and its applications coupled with an abiding, steadfast, and unquestioning trust in science and its management. In an ironic twist, scientific innovations such as the emergence of ecology as a life science and risk analysis eventually helped identify and define the new hazards of technology. The fact that the various adverse consequences of these sciences were unintended and unmanaged by government, and that there was a lack of public policies aimed at remediating these problems, ultimately resulted in growing mistrust and an increasing expression of despair and concern from the public. The questioning of both science as progress and a lack of trust in government to protect the public were two precedents on the pathway to sustainability. Each of the three areas resulted in significant public protests and the earliest environmental movements. Additionally, all three issues were connected to health impacts, but not those about which the public already had experience, that is, breathing bad air, acute poisonings, and accidents; these were entirely new health ailments from the chronic exposure and ingestion of minute chemical residues, resulting in carcinogenesis, mutagenesis, and the accumulation of toxins in children. The view that the environment was a limitless (and without consequence) repository for any and all industrial and chemical intrusions and accumulations was no longer acceptable. This change in the perception of science and a newly ascribed role for both scientists and the public was articulated in two books: *Science and Survival* written by Barry Commoner in 1967, and *Silent Spring* written by Rachel Carson in 1962.

## A Not-Too *Silent Spring*

By the mid-1950s, few warnings had been raised about the hazards of chemical use, but the body of evidence began to mount. Between 1950 and 1965, the pesticide chemical industry grew quickly with over 55,000 chemicals becoming available on the market. Questions arose about the lack of standardized chemical testing protocols, the consistent need to register all chronic chemical hazards, and the need to reexamine those that had been registered much earlier. Under the prevailing registration concept of the 1950s, a chemical pesticide was tested for its efficacy and acute contamination, specifically its effects on agricultural sprayers. Yet science was beginning to detect small residual contamination and human health effects of exposure and ingestion. It was not until 10 to 15 years later that legislation was promulgated to establish new testing standards and the basis for the evidence needed to suspend chemicals that were already in the market.

One of the most famous and impactful books on environmental hazards and the lack of chemical regulation, especially pesticides, was Rachel Carson's *Silent Spring*. Carson was a governmental biologist, and her book revealed the widespread use of the pesticide Dichlorodiphenyltrichloroethane (commonly known as DDT) and its impacts on animals. Her research also established the ability of DDT and other similar pesticides to traverse the entire food chain and ultimately affect human health. She was able to communicate to a large national audience about how small, residual pesticides such as DDT remain in the environment and do not readily break down and dissipate. Moreover, she demonstrated their ability to bioaccumulate in organisms as the chemicals move up the food chain to ultimately accumulate in human tissues, resulting in chronic health problems and birth defects. She provided scientific evidence of how bioaccumulated chemical residues caused problems in the structures of bird eggs, thus leading to the title, *Silent Spring*, intended to convey a powerful image of an outdoor world devoid of birds. It caused eggshells to break, thus threatening the survival of majestic birds, such as the osprey, bald eagle, and peregrine falcon. As the most commonly used pesticide of that era, DDT had been spread everywhere to kill pests and it was long-lasting; thus, human exposure and ingestion resulted in persistent and chronic health hazards. Carson had the skill to take on the complexity of issues in science and biology and write it in such a compelling way that her book became a bestseller. This book stirred organizations into action and became a catalyst for the emergence of local, and ultimately national, environmental and public interest groups.

In addition to her focus on DDT, she and others raised concerns over the use of 2,4,5–Trichlorophenoxyacetic acid (2,4,5-T), an herbicide used in parks to eliminate weeds; it was also linked to birth defects. There were significant warning signs that the use of 2,4,5-T resulted in serious health problems after soldiers serving in the Vietnam War began developing toxicity issues subsequent to their exposure to 2,4,5-T. In addition to these chemicals, other long-lasting chemicals came under suspicion at that particular time, and by the 1970s, actions were being implemented by the (then newly established) United States Environmental Protection Agency to suspend the broad uses of these dangerous chemicals.

## The Nuclear Promise?

The post-World War II era in the United States brought about a promise from industry and science that the commercialization of nuclear power would lead to a long period of peaceful uses of the atom and virtually free energy for the U.S. market. In the late 1950s and early 1960s, however, the public began to have concerns about the serious environmental and health issues connected with nuclear energy. The first national environment movement, started by a largely female interest group in the late 1950s, centered on the health hazards of nuclear fallout from aboveground atomic bomb testing in Nevada. These concerns were specifically focused on the effects from the nuclear residual, radioactive Strontium-90 that was implicated in causing children's bone and brain deformities. The movement coalesced around eliminating nuclear testing because of the deleterious health consequences of Strontium-90.

The debate over atomic testing continued, and the world experienced two serious nuclear reactor events in the 1950s, although both were small and occurred in experimental facilities, as compared to the subsequent Chernobyl and Three Mile Island disasters. One accident was the Windscale accident in Britain (in reality, a nuclear meltdown); the fission material spread large distances from the facility, and extensive areas were cordoned off; cattle near the impact zone were killed; and milk could not be used from these areas. It was one of the first major catastrophes resulting from the use of this new nuclear technology. The second accident occurred at the Chalk River plant located in Canada. The acceptance of the nuclear myth of safe commercial nuclear power and low costs of development and energy production began to dissipate by the mid-1960s as the science of risk analysis started to mature and be used in regulatory decision-making. Again, the confluence of several factors resulted in a society living under a siege of uncertainty from newly discovered hazards: unintended risks of technology and science; growing distrust of both technology and governmental oversight; limitations in institutional capacities to fully understand, manage, and regulate chronic toxicity resulting from environmental exposure; and the always looming insidious and dangerous health problems associated with chemical exposure. Under these conditions, an advanced society should respond in a number of ways: continue to develop scientific knowledge of critical fields, such as risk analysis, ecology, and health sciences; advance knowledge in the associated policy fields; and seek new approaches in regulations to deal with scientific uncertainties. This is exactly what transpired in the 1970s and 1980s.

Nuclear fallout and Strontium-90 were just the tip of the public health iceberg; health hazards connected to nuclear technology demonstrated serious problems at all phases of the nuclear fuel cycle. One of the most vulnerable populations, Native Americans, bore a disproportionate burden of risk from the development of nuclear power. Studies for the Nevada Nuclear Waste Project Office found high levels of cancer rates from exposure to radioactive materials downwind from the aboveground sites of atomic bomb testing in Nevada. Decades later, the Paiute tribe of Indians in particular was extremely sensitive to the proposed use of routes for the transportation of spent nuclear fuel through their reservation for long-term storage at Yucca Mountain, in Nevada. Moreover, years after employment in uranium mines ended in the Navajo Nation, a large number of tribal members were stricken with related cancers and high mortality rates, and some of their homes had to be destroyed and buried. And, still later, nuclear disasters continued to unfold in 1979 with the Three Mile Accident in Pennsylvania; the Chernobyl nuclear plant meltdown in Russia spewing forth radioactive materials across Europe; and, just recently, the earthquake-driven destruction in 2011 of six nuclear reactors in Fukushima, Japan, and its horrific aftermath. In building a sustainable future, what are the principles that should guide us given this history? What are the lessons that we should be learning from this trajectory of history? Projecting this past into our new thinking about the role of sustainability solutions today causes us to pause and think about new tradeoffs. For example, the use of non-renewable fuels results in the emissions of greenhouse gases causing climate change. Even though many countries have accepted the Kyoto Protocol, global levels of carbon dioxide are not declining, but are actually increasing. Thus, it may make sense to substitute non-renewable energy sources for nuclear power plants to produce electric power because nuclear power does not result in emissions of carbon dioxide. However, the risks of nuclear power are perceived to be very high, including concerns over terrorist threats, the lack of appropriate nuclear waste storage sites, and possible accidents throughout the fuel cycle and especially at the sites of power plants. Thus, any decision in favor of developing a new generation of nuclear plants as a way to offset carbon emissions and mitigate climate change presents us with a whole other set of risks.

## A National Environmental Policy: NEPA and EPA

While public interest group activities intensified over pesticides, nuclear energy, and the deterioration of environmental quality, particularly over air and water pollution, multiyear public and legislative efforts were directed at the establishment of an integrated environmental policy for the country. After years of intensive lobbying efforts, the National Environmental Policy Act (NEPA) was established in 1969. This was followed a year later with the establishment of the United States Environmental Protection Agency, the principle executive agency that implements NEPA and all environmental legislation and its regulations. NEPA is significant environmental policy legislation, requiring that decisions affecting the environment be based on evaluations of an "Environmental Impact Assessment." It applies to any environmental project, facility, program, and policy that requires the federal government to provide a permit, oversight, or resources. For example, if a locality or state needs federal government approval or a permit, the federal government has the power to deny or approve the permit based on whether the activity, facility, or policy change creates undue harm to the natural environment or to people. Federal permits or federal government funding is needed for a wide range of projects, such as expanding rangeland for cattle, approval for construction of a non-state highway that may create a significant amount of air pollution, construction of a hazardous waste treatment facility or a recycling plant, or the cleanup of a brownfield site. Accordingly, NEPA would require an environmental impact assessment to identify and measure their potential impacts to the natural environment or people.

Under NEPA, all federal governmental agencies are required to have established methods and procedures to conduct environmental assessments. The strength of NEPA (as well as its limitation) is the process by which an assessment is done. Typically, an initial assessment evaluates whether a proposed action may result in "significant impacts," and, in cases where a determination is made that significant impacts are likely to result, an "Environmental Impact Statement" is needed. An Environmental Impact Statement requires a detailed evaluation of the alternatives to the proposed action, the impacts of each alternative, and ways to mitigate the adverse effects of the likely alternative. One of the more interesting aspects of NEPA pertains to the use of "suitability analysis" and geographical information systems (GIS) mapping as a method to evaluate impacts of proposed land uses on existing land characteristics and sensitivities. This suitability analysis often examines issues such as carrying capacity, risk-benefit analysis of ecosystems, as well as assessing environmental verses economic tradeoffs. NEPA also establishes the public's right to participate in NEPA hearings, and partnerships between local and state agencies to partner with the federal agency or agencies involved in a NEPA deliberation. As part of the process of determining environmental impacts, NEPA also permits litigation against the regulators or industry if the assessment process was not carried out in full compliance of the Act or in the setting of new policies.

The development of significant regulations and regulatory guidelines for actions on hazardous chemicals and technologies were established through long periods of litigation between environmental organizations and the EPA. For example, in the early 1970s, the Environmental Defense Fund (a private entity established in 1967, aimed at preserving nature) sued the EPA for failing to suspend the use of several organo-chlorine pesticides (that had been mentioned in *Silent Spring*) because ample evidence indicated that exposure to such chemicals caused widespread negative impacts to ecological systems and human health. One result of the litigation is that EPA scientists established a set of scientific principles to determine the types and levels of evidence required to deduce carcinogenesis in humans from chronic hazards, and these scientific principles were used to successfully argue in favor of regulating low-exposure chronic hazards.

As mentioned earlier, the EPA developed rules and regulations for managing pollution, pesticide hazards, brownfield regulations and cleanup, and waste management and treatment through the Resources Conservation and Recovery Act of 1976. Later, in the 1980s, the EPA was responsible for the cleanup of the most dangerous toxic sites through the Comprehensive Environmental Response, Compensation, and Liability Act of 1980, commonly known as Superfund. Through this regulatory authority, the EPA regulates the management of hazardous wastes, solid waste, recycling, treatment plants, and implementation issues. In contrast to Carson's days of legislative inaction, the EPA in the 1970s began rigorous initiatives to control the risks of pesticides. It developed scientifically based policies to evaluate the reregistration of pesticides and approaches to discontinue the use of the most dangerous pesticides; required warning labels and use standards regulating how the chemicals could be applied in the field; and, established guidelines, criteria, and scientific principles to ban the use of particular pesticides, especially those that presented an increased risk of severe chronic hazards to humans.

The 1970s represents an era of promulgating, strengthening, and revising the federal government's major environmental legislation and their regulations governing air, water, and land pollution, hazardous waste storage and treatment, and domestic waste management. The implementation of environmental quality concerns and the emergence of citizen participation in the environmental area became codified as part of EPA procedures. It thus constitutes an important period in environmental history.

In recent years, the EPA has taken on new and added responsibilities focusing on sustainability. It has supported regional and state offices dealing with environmental justice issues and established standards and methods for evaluating projects and policies from the perspective of equity considerations. Moreover, as discussed in Chapter 4, the agency has funded studies to demonstrate how to develop neighborhoods and retrofit them to meet green objectives and reduce their carbon footprints. EPA is also working on developing an air quality standard for carbon dioxide, the main source of greenhouse gases.

# Back to the Future: Limits to Growth

From an environmental history perspective, the 1970s were characterized largely by the implementation of environmental policies through NEPA and enforcement of environmental regulations through the EPA, as well as the incorporation of citizen involvement in decision-making. Looking back, it was a time of creative and innovative solutions utilizing the court system to help shape environmental regulatory procedures, and also applications of new fields of study such as risk analysis, ecological sciences, and environmental modeling. During this time, several important books were also published concerning the earth's diminishing carrying capacity because of population growth, the increased use of finite resources, and failing to take actions to protect depleting natural resources. This period ends with four catastrophic events in the late 1970s and early 1980s that helped shape global environmental consciousness and concerns, but it also revealed the lingering public concerns of the unintended consequences of hazardous technology and the ostensible lack of effective oversight and institutional capacities to manage and control complex systems. The four disasters, Three Mile Island, Love Canal, Chernobyl, and Bhopal, have become ominous symbols of the difficulties inherent in making trade-offs between uncertain, high-risk technologies and quick fixes for energy, agriculture, and urban development.

## Limits to Growth

Two parallel threads of environmental history mark this period. One thread is exemplified by regulatory responses to improve the quality of the environment and to address the legacy problems of contamination. The other thread is typified by popular publications on the carrying capacity premise and the pressures that human consumption is placing on natural resources and the possible ultimate societal "collapse" described in Jared Diamond's book, *Collapse: How Societies Fail or Succeed* (2005). Starting in the late 1960s, books such as Paul Ehrlick's bestselling *Population Bomb* (1968), Commoner's *Science and Survival* (1967), and *The Tragedy of the Commons* (1967) by Garrett Hardin, offered the public a view of less-than-optimistic futures should we fail to protect our natural resources and manage them within their limits. However, *Limits to Growth*, published in 1972 (and updated in 2004) by the Club of Rome, captured significant attention and reaction. Using global estimates and assumptions about population and resources, the book was a product of basic global modeling and the consequences on food and other resources given global increases in consumption of non-renewable resources. The modeling results focused on the period from 1900 to the year 2100. Both population and industrial output increase sharply until about year 2030, coinciding with substantial increases in world oil production and food output. While these factors increase exponentially, the world's natural resources slowly decline until between 2020 and 2040. From 2020 onward, industrial output, food availability, and natural resources sharply decline. The most notable decline is in oil production, which plummets and fails by around 2050. Population collapse is possible in these scenarios because of diminishing natural resources due to population growth, consumption, and needs for industrial outputs as life expectancy increases. The book predicted that by 2000, world oil production would decline very sharply, which in reality has not yet occurred, but natural resources are certainly declining.

The argument in *Limits to Growth* has been criticized, but it presents an interesting learning scenario of the global carrying capacity idea. It predates the more current ecological footprint concept and the notion of collapse that we reference in this book. Looking back helps explain why these limits failed to be realized. The discovery of new areas for fossil fuel production and more effective production methods expanded global oil production, and the production of oil from tar sands will likely expand future production even more. Like Malthusian projections, exponential population growth and consumption of finite resources cause overshoot of the planet's carrying capacity. This idea is similar to, and based on the same logic as, the Ecological Footprint concept that was addressed in the 30-year update of *Limits to Growth* (2004).

## The Importance of Love Canal

While numerous accidents and disasters unfortunately shaped our environmental history (as identified in the Timeline in this chapter), from the perspective of sustainable cities, the Love Canal event provides significant insights and imparts substantial knowledge concerning the need for sustainable urban land practices. The event itself and its causes reflect one of the worst examples of land ethics and practices—ones that we may now observe to be profoundly contradictory to sustainability goals.

As early as the 1920s, a chemical firm located in Niagara Falls, New York, emptied its hazardous wastes into Love Canal, a dry unfinished canal abutting its plant. Over the years, the plant became nonoperational and the canal was no longer visually apparent because of the addition of topsoil on the site. In the mid-1950s, Niagara Falls approved a proposal for a subdivision development. Thus, despite warnings from the chemical company, a neighborhood and school were established—on and adjacent to land that was highly contaminated with over 20,000 tons of hazardous industrial wastes and byproducts. Approximately 20 years later, the toxic neighborhood was "uncovered" by a group of Love Canal residents when they documented a clustering of serious illnesses among the residents and schoolchildren living there. In their initial response to these residents, local officials strenuously denied that any type of health or environmental issues existed.

After an environmental review, a substantial portion of this neighborhood proved to be unlivable. Love Canal became ground zero of a multi-year, highly contentious battleground for remediation, relocation, and health reparations. Upon state and federal recognition of the dire nature of this problem, the federal government responded (for the first time) to this type of human-caused disaster by providing emergency funds for relocation and recovery.

Like a slow-moving but highly lethal exploding bomb, this human-caused disaster sent shockwaves around the country. The public asked how it could have happened considering all of the regulations in place focusing on environmental quality. They pondered the notion that if this had happened in Love Canal, so many years after toxic chemicals were buried and hidden, where else would we discover hidden toxics of the most dangerous types? Who is responsible for this disaster, and who will be accountable for damages, such as property damage, medical expenses, cleanup, and reclamation: the developers and owners of the land, the owners of the chemical company, or the municipality for permitting the development of residential houses and school? Under the current ethics and practices of urban sustainability, it would be unimaginable for this disaster to have occurred.

## The Sustainability Movement: A Brief Overview

The Timeline that accompanies this chapter identifies the principal international conferences, governmental reports, legislation, and significant events that have shaped the framework of sustainability. In this section, we first outline the key historical United Nations conferences that had a major impact on implementing urban sustainability. We then identify important climate change reports and events because climate change is central to our thinking about sustainability and how cities will cope with its increasing impacts.

### Global Climate Change

At its core, global climate change may be seen as a consequence of global warming (see Chapter 8). As part of this historical overview, climate change has become a central topic within urban sustainability, which actually predates the Brundtland definition of sustainable development. Climate change is an urban sustainability issue from three different viewpoints:

1. Most of the carbon dioxide emissions responsible for climate change are generated in cities from the transportation and building sectors of the economy through the burning of fossil fuels for gasoline and the cooling and heating of buildings.

2. Urban form in terms of sprawl and low-density cities requiring massive automobile use between residential areas and employment centers is an indirect source of greenhouse gases. Therefore, urban design that emphasizes "green" design and New Urbanism principles, higher-density neighborhoods, mixed land uses (as in transit orientated development), and public transportation systems has the ability to reduce carbon dioxide emissions.

3. As Chapter 8 discusses, cities will be largely impacted by global climate change, and some cities are already starting to develop adaptation strategies to mitigate and reduce and climate based adverse impacts, primarily through climate action plans.

The concept of climate change had its start in the 1980s, although scientific research and climate modeling in this area was already ongoing in the 1970s. In 1983, the United States National Academy of Sciences (NAS) issued one of the first reviews of the possible effects of increasing carbon dioxide emissions and linked this increase to human-caused activities. The report concluded that global carbon dioxide levels will increase and that, as a result, "unforeseen consequences" will occur in the future. In hindsight, looking back from 2012, this forecast has been accurate; yet, despite the Kyoto Protocol's 1997 international call to reduce emissions to 1990 levels, this goal has not been achieved. And some of the "unforeseen events" identified in the 1983 report have become apparent sooner than projected by the climate modeling.

By 1990, three events transpired to turn climate change into a public policy issue. First, scientific testimony before Congress that climate change has been occurring resulted in public concern and the beginning of governmental responses. Second, in 1988, the Intergovernmental Panel on Climate Change (IPCC) was founded by the World Meteorological Organization and the United Nations Environmental Program. The IPCC has become the leading institution for the regular assessments and evaluation of scientific findings related to climate change and its impacts. The first IPCC report in 1990 had similar results as the 1983 NAS report; it found that temperatures were rising and that climate change was highly likely in the future. The third event was the 1992 United Nations Conference in Rio de Janeiro that laid the foundation for reducing the world's carbon footprint with the declaration of the United Nations Framework Convention on Climate Change. By 1997, the Kyoto Protocol was signed by most, but not all, countries. This Protocol had as its goal the reduction of greenhouse gas emissions by 5.2 percent below the 1990 emissions levels by 2012.

By 2005, the Kyoto Protocol was signed by 35 developed countries knowing that the 2012 goal would likely not be reached. The United States never signed the protocol. In 2007, the fourth and latest IPCC report was released and argued that a scientific consensus had been reached regarding the causes of climate change; namely, that it is mostly caused by human activity and that more serious environmental impacts are foreseen. Lastly, in 2009, the Copenhagen Accord called for the continuation of the Kyoto Protocol beyond 2012 and emphasized the role of climate mitigation and adaptation strategies (see Chapter 8). Approaches of major import today and into the future in terms of urban sustainability and climate change include taking steps to:

1. evaluate how "green urban design" can reduce the carbon footprint of cities;

2. determine how we can develop scenario-based plans to deal with urban complexities and develop mechanisms for effective anticipatory governance dealing with future global climate change impacts;

3. determine how we can improve our ability in "futures thinking" to incorporate sustainability challenges such as climate change impacts on cities and enhance urban resiliency by incorporating adaptation policies; and

4. learn how we can establish policy measures at all levels of government to mitigate greenhouse gas emissions. A move toward new nonrenewable energy technologies must be consistent with the equity, economic, and environmental domains inherent in sustainability thinking.

## United Nations and International Conferences

At the time in the United States when Ehrlich published *The Population Bomb* and NEPA was being formulated in 1968, UNESCO (United Nations Educational, Scientific and Cultural Organization) held its Biosphere Conference to discuss the threats to the biosphere, including loss of biodiversity, environmental impacts from urbanization, and even climate change. As one of the earliest collaborative efforts at the global environmental level (even predating the United Nation conferences on sustainability), it crystallized thinking about the need for global responses and education about environmental change. Unfortunately, a global political action agenda was not initiated;

this had to wait two decades. Although not often mentioned today, this conference constituted an important precursor to later thinking about the importance of integrating environmental issues with economic development. Four years later, in 1972, the United Nations Conference on the Human Environment in Stockholm established an international foundation to tackle global environmental issues. Importantly, the theme centered on the "human environment" and discussions took place regarding poverty and human-caused environmental change, including climate change, ecosystem disturbances, deforestation, and desertification.

Two years after Lester Brown published his book *In the Human Interest* in 1974 and two years before the nation would discover the Love Canal tragedy, the United Nations Habitat Conference took shape. The discussions and debates identified specific effects of human activity on the environment, but the specific focus was on the deteriorating conditions of global settlements, especially in developing countries. In terms of "habitat," the focus was on poverty, population growth, poor conditions of human settlements, and an action agenda for improving settlements and livability. Known as the "Vancouver Declaration on Human Settlements," the conference report set the structure for urban sustainability and actions. Protection of ecosystems, restoring environmental and natural resource assets, and reducing pollution and exposure to toxins comprised one component of the declaration. These were placed in a much larger context of improving the quality of life of settlements (i.e., cities) through meeting the basic needs of populations for food, health, shelter, education, and especially quality water supplies. The deterioration of settlements was seen as an outcome of global socio-economic inequities, rapid population growth, uncontrolled urbanization, and poverty. Following from the United Nations Conference on Human Settlements, the momentum now swung toward an integrative framework for global progress and reversing deleterious living conditions. It was the Human Habitat Conference that brought together the importance of planning and developing policies in cities based on economic development, environmental actions to reduce pollution, and community well-being through equity, health, adequate shelter, and other sustainability factors.

The Vancouver Declaration served as an early driving force for sustainability practice at the urban level. It argued for a strong proactive role for planning and designing cities and developing well-conceived and balanced land policies. It supported environmental justice pursuits, development of regenerative waste streams, preservation of natural places in cities, the need to be sensitive to local urban ecosystems during development, creation of a balance between development and infrastructure, and preservation of important historical and cultural places. Other critical elements are found in the Declaration that today are fundamental for establishing sustainable cities: citizen involvement and participation in all aspects of habitat development; design or development at the "human scale"; special focus on planning for the needs of disadvantaged groups; preservation, restoration, and improvement of natural systems in urban areas; and mitigating actions to prevent and prepare for disasters. A missing element concerned the concept of "meeting future needs" through the reduction in our consumption of natural resources to ensure carrying capacity; this concept would not be introduced until almost 10 years later by the Brundtland Commission.

The importance of the 1987 report "Our Common Future" (known as the Brundtland Commission report), where sustainable development is defined in a way that is generally accepted by the public, is covered in Chapter 1. Sustainability literature demonstrates a plethora of definitions of sustainability, but the Brundtland definition of "development that meets the needs of the present without compromising the ability of future generations to meet their own needs" has both longevity and popular appeal. As a compromise between the industrial, advanced countries and their emphasis on environmental assets and pollution abatement, and the developing countries, which placed importance on economic growth and poverty reduction, the operating definition of sustainability became a framework that balances economic development and employment, social well-being and community capital, and environmental stewardship—representing the ideas behind the three pillars of sustainability. This report was critically important for the trajectory of sustainability thinking over the next 25 years. For example, the use of the Gross National Product (GNP) for measuring the wealth of nations was no longer an appropriate indicator. Since 1993, the United Nations Human Development Index has been used as an indicator of a country's well-being. The Index consists of four measures—poverty, literacy, education, and life expectancy measures—a considerably more complex and telling indicator than what is revealed by a simple measure of national productivity encapsulated by GNP. By 1993, sustainability indicator initiatives were underway, and now, there are over 250 community indicator systems, using a more appropriate set of indicators than the ones used in most conventional city indicators of the past. "Sustainable Seattle" was one of the earliest indicator systems developed around the sustainability framework and is viewed by many today as a model indicator system (http://www.sustainableseattle.org/whoweare).

Five years later, the United Nations organized the Earth Summit (UN Conference on Environment and Development) in Rio de Janeiro, Brazil. By this time, United Nations delegates were moving toward implementation strategies, policy development, and an array of local initiatives to advance sustainability practices and initiatives. The central topics included alternative sources of energy, water security, climate change mitigation, and local sustainability initiatives, among others. One of the most important statements that emerged from the Summit (which later became the most politically controversial), was an agenda for sustainable development actions for the twenty-first century. For the purposes of this historical overview on sustainable cities, it is important to note that Agenda 21 specifically addressed the planning and policies needed for sustaining urban areas and communities. It promoted urban sustainability through applications of energy efficiency, transportation systems, land management, and climate change research, among other topics. As a global action agenda, Agenda 21 is exceptional in its promotion of the importance of public participation in all sustainability programs and as a means for sustainability policy development. An excellent summary of the urban dimensions and action items of Agenda 21 is contained in Haughton and Hunter's 1998 book *Sustainable Cities*. The following action items are adapted from that book:

1. Provide adequate shelter for urban residents at local and international levels.
2. Improve urban management systems.
3. Promote sustainable land use planning, including the use of private-public partnerships.
4. Establish integrated infrastructure systems to avoid and reduce environmental damage.
5. Develop energy efficient technologies through the use of renewable energy and transportation systems based on renewables.

6. Develop planning processes for disasters in all its phases—preparedness, response, recovery, and reconstruction.

7. Promote sustainable design principles including materials, energy efficiency, and urban land uses.

As Agenda 21 was being developed with its emphasis on implementing policies and programs for sustainability practices at the city level, two other influential works in the sustainable urbanism arena emerged to ground design into the sustainability framework. The first is the "Hannover Principles: Design for Sustainability" developed in 1992 by William McDonough, an architect, and a team of experts evaluating sustainability charrettes. These design principles demonstrated the interdependence of natural processes and human activity and our ethical responsibility to the future. Reducing waste streams, reusing materials, practicing regeneration, buying local materials, and protecting nature were the ideas inherent in the principles, which also laid the foundation for his next book *Cradle to Cradle* a decade later in 2002.

| The Hannover Principles |
| --- |
| 1. Insist on rights of humanity and nature to coexist. |
| 2. Recognize interdependence. |
| 3. Respect relationships between spirit and matter. |
| 4. Accept responsibility for the consequences of design. |
| 5. Create safe objects of long-term value. |
| 6. Eliminate the concept of waste. |
| 7. Rely on natural energy flows. |
| 8. Understand the limitations of design. |
| 9. Seek constant improvement by the sharing of knowledge. |

Another foundational work that addressed the importance of sustainable urbanism was written by Duany, Plater-Zyberk, and Krieger titled *Towns and Town–Making Principles* in 1991. Their strategies advanced mixed-use development, compact development with associated open space, the creation of walkable environments, and transportation alternatives. These goals as well as others are now well-established under the framework of New Urbanism. Other objectives of this movement include building with a sense of community, protecting environment assets, and reducing automobile use. New Urbanism applies sustainable design concepts to reduce the carbon footprint, which was the theme in Peter Calthorpe's recent book, *Urbanism in the Age of Climate Change* (2010). Continuing the themes related to community place-making, pedestrian-based neighborhoods, and social capital formations in cities are two foundational books: *Ecological Design* by Van der Ryn and Cowen (1997) and *The Ecology of Place: Planning for Environment, Economy, and Community* by Beatley and Manning (1997). Ecological Design helped influence sustainability from concept to design practice by bringing together the concepts of lifecycle assessment of materials, building with local materials, bio-mimicry, and reuse of materials. The book is also important for demonstrating the importance of collaborative design and characterizing the differences between conventional and sustainable design principles among a set of criteria.

## Reversing Urban Legacy Problems

During the last quarter century, since Brundtland, sustainability has been addressing our past urban mistakes. We need to correct these errors and seek their remediation, prevent their reoccurrence, and reutilize deteriorated land into viable, livable places. The integrative framework of urban sustainability directs cities to examine a set of goals that include community well-being, economic development, social equity, and environmental stewardship, all in balance with each other, in every urban plan and program. One issue that has emerged from the many Superfund-related problems is the environment justice movement and the attention paid to those minority communities that experienced a disproportionate level of risk by living near contaminated areas. Urban wastelands still exist in central cities (and are now even found in some suburbs) without healthy neighborhoods and socio-economic resiliency to overcome their liabilities.

As discussed in Chapter 4, one of the major catalysts for the environmental justice movement was the discovery that disproportionally more minority and low-income people were exposed to hazardous and contaminated substances resulting from geographical proximity to contaminated sites. Environmental justice is at the cornerstone of efforts to remake cities into sustainable cities. These activities include assessments of differential access to urban amenities such as parks, toxic site remediation, cleanup of contaminated groundwater systems, relocation of public housing, investments in deteriorating neighborhoods to provide local employment, and brownfield redevelopment.

While we still have a long way to go to remediate brownfield sites in central areas of cities (especially old industrial zones), their redevelopment encapsulates all of the dimensions of urban sustainability. For example, contaminated sites first need to be cleaned up, and then an assessment is needed to determine if the industrial buildings can be reused or modified for similar uses, or utilized for entirely different purposes, such as playgrounds and parks. Chapter 11 provides numerous examples of reusing old industries for public infrastructure and enhancing ecosystems, especially through open space planning.

Place-making and recycling outdated and obsolete land uses into different and viable uses is an important aspect of urban sustainability and is a central theme in Timothy Beatley's 2012 book, *Green Cities of Europe: Global Lessons on Green Urbanism*. Many of these brownfield redevelopments can form the basis of a regenerative neighborhood that provides new employment opportunities and mixed uses. Often these redevelopments are based on visioning participatory processes involving local residents, partnership building between the private and public sectors, open space and mixed uses, and opportunities for small-scale startup businesses, including Portland Streetcar development in Portland, Oregon; Santa Fe Railyard Park and Plaza in Santa Fe, New Mexico; and Benton Harbor, Michigan Golf Course located on a remediated former car factory site.

# The Next Decade 2010–2020

The last half of the twentieth century saw amazing and rapid changes in the ways in which the country responded to declining environmental quality and the hazards of technology. In the 1970s and 1980s, a new federal agency, EPA, developed legislation and regulations to contend with the issues relating to water quality, air quality, pesticide hazards, hazardous wastes, and remediation of toxic sites. These were established after expressions of public concern over environmental problems coincided with the evolution and development of ecological and biological sciences, the science of risk assessment, biophysical modeling, and detection technologies, among others. The concept of sustainability slowly developed over time—predominately as a solution for the problem of carrying capacity and conservation. This approach applied until 1987, when a compelling yet equivocal definition of sustainable development was created, one that could be used to address the problem of meeting an array of current needs and assuring that future needs would be met as well. Due to threats to the environment and environmental quality and health, sustainability implored examining the ecological footprint as a relationship involving consumption, natural resources, and waste products. In the 25-year period since Brundtland, global initiatives have led the way toward directing sustainability goals into action and programs at the (considerably more realizable) local level.

As urban areas continue to explode in population with a majority of the world now living in cities, cities will become the focal point of sustainability efforts. What can we expect sustainable practices to look like in cities in this decade?

1. *Building Resiliency*. Given the global economic recession, we can expect more efforts in understanding and implementing programs in socio-ecological resiliency, but also in resiliency building of urban areas that are vulnerable to a host of threats including climate change impacts.

2. *Emergence of Sustainable Urban Design*. The urban form issues of the twentieth century continue to exert a significant toll—sprawl, undiminished and growing carbon dioxide footprints, disconnected neighborhoods, children's health issues, and new forms of environmental injustice such as food deserts. We can expect momentous growth in cities' interest in green design initiatives. These initiatives will integrate neighborhood design with local economic development and public transit. Moreover, design metrics will soon develop, merging spatial analysis with design and health indicators.

3. *Innovative Decision-Making and Policy Tools*. Given high levels of uncertainty in local decisions, especially related to global climate change impacts, we can expect to see the development of advanced tools that guide policymakers, such as robust scenario-based modeling of urban futures, public visioning and participatory processes, collaborative design, and adaptation tools, among others.

4. *Climate Action Planning*. We anticipate a growing interest among cities to advance climate action planning to help mitigate greenhouse gas emissions through urban planning and energy efficiency, as well as through innovative technologies and the development of adaptation plans to address future unanticipated threats.

5. *Urban Ecological Planning*. Cities will expand their planning to ensure that the interaction between human and ecological systems is viable.

The identification and protection of ecological systems within and between cities will become more important.

6. *Sustainable Indicators*. We can expect a renewed interest in developing indicators with citizen participation programs in sustainability.

7. *Local Food Systems*. Cities will invest in and support the development of local food systems and urban agriculture.

8. *Eco-City Policies*. Influenced by eco-cities and eco-neighborhoods such as Curitiba, Brazil, Freiberg, Germany, and Civano in Tucson, Arizona, cities will begin to ask how a multifaceted and integrative approach to sustainable cities can be accomplished. It will be a period of intense policy and land planning activities, with cities perhaps taking their cues from an updated SustainLane (2008) sustainability ranking system of cities.

# A Personal Afterthought by K. David Pijawka

*After several years of intensive effort on modeling the planet's future population growth and its levels of consumption of food stock, nonrenewable fuels, natural resources, and associated pollution,* Limits to Growth *was published in 1972. As a university student, the publication was immeasurably influential and served as basis for much heated debate on the role of population, assumptions used to calculate the projections, and what humankind could do to avoid collapse or at least slow the rate of decline. We students were also very much influenced by the "hazards school of thought" where there are possible adjustments (now called adaptation strategies) to reduce vulnerabilities to threatened socio-ecological systems and communities. This was prior to the global emergence of sustainable development in the 1980s and its manifestation on cities starting in the 1990s.*

*We were making progress—at least it seemed like we were—in finding and implementing sustainable solutions. At the university, we were establishing new educational programs in sustainability and discussing learning outcomes in sustainability courses; issues of local environmental injustice drew us into public discourse and equity research; we explored analyses for walkable neighborhoods and LEED (Leadership in Energy and Environmental Design) neighborhood ratings; exploring land value impacts of a light rail system, and policies needed to enhance green building programs; and studying public perceptions and beliefs related to global climate change. And then, in 2004, the 30-year update of* Limits to Growth *was published. Now, using the "Ecological Footprint" metaphor, we learned that the world's population footprint is beyond the capacity of the planet and growth will likely end in the twenty-first century: the argument is that the current ecological footprint equates to 1.2 earths, exceeding the earth's carrying capacity. The capital needed to keep resources flowing will increase to the point of diminishing returns. The indicators of collapsing natural resource assets are all known. The questions I have, and urge you to consider, are—*

*Can all of the small incremental sustainable solutions we apply to cities work to reduce the current footprint to a sustainable level where carrying capacity is leveled off?*

*What are the adaptations needed to avoid or slow down urban collapse?*

*What role can planning play to stem (or at least mitigate) these trends to make a more habitable, sustainable, and just urban realm?*

## ■ LESSONS LEARNED FOR ACHIEVING SUSTAINABILITY

Sustainability needs more precise operational definitions or frameworks; the existing definitions have been argumentative and debated. This has caused confusion and misunderstandings, but also given the field much-needed attention. To achieve sustainability, interdisciplinary thinking needs to be at the center; while we can discuss this in theory, it is often difficult to put into practice. The public needs to be involved in meaningful and transparent ways to help provide vision and strategies, but also support for sustainable solutions. Longevity often is not met, yet sustainability policies and plans require long lead times, public input, and transformative change. Over the long-term, small incremental changes toward sustainability have been implemented, but the environmental problems overall have not been changed substantially. As just one example among many discussed in this chapter, brownfield redevelopment in central cities offers the United States an opportunity to meet sustainability goals for the country—toxic cleanup, recycling of land, economic development and green jobs, remediation of environmental inequities, and obtaining the input of persons living in places of despair and hope.

# DISCUSSION QUESTIONS

1. How is the Dust Bowl a problem of human-ecological systems, and how could it be looked at through resiliency thinking?

2. What can be discerned about how to build sustainable cities today based on Ebenezer Howard's 1898 book? Is it relevant today?

3. How important are the ideas from *Limits to Growth* to the concept of sustainability?

# Earliest Urbanism

*Charles Redman*

## ▨ WHY THIS CHAPTER IS IMPORTANT FOR UNDERSTANDING SUSTAINABILITY

History holds many lessons for better understanding the operation of modern cities and possible directions for developing urban sustainability. Although more people reside in modern cities than in the past and the technologies we use are dramatically different, human interactions and the ways in which we organize ourselves are very much the same. If utilized carefully, history can provide seemingly countless examples of how people around the world cooperated to live in ever larger settlements, how they solved problems, and, in many cases, how they sowed the seeds for their own collapse. Sustainability is about solving problems as societies confront change, successful human interaction over long periods, and preventing imbalances between the extraction of resources from our natural environment and its ability to regenerate those resources. The advantage of using history over relying only on contemporary studies is that we know how decisions and actions played out over time, and whether they led to further growth or to decline and abandonment. One particularly insightful message from the past is that the collapse of many cities and states occurred when they appeared to be at their peak of power and sophistication, and not after long periods of decline. This message may have direct relevance to our own situation and lead to a better understanding of how and why such collapses could have happened repeatedly to the "great" societies of the past; it may help us redirect our trajectory toward sustainability instead of collapse.

## ▨ KEY CONCEPTS AND TERMS

*After reading this chapter, you should understand and be able to discuss the following:*

coupled human-nature interactions; ecosystem management; human-environmental dynamics; maximizing short-term returns with little concern for long-term consequences; regenerative capabilities; resilient socioeconomic unit; social organization; and The Urban Revolution.

## Introduction

One of the most significant and informative milestones in the history of human societies was the growth of the first cities in the Near East. This process, often called **The Urban Revolution**, involved much more than just an increase in the size of settlements: it included fundamental changes in the way people interacted, in their relationship to the environment, and in the very way they structured their communities. Processes and institutions that began at this time, some 5,000 years ago, have continued to evolve, forming the basic structure of urban society today. Although ancient cities emerged in various regions of the world, this chapter focuses on the process as it occurred in the Near East, and in particular, Mesopotamia, for three important reasons. First, cities appear in Mesopotamia as early as, or earlier than, anywhere else;

**The Urban Revolution** - processes that originated during the growth of the first cities in the Near East; encompasses the behaviors that simultaneously occurred as people began to reside in urban communities, such as the cultivation of crops, herding of animals, the mass production of goods, and the development of a writing system.

second, cities and their societies have direct links with developments in neighboring regions and can be traced as ancestral to developments in many parts of the modern world; and third, we can identify early examples of **human-environmental dynamics** that are still operating today.

Writing, a system of laws, the wheel, the plow, metallurgy, mathematics and engineering principles—all commonplace in our modern world—were first developed in the cities of Mesopotamia (present-day Iraq and southwestern Iran). Despite the vast scope of these technical innovations, the most significant developments were those of **social organization**. A quantum leap occurred in the number of inhabitants living in the largest settlements, and with this growth, a transformation occurred in the way people dealt with each other and with their environment. The physical environment of Mesopotamia and the surrounding regions provided promising ecological conditions for the early introduction of agriculture and the subsequent growth of the first urban society. An awareness of these conditions, and how they supported the human-nature relationships that were to emerge, is essential to a thorough understanding of **coupled human-nature interactions** today.

Image © Steven Wright 2012. Used under license from Shutterstock, Inc.

**Historic map of Iraq dated 1872 showing "Mesopotamien," which is German for Mesopotamia.**

# The Environmental Stage

Mesopotamia is a large, arid alluvial plain created by two major rivers—the Tigris and the Euphrates—and is surrounded on two sides by better-watered mountainous zones. The region's climatic pattern is one of summer drought and winter rainfall, although the lowland plain receives minimal rainfall and the people there derived most of their water from the rivers. In the south, where the Tigris and Euphrates rivers join and eventually empty into the Persian Gulf, the land is almost flat and there are many marshy areas. Moving upstream, to the northwest, the slope is small, but it increases perceptibly, giving rise to more clearly defined watercourses surrounded by arid plains. Effective natural levee formation in the southern reaches of the Mesopotamian plain strongly influenced their selection for settlement locations.

Furthest from the rivers were lowland areas that were marshes during the flood season and supported natural grasses the rest of the year, making them useful for grazing animals. Nearer the rivers, farmlands developed if they were within reach of irrigation water from the river. Those fields closer to the river were preferable in that they often were better drained, more productive, and had more secure access to irrigation. Along the riverbanks were the natural levees, which were higher and better drained than the surrounding plain. These were the best locations for intensive cultivation and settlement. The levees had several natural advantages: they were fertile, quickly drained after floods, and were least vulnerable to winter frosts. Equally important, as the population density of farmers increased, the levees gave access to river water during years in which the river level was low and not all fields could be adequately irrigated.

Moving further upstream, to the northerly areas of the Mesopotamian plain, the gradient increases, the landscape becomes rolling, and the rivers cut deeper into the landscape, making irrigation more difficult. Continuing further north, the major rivers and their tributaries cut across a series of increasingly high ridges and ultimately reach the Taurus Mountains, to the north, and the Zagros Mountains, to the northeast. Proximity to these uplands and the large tributary rivers provided natural advantages to settlement in the north, such as access to stone and timber for building, while the vast stretches of relatively easily irrigated land in the south facilitated population growth there.

Pre-urban, Neolithic settlement (8000–5000 BC) of Mesopotamia concentrated in the uplands, with only a few settlements around the margins of the lowlands where the upper reaches of the rivers and their major tributaries intersected in what are now southeastern Turkey and the Irano-Iraqi borderlands. The earliest that researchers have found evidence of any substantial settlement in southern Mesopotamia is approximately 5500 BC. Between 6000 and 4000 BC, however, the area of settlement expanded from the uplands to include more and more of the Mesopotamian plain. This was not a rapid migration in terms of a single lifetime; it took many generations to learn how to manage crops and animals in the heat and aridity of the lowlands. At first, expansion was limited to areas of possible, although unreliable, rainfall. Subsequently, with the aid of primitive irrigation systems, settlers moved into areas of the plain that previously could not be cultivated by rainfall alone.

# Processes of Change

History offers many lessons relevant to sustainability about how humans and their societies have recognized and responded to challenges and opportunities of their human-natural environment. Three of the basic approaches to problem solving in antiquity were: (a) mobility of people to available resources; (b) **ecosystem management** to secure enhanced local growth of produce; and (c) increasing social complexity encoded in formal institutions that guided an ever-expanding range of activities. These solutions were fundamental to the rise of early civilizations, are instrumental in the design of sustainable cities in the future, and continue to evolve.

The mobility of people to available resources has dominated the human approach to securing adequate subsistence for the vast majority of human existence. Until approximately 10,000 years ago (and more recently in many regions), virtually all people had to move among several locations each year to take advantage of the seasonality of ripening resources. This movement pattern was disrupted by the introduction of agriculture, which allowed the establishment of year-round settlements in most regions of the world. Agriculture is an example of the second approach to problem solving noted above, ecosystem management for enhanced productivity. This has proven to be an astonishing successful solution to feeding an ever-increasing global population, thereby allowing virtually all people to live in permanent settlements. In fact, the advancement of agriculture and the infrastructural improvements made to enhance productivity were strong incentives for the spread and growth of sedentary communities. Scholars believe that a highly effective socio-natural pattern emerged from millennia of experimentation—called the village farming community—and became the dominant settlement form across the globe. Consisting of between 1 and 500 people, village farming communities were the most enduring and widespread type of community because they had flexibility in their sources of subsistence, and they achieved balance between the extraction of natural resources and the resulting regeneration of the local ecosystem. Although beginning as early as 10,000 years ago in the Near East, the concept spread to most continents, and similar descendent communities housed over half the world's population as recently as the middle of the twentieth century!

**Ecosystem management** - the use, protection, and conservation of our environmental resources in a way that seeks to ensure their long-term sustainability. This concept considers humans and the environment as a single system rather than as individual parts.

**Resilient socioeconomic unit** - characterizes the interconnectedness between the human inhabitants and the economy of a place in a way that promotes the ability to bounce back and recover after a disturbance or crisis.

The village farming community proved to be a highly **resilient socioeconomic unit**, yet some of these communities expanded on their approach to ecosystem management to the point where larger aggregations of people were necessary to supply the required labor. However, these larger populations also underwent a transformation in the social order, which was largely

Image © George Allen Penton, 2012. Used under license from Shutterstock, Inc.

**Farming community in the Middle East.**

achieved through innovations in social complexity. This is at the heart of what scholars call The Urban Revolution, and it appears to have occurred first in Mesopotamia.

# The First Cities

The formation of the first cities and their linking together as one civilization on the Mesopotamian plain was relatively rapid, considering the scope of the social and technological changes involved. Only approximately 2,000 years after the earliest known occupation of this region, in about 5500 BC, cities emerged, along with attendant traits of urbanism, such as writing, the construction of monumental buildings, and craft specialization. The rise of these early cities was not simply the growth of large collections of people—rather, it involved communities that were far more diverse and interdependent than their predecessors. Relative independence and self-sufficiency characterized village farming communities, but they also limited the growth of these communities. Specialization in the production of various goods and complex exchange networks helped urban societies grow. Cities were also interdependent with their surrounding towns and villages, and they developed ways to obtain goods and services from them. The development of effective irrigation agriculture, the manufacture and widespread exchange of goods, and the advance of science and mathematics were fundamental to the growth of cities. Additionally, changes in the social realm, such as class-structured society, formalized systems of laws, a monopoly on the use of coercive force, and a hierarchical, territorially based government made cities possible and continued to characterize their successful operation.

A landscape-productivity-human relationship evolved in villages and towns, enabling the growth of large, diverse populations that aggregated into cities. As positive as these "advances" were in terms of productivity and competitiveness, they also led to maladaptive relationships and created an increase in long-term risks. One set of new relationships was established as the concept of private property emerged to replace both a generally weak sense of ownership and the concept of community ownership. It is hard to say what came first, but these new relationships evolved when farmers could both produce more food than their families required and find ways to store this surplus for later use or trade. This led some farmers to produce a surplus to guard against future bad harvests; however, one could only eat so much, and a variety of factors limited the amount of food that could be effectively stored. Hence, the stimulus to produce a surplus remained limited in most farming villages. What may have changed this relationship, and was key to the growth of urban society, was the ability to transform locally produced surplus food and goods (through purchased, specialized labor, and exotic goods) into enduring prestige items associated with elevated status. This only existed in areas where a new social order occurred that acknowledged classes with differential wealth (access to productive resources), power, and status. An ideology (through religion, myth, constructed history, and law) legitimized the existence of elite classes and their precious goods that helped identify them. Another dynamic that coevolved with private property, surplus production, elite goods, and hierarchical class society was the reliance on inheritance for membership in these classes. Merit, strength, agility, and intelligence certainly were important, but which family, clan, or class a person was born into set limits on his future potential in the age of early cities, and to some extent, continues to operate today in certain cities.

## Cities Going Global

Organizing society into hierarchically stratified classes became widespread along with urbanism, coming to characterize most regions of the world up to the present day. This social framework, along with a widely accepted ideology legitimizing it, was an effective means of organizing large groups of people and large-scale productive activities. People have always sought to make sense of the world around them and to determine how to relate to other people. Myths, histories, and ethics often were organized into formal religions that helped people understand their place in the world, and simultaneously, justified the unequal allocation of rights and prescribed appropriate ways to behave. In time, territorially based authority also emerged, largely through successful military action and monopolies on the use of coercive force. This secular authority also needed a source of legitimization, which emerged as constructed histories, legal codes, and institutions of management and enforcement. Although they often cited different rationales, governing authorities based on religious or secular justification served many similar purposes in creating a framework for the effective functioning of large populations and controlling vast tracts of land. Not surprisingly, the two interacted closely, and they have often been unified into a single entity or a closely cooperating team. Hence, in the newly emergent urban society of Mesopotamia, and later elsewhere across the globe, people produced more goods, and larger numbers of people could live in a single community and be marshaled as a labor force. This was possible because sacred orders were established and widely accepted that legitimized the social order and prescribed appropriate behavior, and because security was provided through a monopoly on the use of force and formal systems of laws. Respect for this new social and governing order was often reaffirmed through the construction of massive monuments, the performance of complex rituals, and expression through large-scale representational art. The concentration of people, stored supplies, and elite goods led to early cities being targets for raiding and organized military activity, prompting further investment in defensive walls and armies to defend cities. This cyclical relationship of the concentration of wealth leading to military aggression leading to the investment in armies is a cycle that dominates all of human history and can be seen operating today.

Image © Persep<edusa, 2012. Used under license from Shutterstock, Inc.

**Dating back to 3500 BC, Mesopotamian art war intended to serve as a way to glorify powerful rulers and their connection to divinity.**

# Are Cities Maladaptive?

Unfortunately, other responses that originated to aid the facilitation of solutions to help solve problems have also established detrimental cycles that threaten the very existence of the societies that developed them. For example, large numbers of people aggregating into cities allowed for specialization of labor and other efficiencies, but it also meant that most people would not be able to grow their own food. Hence, people in the rural countryside were responsible for growing enough food for both themselves and city dwellers in an amount to offset the cost of transport and distribution. This arrangement put a tremendous burden on farming communities to produce much more than they would if the farmers alone made the decisions. As differing segments of the population grew more divergent in their societal roles, so did their objectives and understanding of the situation. For instance, farmers in the earlier village farming era more intimately understood the landscape and productive systems and were inclined toward conservation practices wherein they balanced extractive activities with the **regenerative capabilities** of the land. The urban elite, on the other hand, were more focused on the net yield they could extract from the countryside and insisted on maximum production, with little knowledge of or concern for the potential deleterious effects on the rural landscape. In an ideal hierarchical society, even though decision-making authority is concentrated at the top, knowledge would travel up the hierarchy, and informed decisions would thus be made. However, it is somewhat surprising that this was seldom the case and that the dominant pattern was **maximizing short-term returns with little concern for long-term consequences**. Archaeological evidence attests to repeated instances of intense environmental degradation in the regions around cities, and the impact of urban demand on the rural countryside is still evident today.

In addition to making ill-advised decisions leading to excess extraction of resources, individuals and societies are regularly forced to make decisions in response to changing conditions. These conditions might be a change in climate, such as less rainfall, a change in local environment, such as soil erosion, or a change in the cultural or technological context, such as new neighbors or the introduction of new subsistence strategies. Changes like these are normal, and they were frequent in the past and are still common today. Jared Diamond, in his book *Collapse: How Societies Choose to Fail or Succeed*,[1] points to errors in decision-making as a primary cause of social collapse. Such errors occurred in a variety of contexts, such as not recognizing the significance of an important change in conditions; recognizing the change, but misdiagnosing the appropriate response; or waiting too long before responding. Unfortunately, many of today's leaders have apparently not learned from the past and are unable or unwilling to respond to the varied significant changes currently taking place around us. This is strikingly similar to the behavior of the collapsed civilizations about which Diamond warns us.

Other "urban efficiencies" create their own challenges. Many of the world's devastating contagious diseases were virtually nonexistent until the growth of dense urban populations. The spread of the plague, small pox, measles, cholera, and many other diseases can be traced to a combination of close association between humans and domestic animals, and living in large, dense populations. Cities were the centers of

**Regenerative capabilities** - the processes of renewal, restoration, and growth that make ecosystems resilient to natural events in order to prevent irreversible damage.

**Maximizing short-term returns with little concern for long-term consequences** - this concept encompasses the idea that many decisions made by those individuals with authority and power often focus solely on increasing short-term benefits, such as the accumulation of money, without considering long-term consequences of those decisions, such as degradation of the environment.

people, economic activity, and the arts, but until public health innovations of the twentieth century, they were also the centers of disease, many of them fatal. Large urban populations also created new challenges that were unknown when the largest communities were only several hundred people or less. For example, knowing who everyone is in the community and how to act toward them is no longer feasible when the community's population exceeds 500 people. Similarly, less tranquility and security breakdown are evident as population grows larger, requiring the introduction of formal, impersonal solutions to human interactions and security. Certain other challenges become more complex as the population enlarges, such as the transport of people and goods, sanitation, and an adequate supply of potable water and food. Often, these issues are addressed by formal institutions that unfortunately raise the monetary cost of being an urbanite and also increase residents' dependency on the central authority.

## ■ LESSONS LEARNED FOR ACHIEVING SUSTAINABILITY

Several lessons are apparent from this review of earliest urbanism. First, humans are amazingly successful at self-organization to promote their survival in the face of virtually any environmental challenge, but many of these solutions have unanticipated costs, with continuing impacts on future societies. People manage their socio-ecosystems according to how they perceive the opportunities and risks, and how they value the alternatives. However, this valuation process may appear very different to people in different social positions, and the true "costs" of some alternatives are not recognized at the time, and may even threaten the society's very survival. There is also the problem that challenges may take unrecognized forms because they occur in a new context and people have not retained the knowledge of the past occurrences. Moreover, people may choose to ignore or minimize the expected impact of the challenge because they may be unwilling to bear the costs of responding appropriately. However, once there is recognition, people do respond to problems and opportunities, and they do so by transforming biota (the flora and fauna of the region), landscapes, technologies, and their built environment so that the immediate, net yield for humans is increased even though native biota and earth systems may be degraded. Unfortunately, we do not yet know how serious these threats are and if they will eventually undermine the sustainability of cities. Nevertheless, we must devote ourselves to forming a better understanding of the impacts of our decisions and the pathway toward a more sustainable existence.

Several lessons that inform sustainability stand out from the past. The first is that environmental, social, and technological change is to be expected and, therefore, individuals and societies must prepare themselves to respond to those changes in sustainable ways. The second is that there will be tradeoffs in taking virtually any action to respond to these challenges. That is, some parts of the system will benefit, but other parts of the system will likely be diminished. Hence, we must continually strive to gain a thorough understanding of the interconnectivity of all social-ecological systems and recognize that cascading and unintended consequences may often result to even our best-intentioned actions. Third, the world and its challenges are perceived and valued differently by people in different positions within society. What may appear to help one segment of society may hurt another. All too often, because decision makers are in positions of power, they act in ways that further their own power and wealth, often at the expense of other segments of society. This inequality in power, wealth, and access to resources that characterizes our contemporary world has very old origins. In designing a more sustainable world, we would be well-advised to carefully study how the formation and growth of early cities resulted in societal inequality, and strive to discern and implement solutions to reverse this disparity.

## Supplemental Readings

Diamond, J. (2005, January 1). The ends of the world as we know them [Op-ed]. New York Times. Retrieved from http://www.nytimes.com/2005/01/01/opinion/01diamond.html?_r=1

Butzer, K. W. (2012). Collapse, environment, and society. *Proceedings of the National Academy of Sciences of the United States of America, 109*(10), 3632.

Choi, C. (2012, May 28). Huge ancient civilization's collapse explained. *LiveScience.* Retrieved from http://www.livescience.com/20614-collapse-mythical-river-civilization.html

# DISCUSSION QUESTIONS

1. How does coupled human-nature interaction affect urbanization?

2. What was The Urban Revolution?

3. What were some of the changes farmers underwent after urbanization?

4. What were some of the impacts, either positive or negative, on ecosystems due to urbanization?

# Environmental and Social Justice

*Martin A. Gromulat*
*K. David Pijawka*

## ▮ WHY THIS CHAPTER IS IMPORTANT FOR UNDERSTANDING SUSTAINABILITY

As one of the three pillars of sustainability, equity is a key component of a sustainable society. We cannot achieve sustainability without addressing the economic and social inequities that exist within our country and globally. Environmental justice is rooted in the notion that all people are entitled to the same degree of protection from environmental hazards and to equal access to the decision-making process. Thus, to become sustainable, we must develop policies and make decisions that not only aim to safeguard our natural resources, but that also consider how to ensure that all members of society benefit from the results equitably.

## ▮ KEY CONCEPTS AND TERMS

*After reading this chapter, you should be able to understand and discuss the following:*

brownfields; brownfields revitalization; Brundtland Commission; corrective justice; distributive justice; Environmental Protection Agency; environmental racism; Executive Order 12898; food deserts; procedural justice; public participation in decision-making; social justice; and urban farms.

## Introduction

**Social justice**, or equity, is one of the three pillars or domains of sustainability. The concept of social justice is based on the belief that everyone deserves equal economic, political, and social rights and opportunities, regardless of their gender, race, ethnicity, religion, income, or culture. Environmental justice can be seen as an integration of social justice and environmentalism; it has its roots in the tenets of environmental law, civil rights law, and societies' struggles to achieve social, racial, and economic equality. Environmental justice encompasses two key concepts: the concept of environmental equity, which focuses on the idea that environmental hazards should not be disproportionately distributed among specific segments of the population,

**Social justice** - the belief that everyone deserves equal economic, political, and social rights and opportunities, regardless of their gender, race, ethnicity, religion, income, or culture.

**Scales of Justice: Earth vs. Money.**

Image © Imagewell, 2012. Used under license from Shutterstock, Inc.

and the concept of "**environmental racism**," which abhors any policy or practice that differentially affects the environment of individuals or communities based on their race.[1] Environmental justice issues can be found in practically all aspects of environmental law, including permitting facilities, enforcement, cleanup of polluted sites, and **brownfields** redevelopment. Environmental inequalities are also intertwined in land use and transportation issues, civil rights cases, international human rights issues, and tribal law.

In the United States, the **Environmental Protection Agency (EPA)** serves an important function in upholding environmental justice and was one of the first governmental organizations developed to respond to such inequities. The EPA's stated goal is to "provide an environment where all people enjoy the same degree of protection from environmental and health hazards and equal access to the decision-making process to maintain a healthy environment in which to live, learn, and work."[2]

In this chapter, we examine the concept of environmental justice by considering its historical context, analyzing why equity is vital to sustainability, and exploring real-world examples of environmental injustice and how they may be avoided, mitigated, or eliminated in the future. The goal of this chapter is therefore twofold: first, to examine the complexities presented by environmental inequity in our cities and globally; and second, to explore opportunities to achieve equity while advancing toward sustainability.

Issues surrounding social and environmental justice often raise more questions than answers, and the struggles that inequity raises can be both complex and emotional.[3] As you read about this concept, one particularly important question to keep in mind is whether a city can truly be sustainable if it lacks environmental justice or equity.

## The Four Traditional Notions of Justice

Before you can understand the concept of environmental justice, it is helpful to first understand what is meant by "justice." Four traditional notions of justice are implicated by environmental justice issues, as discussed below. Many of these justice values were first conceptualized by Aristotle (384 BC–322 BC), the great ancient Greek philosopher.

1. **Distributive Justice**: This is defined as the right to equal treatment in terms of the equitable distribution of goods and opportunities. The focus is on the fair distribution of outcomes, as opposed to focusing on the processes by which those outcomes are achieved. In the environmental context, distributive justice involves the equitable distribution of both the burdens resulting from environmental hazards and the environmental benefits provided by governmental and private sector programs. It most often involves concerns about the disproportionate public health and environmental risks borne by minorities and lower-income individuals. In the United States, a long history of research shows a correlation between low-income groups and pollution. On a global scale, many of the burdens associated with climate change, such as flooding, desertification, and extreme storms, are likely to be felt most severely by the most economically disadvantaged people in the world.

Aristotle is often credited with the first formulation of the concept. He explained it as involving "the distribution of honor, wealth, and the other divisible assets of the community, which may be allotted among its members."[4] In the United States, as well as many other places across the globe, issues of distributive justice primarily focus on concerns about rampant poverty and racism, as well as debates about the fairness of affirmative action policies that grant preferential treatment to particular racial or gender groups.

2. **Procedural Justice**: This is defined as the equal right to treatment in terms of the political decisions about how goods and opportunities are to be distributed. Unlike distributive justice, the focus is on the fairness of the decision-making processes rather than on the outcomes. An example of an effort to address procedural injustice in the environmental context can be seen in President Bill Clinton's Executive Order (discussed below), which directs governmental agencies to ensure greater public participation and access to information for minority and low-income populations. Aristotle originally referred to this concept as the need for all individuals to have an "equal share in ruling and being ruled."[5]

**Procedural justice** - the equal right to treatment in terms of the political decisions about how goods and opportunities are to be distributed; its focus is on the fairness of the decision-making processes rather than on the outcomes.

3. **Corrective Justice**: This type of justice involves fairness in how punishments are assigned for breaking laws and how damages to individuals and communities are addressed through the duty of the responsible party to repair the losses for which it is responsible. In the environmental context, corrective justice refers not only to fairness in allocating punishment to polluters, but also includes the duty to compensate individuals and communities that were negatively affected by their actions, including cleaning up and remediating resulting contamination. One example of such an injustice is the prevalence of brownfields in minority and low-income neighborhoods, which are discussed below.

**Corrective justice** - involves fairness in the way in which punishments are assigned for breaking laws and how damages to individuals and communities are addressed through the duty of the responsible party to repair the losses for which it is responsible; also known as retributive justice, it is concerned with punishing or rewarding an individual.

4. **Social Justice**: This is the primary goal of the environmental justice movement. It focuses on integrating environmental concerns into a broader perspective emphasizing social, racial, and economic justice. President Clinton's Executive Order also acknowledged the importance of social justice by directing federal governmental agencies to consider the economic and social implications of the agencies' environmental justice activities. Aristotle first formulated a theory of social justice that remains very consistent with our modern view of justice.

# Historical Context of the Environmental Justice Movement

Grounded in the struggles of the 1960s Civil Rights Movement in the United States, African-American communities in the 1980s began venting their long-standing frustration amid accusations of environmental racism because they had been disproportionally exposed to higher environmental risks than other communities.[6] Groups began questioning the locations of landfills, hazardous waste facilities, and industrial activities, as well as other land use practices in their communities. Minority communities are affected disproportionately more often than other segments of society by the presence of industrial facilities, waste treatment plants, and landfills, which are predominantly located in close proximity to the communities in which these groups live and work.

A 1987 study by the United Church of Christ's Commission for Racial Justice revealed that 60 percent of African-Americans and Hispanics in the United States reside in neighborhoods where hazardous wastes are dumped. The study also showed that 50 percent of the children suffering from lead poisoning are African-American, while pesticide poisoning primarily afflicts Hispanic farm workers and their children. This study was updated and published in a report "Toxic Wastes and Race at Twenty 1987–2007: Grassroots Struggles to Dismantle Environmental Racism in the United States." Using demographic data from the 2000 Census and improved research methods, the report indicated that minority and low-income populations were more heavily concentrated around facilities that use, store, or generate contaminants than what previous studies had found. The 2007 report found that minority groups constituted 56 percent of those living within approximately two miles of where hazardous waste facilities were located, in spite of representing only 30 percent of the national population at that time.

The discovery that minority and low-income populations were being exposed disproportionally to increased levels of hazardous and contaminated substances solely because of their geographical proximity to contaminated sites became one of the major catalysts for the environmental justice movement. The first major publication on this topic was by Robert D. Bullard in 1990 titled "Dumping in Dixie: Race, Class, and Environmental Quality." His research indicated that solid waste facilities were predominantly and disproportionately located in minority neighborhoods. The book starts with the premise that all Americans have a basic right to live in a healthy environment and chronicles the efforts of African-American communities, empowered by the Civil Rights Movement, to link environmentalism with issues of social justice. The results of these studies, as well as subsequent ones, showing that minority and low-income communities are disproportionately victimized, lends direct support to the notion that environmental justice is at the cornerstone of efforts to remake present-day cities into sustainable cities. These activities include assessments of differential access to urban amenities such as parks, toxic site remediation, cleanup of contaminated groundwater systems, relocation of public housing, investments in deteriorating neighborhoods to provide local employment, and brownfield redevelopment (as discussed below).

In 1990, the Congressional Black Caucus, a coalition of academics, social scientists, and political activists, met with EPA officials to discuss their allegations that minority and low-income populations suffered greater risks from environmental hazards than nonminority populations. In response, the EPA created the Environmental Equity Workgroup, which produced a report in June 1992 that supported the allegations and made 10 recommendations for addressing the problem. One of the recommendations was to create an office to address these inequities and, thus, the Office of Environmental Equity was established in November 1992 (it was later changed to the Office of Environmental Justice in 1994).

On February 11, 1994, President Bill Clinton signed **Executive Order·12898** titled "Federal Actions to Address Environmental Justice in Minority Populations

**Executive Order 12898** - officially titled "Federal Actions to Address Environmental Justice in Minority Populations and Low-Income Populations," it aimed to promote nondiscrimination in federal programs that affect human health and the environment, and to increase public participation in decision-making by minority and low-income communities in matters relating to human health and the environment.

and Low-Income Populations," to focus federal attention on the environmental and human health conditions of minority and low-income populations with the goal of achieving environmental protection for all communities. The Order aimed to promote nondiscrimination in federal programs that affect human health and the environment, and to increase **public participation in decision-making** by minority and low-income communities in matters relating to human health and the environment.

As mentioned earlier, the EPA is responsible for implementing and enforcing a variety of laws and regulations affecting our environment; with that responsibility, it has the authority, and sometimes the obligation, to consider and address environmental justice concerns. These laws often require that the EPA consider a variety of factors such as public health, social costs, and welfare impacts in its decisions. Some statutes direct it to consider minority and disadvantaged populations in setting environmental standards. In all cases, the way in which the EPA chooses to enforce its authority can significantly affect the achievement of environmental and social justice.[7]

Issues of environmental justice gained global attention in 1987 with the **Brundtland Commission**, which crafted the classic definition of sustainability. The Commission advanced an understanding of the link between economic growth of the poorer nations and global environmental protection. It argued that poorer countries must have the opportunity to develop economically to support sustainable practices, and that richer countries must develop policies that promote environmental conservation with economic development. Additionally, to bring attention to these social and environmental injustices, the United Nations established February 20 of each year as the World Day of Social Justice.

The environmental justice movement in the United States largely was inactive during President George W. Bush's administration. In fact, environmental justice policy at the federal level has not made much progress in the past 10 years. However, much-needed attention to environmental justice was raised in 2007 by hearings held in the Senate, which focused on the EPA's handling of environmental justice matters, and by the release earlier that year of the updated "Toxic Wastes and Race at Twenty: 1987–2007" report mentioned above. Because of the stalemate at the federal level, considerable efforts have been made at local levels to develop environmental justice policies. Currently, 41 states have some policy on environmental justice. Over time, the environmental justice movement has succeeded in raising public attention and spurring some government efforts on these issues. While growth has occurred recently in the number of global social movement organizations concerned with environmental justice and human rights, arguably the most important components of the movement are the domestic local, regional, and national organizations in the various nations and communities in which scores of environmental justice battles continue. Today, environmental justice and human rights movements are merging together as a global force for social change and democratization, focusing on changing governmental and corporate policies concerning hydroelectric power, incineration, and mineral extraction, among others, while seeking solutions for sustainability and social justice. These global movements may serve to reignite the environmental justice movement in the United States, where this movement began.[8]

**Public participation in decision-making** - pursuant to the Executive Order on environmental justice, to increase public participation in decision-making, federal agencies must solicit public recommendations and allow public participation in developing and implementing environmental justice strategies, and must create accessible and understandable public documents.

**Brundtland Commission** - a United Nations commission responsible for creating the classic definition of sustainability: development that meets the needs of the present without compromising the ability of future generations to meet their own needs.

# Local and Global Environmental (In)justices

## Food Deserts

One example of an environmental justice issue that prevails throughout the United States is the overabundance of "**food deserts**" in minority and low-income urban communities. Food deserts are those areas where inexpensive, nutritious food is virtually nonexistent, or is located in supermarkets generally more than 10 miles away. Since many urban residents, especially in low-income areas, lack personal vehicles, they are unable to travel easily to distant supermarkets and often depend on small, local convenience stores where prices are high, products often consist of highly processed food, and fresh fruit and vegetables are of poor quality or nonexistent. Unfortunately, it is often easier and less expensive to purchase fast food and low-nutrition processed foods than it is to buy fresh fruits and vegetables. As a result, the current generation of inner-city youth rarely eats fresh foods, generally does not know how to cook them and, in many cases, cannot even identify them.

One of the causes of food deserts began in the 1970s, when hundreds of supermarkets began to move away from minority urban neighborhoods into suburban communities that provided accessible parking and more affluent customers. In addition, the recent proliferation of large-scale "supercenters" primarily located far from inner-city neighborhoods, are taking the place of smaller grocery stores. Thus, the smaller grocery stores that had been servicing the food needs of local residents closed down and further food desertification took place. A recent study showed that in several states, four times more supermarkets are found in neighborhoods with a majority white population than in those with a predominately minority population.[9] Fortunately, in many cities across the country, **urban farms** are beginning to take shape, not only growing and providing accessible and affordable fresh fruits and vegetables, but also educating children and adults about where food comes from, how it's grown, and its nutritional benefits.

## Brownfield Contamination

Another example of the disproportionate environmental impact on low-income and disadvantaged communities in the United States is the overabundance of brownfields in the cities and neighborhoods in which these populations live and work. Brownfields are abandoned or underused properties, generally consisting of industrial or commercial facilities, which often contain environmental contamination due to the prior use or storage of hazardous substances. They often leave a toxic imprint on the land, for example, with submerged drums full of hazardous materials still continuing to corrode and pollute the surface of these sites. Examples of historical uses associated with these sites include deserted gas stations and vacant automobile repair shops, old factories, mills and foundries, and landfills, dump sites, and junkyards. Unfortunately, brownfields most frequently are located in poor, primarily minority communities.[10] The EPA estimates that more than 450,000 brownfields exist in the country.[11] **Brownfields revitalization** is one example of the environmental justice movement in action: it focuses on correcting the environmental harms disproportionately suffered by minority and low-income communities. The EPA's "Brownfields Program" provides funding

---

**Food deserts** - urban and rural communities where inexpensive, nutritious food is virtually nonexistent, or is located generally farther than 10 miles away.

**Urban farms** - the growing, processing, and distributing of food and other products through intensive plant cultivation and the raising of animals in and around cities.

**Brownfields revitalization** - the cleanup of, and reinvestment in, brownfields that helps protect the environment, reduces blight, and takes development pressures off of green spaces (agricultural, recreational, and ecological reuse) and working lands.

specifically for assessment and cleanup of brownfields, as well as environmental job training to enable local community members to participate in restoring their own neighborhoods.[12]

Abandoned industrial steel mill in Bethlehem, Pennsylvania.

## The Bhopal Disaster

Another example, this time concerning the perpetuation of a global environmental injustice, was the December 1984 leakage of 27 tons of lethal methyl isocyanate from the Union Carbide factory in Bhopal, India, resulting in one of the world's worst industrial catastrophes. Methyl isocyanate is used to produce pesticides and is extremely toxic to humans even from short-term exposure. This is an example of international injustice because the European country where the pesticide was manufactured prohibited the production of the pesticide's active ingredient—one of the most toxic known in its own country—but shipped the manufacturing to a developing country that lacked the regulatory safety controls of the parent country. India's federal government claims that 5,295 people died and 4,902 suffered permanent disability as a fallout of the disaster. Activists say the number is even higher than this and local organizations in Bhopal estimate that approximately 25,000 people died and several thousand more people suffered permanent or partial disabilities. In 1989, a partial settlement was made with the Indian government, where U.S.-based Union Carbide agreed to pay out approximately $470 million in compensation.

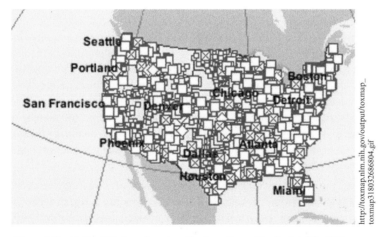

Map of the United States showing the location of industrial facilities that manufacture, process, or use significant amounts of toxic chemicals (in blue), and contaminated sites (in red).

During a rally to mark the twenty-sixth year of the Bhopal disaster, victims walk with an image of Union Carbide's former CEO Warren Anderson, seeking his extradition to stand trial.

The victims were not consulted in the settlement discussions, and many felt cheated by their compensation of between $300 and $500. Allegations have been made that Union Carbide has refused to cleanup the site, provide safe drinking water, fairly compensate the victims, or disclose the composition of the gas leak, information that doctors could use to treat the surviving victims properly. As recently as June 2012, a New York federal court dismissed all claims by Indian plaintiffs against Union Carbide for any environmental fallout from the gas leak. The lawsuit sought damages to pay for the removal of pollutants from the site, compensation to residents whose water source was contaminated, and monitoring of the health of local residents.

## ■ LESSONS LEARNED FOR ACHIEVING SUSTAINABILITY

The lifestyles of the richest and poorest communities pose the greatest threat to the sustainability of our natural resources, but for very different reasons. The affluent communities consume vastly more than their share of resources, more than the planet can provide for everyone. The poorest, however, have little alternative but to use resources in a short-sighted way based on their circumstances. When people must choose between resource conservation and staying alive, they cannot integrate sustainability considerations. Thus, sustainability has the best chance of being successful when it goes hand-in-hand with fostering equity for the disadvantaged members of our society, in terms of economic, social, racial, and environmental justice. An ethical approach to sustainability suggests that society not only has an obligation to eliminate wasteful uses of resources among the affluent, but also that it has an obligation to foster equity among the disadvantaged, while maintaining environmental resource protection.[13] To succeed, sustainability must focus on a balanced approach to decision-making that considers the social, economic, and environmental goals and objectives of all groups in our society. One current environmental justice concern relates directly to a key goal of sustainability: climate change has been shown to create unequal impacts on minority populations, indigenous peoples, the poor, and developing countries. Thus, to develop sustainable solutions to deal with the negative effects of global climate change, we must also address the inequities of the risks and burdens the disadvantaged groups in our society face.

As we have seen, the concept of environmental justice, and later smart growth, both have roots in the Civil Rights Movement and developed in part as a response to dissatisfaction with the lack of public investment in urban renewal, particularly in low-income and minority neighborhoods.[14] Increasingly, neighborhoods are incorporating smart growth principles and environmental justice goals in an attempt to achieve environmentally and economically sustainable developments in their communities. As part of this effort, the EPA is drafting a report entitled *Creating Equitable, Healthy, and Sustainable Communities: Strategies for Advancing Smart Growth, Environmental*

*Justice, and Equitable Development* that can be used by community-based organizations, local and regional decision-makers, developers, and other stakeholders that operate in minority, low-income, tribal, and otherwise disadvantaged neighborhoods as they strive to implement equitable development specific to their own communities.[15]

## Supplemental Readings

Hakim, D. (2012, June 13). Cuomo Proposal Would Restrict Gas Drilling to Struggling Region: Metropolitan Desk. *New York Times*, pp. A.1. Retrieved from http://www.nytimes.com/2012/06/14/nyregion/hydrofracking-under-cuomo-plan-would-be-restricted-to-a-few-counties.html?_r=1

Lebiednik, S., Guhathakurta, S., Pijawka, K. D., Ashur, S., & Blair, J. (1998). Environmental equity in central cities: Socioeconomic dimensions and planning strategies. *Journal of Planning Education and Research, 18*(2), 113–123.

Mohai, P., Pellow, D., & Roberts, J. T. (2009). Environmental justice. *Annual Review of Environment and Resources, 34*(1), 405–430.

# DISCUSSION QUESTIONS

1. What is the relationship between environmental justice and sustainability?

2. What are the four traditional notions of justice, and how do they relate to environmental justice?

3. Does your community have any environmental injustice issues or concerns, and if so, what can be done to help ameliorate them?

# Managing Water Resources: The Central Issue for Sustaining Life

*Ray Quay*

## ■ WHY THIS CHAPTER IS IMPORTANT FOR UNDERSTANDING SUSTAINABILITY

Water sustainability, though in itself it represents a critical challenge, cannot be separated from the general concepts of social, environmental, and economic sustainability. Water is critical to each of these three aspects of sustainability. Water is required to sustain human life, but it also plays an important role in lifestyle and culture. The landscapes that we find desirable, our preferences for recreation, and our habits and technologies of hygiene and health depend on adequate water. The ecosystems of our lands heavily depend on freshwater. Riparian areas, wetlands, lakes, and rivers provide critical habitat and ecosystems services, which depend on adequate water to sustain them. Our economies also heavily depend on adequate water supplies. Agriculture and most industrial processes require water. Goods are shipped via rivers. Most tourism-based economies depend on water and snow for recreation. Thus, water is a foundation in multiple aspects of sustainability, which likely will mean that as we manage sustainability of our communities, tradeoffs in water use may be required. We may need to change some aspects of water use for lifestyle, to ensure adequate water for the environment or economy. Or we may need to accept some loss of environmental quality or ecosystem services because less water is available for the environment.

## ■ KEY CONCEPTS AND TERMS

*After reading this chapter, you should understand and be able to discuss the following:*

Active Management Areas; adaptation; anticipatory governance; Central Arizona Project; climate change; Colorado River Compact; complex adaptive systems; decision tree; foresight; gallons used per capita per day (GPCD); global climate models; groundwater; recharge; reclaimed water; renewable resource; resiliency; riparian areas; stressed; surface water; sustainable yield; uncertainty; wastewater treatment; water cycle; water demand; water supply; water quality standards; water sustainability; and watersheds.

## Introduction

Water is essential for the survival of life as we know it, and its abundance or lack thereof has been a major factor in the growth or decline of almost every human civilization. Today, adequate **water supplies** to meet current and future worldwide needs of humans and the environment could be one of the greatest challenges of the twenty-first century. This challenge is in response to an emerging global water crisis of three interrelated dimensions: the lack of sanitary water and wastewater conditions in developing countries; degradation of freshwater supplies and associated habitats by human action such as pollution; and a looming shortfall between freshwater supply and demand in urban and rural areas. These problems are further complicated by the fact

**Water supply** - the total amount of water available to be used to meet water demands.

that they are not uniform for all parts of the globe. Since the adoption of the United Nations Millennium Development Goals in 2000, the percent of people worldwide that do not have access to sanitary water decreased from 24% to 11%, and those who do not have access to sanitation facilities decreased from 51% to 33%. These are significant achievements, but in sub-Saharan Africa, 60% do not have access to sanitary water and 70% do not have access to sanitation.[1] In 2010, it was estimated that 80% of the world's population lived in an area impacted by degradation of a river system. This impact also has global spatial patterns. Some countries are able to deploy technology to reduce these threats, while others, such as Africa and South Asia, are more limited in their ability to do so.[2] This creates a significant regional problem given that, in 2005, it was estimated that 54% of China's seven main rivers were unsafe for human consumption.[3] Lastly, many developed and undeveloped countries already have highly **stressed** water supplies. It is estimated that globally 1.4 billion people live within **watersheds** where demand exceeds available water supplies[4] and that half of the world's 16 largest cities are experiencing freshwater shortages.[5] This gap in water supply and demand will likely increase with continued growth and possible **climate change** impacts. These three issues of water crisis would require more space than afforded by this book, thus, this chapter focuses on this last issue. How we manage demand and supplies of water to maintain a sustainable water supply, especially in our cities, under conditions of change and **uncertainty** will be the most critical issue to our future.

**Water sustainability** can be defined in the terms of the 1987 Brundtland Commission report as the ability of institutions to manage water in a manner that meets the needs of present social and environmental systems without impairing the ability of future generations to do the same. There is no silver bullet to accomplishing this goal. As this chapter will present, water sustainability is a complicated issue fraught with high uncertainty about the future state of social and environmental systems. Four conditions of water resource sustainability should be considered:

1. Availability of freshwater supplies under conditions of uncertainty, including long-term drought, climate change, and regional growth.

2. Ability to provide infrastructure needed to store, withdraw, treat, recycle, and deliver water for power, agricultural, and domestic use.

3. Ability to manage power, domestic, industrial, and agricultural demand for water.

4. Ability of private and public water management institutions to anticipate and adapt to changes within social and environmental systems.

Though water sustainability is a global issue, this chapter focuses primarily on sustainability of water in the United States. It will examine each of these four conditions of urban water sustainability.

# Water as a Renewable Resource

Water is essential for life and developments, and fortunately, it is plentiful. On earth, 97% of the surface is covered by water and only 3% by land. However, most of the life that exists on land needs freshwater, which represents only a small portion of the earth's total water supply. Less than 2.5% of the earth's water is freshwater, and over half of this freshwater is for now locked in ice caps, glaciers, and permanent snow

**Stressed** - the result of a change that threatens the functionality of a system.

**Watersheds** - the geographic extent from which rainfall will eventually flow into a river or lake.

**Climate change** - long-term deviations from historical records of precipitation, temperature, and storm intensity.

**Uncertainty** - lack of knowledge about when or what will be a future state.

**Water sustainability** - based on the Brundtland Commission definition of sustainable development, the ability of institutions to manage water in a manner that meets the needs of present social and environmental systems without impairing the ability of future generations to do the same.

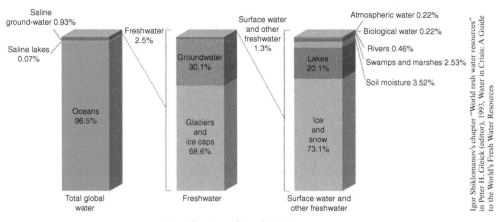

Igor Shiklomanov's chapter "World resh water resources" in Peter H. Gleick (editor), 1993, Water in Crisis: A Guide to the World's Fresh Water Resources

**Distribution of Earth's Water.**

mass. Less than 1% of the earth's total water is freshwater available for use by life on the earth's landmasses.[6] Even this 1% is not evenly distributed across the earth's land-masses; some areas such as the northern and tropical forests have more, and desert areas of the southwest United States and northern Africa have less.

Water, including freshwater, exists within a natural cyclic system that moves water from the oceans to the land and back. Solar radiation evaporates water from the oceans and **surface water** on land. This evaporated water condenses into clouds and eventually precipitates as rain and snow on land and over the oceans. On land, some of the rain and melted snow becomes surface water flowing into streams and rivers and eventually back to the oceans. Some surface water is stored in lakes. Some percolates into the ground and into **groundwater** aquifers. Water in the aquifers moves underground, eventually reemerging at springs that flow back to the oceans via streams and rivers. This **water cycle** makes freshwater a **renewable resource** that is constantly replenished as water moves from the oceans to the land.

**Surface water** - the water that flows or is impounded on the surface of the earth, such as that found in rivers and lakes.

**Groundwater** - water found underground in aquifers.

**Water cycle** - the cyclic process that continuously moves water back and forth between the land, oceans, and the atmosphere.

**Renewable resource** - a resource that continually renews itself through natural processes.

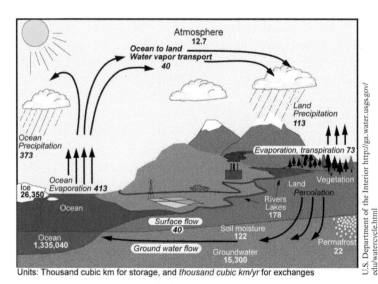

U.S. Department of the Interior http://ga.water.usgs.gov/edu/watercycle.html

Units: Thousand cubic km for storage, and *thousand cubic km/yr* for exchanges

**Hydrological Cycle.**

Not all paths of the water cycle occur in the same time frame or in the same place. The time it takes for **recharged** water to move into and through an aquifer can vary from decades to centuries. Shallow water aquifers are more closely linked to surface waters and can often be found in association with a river. Water will percolate into these aquifers quickly; however, the volume of supply is often limited, and high-volume pumping quickly can deplete these aquifers. They are also susceptible to contamination from surface sources such as septic tanks. Deepwater aquifers contain water that may be centuries old. Typically, they are within geologic formations that can span hundreds of square miles and contain large volumes of water. Although their location is independent of surface water features, they are often recharged where rivers and streams cross over them. Given their volume and depth, recharge can take decades to centuries. Surface water can also take a slower path as glaciers and permanent snowpacks can store water for decades to centuries. One growing problem is the pumping of groundwater supplies at a rate faster than they are being recharged.

# Demand for Water

The availability of freshwater has been a key factor in the rise and fall of ancient civilizations.[7] Humans use water for numerous purposes. Obviously, we need water to drink. We use it to bathe ourselves, wash and cook our food, and dispose of human waste. We use it to irrigate our crops and raise animals. We use it to produce raw materials and goods, to produce electricity, and occasionally, to fight fires. We also use it for less critical activities such as for watering lawns and gardens, swimming pools, and fountains. It is estimated that for 2005 in the United States, 210 billion gallons of water per day were withdrawn from various sources of water for these activities. Not all of this was freshwater; 15% came from saltwater sources. Thermoelectric power production was the largest use of this water in 2005, using 41% of the total freshwater withdrawn and almost all of the saltwater. With 37% of the total, irrigation was the next largest use of freshwater. Public systems represented 13% of the freshwater withdrawn.[8] One of the goals of sustainability is to assure long-term safe drinking water supplies for every person in the world. Unfortunately, this goal has not been reached.

Most people in the United States get their water from a public system. These public systems vary from a single well serving a dozen customers to large systems serving millions of people using multiple sources of water. These systems deliver water that must meet national **water quality standards**. Typically, the water is collected from a groundwater or surface water source, treated within a water treatment plant, and delivered via pipes to individual customers. How much water each of these public systems uses and for what purpose can vary widely between systems and regions. Several key factors can account for these differences. Climate has an impact on water use. Dryer and hotter climates will require more water to meet demands for outdoor water use, such as landscape irrigation, pools, and cooling towers. Southern parts of the United States, such as Southern California, Arizona, and Florida, can have two or three growing seasons. Thus, agriculture water use can be much higher on an annual basis. Cities with older water systems, such as Boston, have high rates of unaccounted for water, essentially water that leaks from main water lines, in some cases, as high as 30% to 40%. Newer cities such as Phoenix, Arizona, may have less than 6% unaccounted for water. A common standard measure of the efficiency of water use for a public system is total **gallons used per capita per day (GPCD)**. GPCD varies between and within regions, ranging from as low as 50 to as high as 400. When compared to other countries, the United States has some of the highest GPCDs in the world.

Gallons used per capita per day (GPCD) - a measure of water use efficiency for a community.

Within these public systems, residential or domestic uses represent the largest volume of water use, on average, 60% to 70% of total public water supplies in the United States. Domestic water use can be separated into two types of uses, indoor water use and outdoor water use. Unfortunately, measuring indoor and outdoor water use is not easy, and estimates of what percent is used for each are generally based on methods that amount to being educated guesses. Estimates of the percent of outdoor water use vary from 15% to 60%, with the range a function of how much water is used outdoors, not how much is used indoors, and primarily due to local climatic conditions. Outdoor water is used for a variety of purposes with irrigation of grass, gardens, and trees being the largest, and cooling towers and pools in warmer climates representing a second major use. Most of suburban America is landscaped with turf, utilizing significant water volume. Cities in northern latitudes with high amounts of annual rainfall, such as Seattle, Washington, have natural rainfall that is adequate to support most landscapes and thus less water is needed for irrigation. Cities in dryer regions, such as Phoenix, have high rates of evapotranspiration and less rainfall requiring more water to maintain turf and pools. Outdoor water use is also a factor of the seasons, with more being used in the summer months than winter months.

Examples of this are outdoor and indoor water use for Atlanta, Las Vegas, and Seattle. Though total GPCD varies from 165 for Las Vegas to just over 60 for Seattle, indoor water use only varies from 54 to 71 GPCD. Average per capita indoor water use does not vary much between regions in the United States or from one season to the next, but can vary based on the age of the home and the number, income, and age of residents in the home. Typically, over half of indoor water use occurs in the bathroom with most of that coming from the toilet. Another 25% is used in the laundry room by the clothes washer. But these ratios are changing. In the United States, federal standards for water efficiency have greatly increased the efficiency of new toilets, shower heads, and faucets, and most manufacturers now produce more

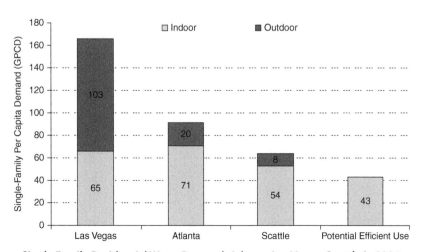

**Single Family Residential Water Demand: Atlanta, Las Vegas, Seattle in 2004.**

efficient clothes washers and dishwashers. As a result, newer homes will typically have more efficient appliances and thus lower average water use. Much of the decline in per capita water use over the last 20 years can be attributed to these efficiency improvements.

Most water-resource planning focuses on the human uses of water, but water is also critical to the function of natural environments. **Riparian areas** adjacent to streams and rivers depend on shallow groundwater replenished by the river or stream and often are critical habitat for wildlife. Some habitats require year round stream-flows, while others have adapted to intermittent streamflows. Habitats in upland areas are dependent on seasonal rainfall and snowmelt. Many species of fish require specific levels of streamflow to breed. Changes that reduce streamflow can result in changes to these habitats. Such changes arise from several causes. Damming rivers and streams, over pumping or altering natural recharge of aquifers that are a source of water for streams, and reduced precipitation due to climate change all can result in reduced streamflows. Such changes are one factor in the steady loss of riparian habitat in the United States.[9]

# Water Supply

In ancient times, humans relied on three primary sources of freshwater: rainfall; surface waters that could be found in rivers, lakes, and springs; and groundwater available from shallow wells. From the earliest periods of human civilization, humans built infrastructure such as canals, wells, and impoundments to store and convey freshwater from where it was found to where it was needed for agriculture and consumption. As civilization advanced, our methods of obtaining, storing, and delivering freshwater allowed us to withdraw, store, and deliver more water over longer distances. Today, this technology varies globally from methods not much more advanced than those used by ancient civilizations to highly advanced systems of reverse osmosis to remove salt from seawater. Sources of freshwater vary from one region to another. In some regions, groundwater from shallow aquifers is widely available, while other regions must use modern pumps to access aquifers that exist thousands of feet below the surface. Some regions have access to surface water from lakes and rivers, while in other regions, water supplies are scarce and the lack of surface or groundwater limits human activities. Many major urban areas, such as Boston, New York, San Francisco, Los Angeles, and Phoenix, move water from watersheds hundreds of miles away to meet the **water demand** of their region. The below image shows the 337-mile long **Central Arizona Project** canal that diverts water from the Colorado River to Phoenix and further south

**Central Arizona Project canal.**

to Tucson mostly for municipal water needs plus water for Indian tribes, who have regained their historic rights to water through federal legal challenges.

Freshwater supplies can be organized into three major sources: groundwater, surface water, and **reclaimed water**. In the United States, on average, the primary source of freshwater is from surface waters (77%) with the rest coming from groundwater (23%).

**Reclaimed water** - sewage treated to a level of water quality suitable for reuse or recycling.

The availability of surface water for each region is a function of the climate, topography, and the dynamics of the water cycle within the region. For most regions, surface water comes from seasonal precipitation that gathers on upland areas flowing into streams and rivers to lower areas. Large watersheds with high volumes of rainfall, such as the Mississippi River, can sustain flow across the whole year with some ebb and flow resulting from the season. Smaller watersheds and those with low rainfall may only flow during the wet season. Some areas have natural storage within snowpacks at higher elevations. Snow accumulates in the winter, slowly thawing in the spring delivering water to streams and rivers. Some parts of the United States, such as the southwest, have built dams to catch and store water during the wet season so it can be released during the dry season.

This variability in streamflow is not just seasonal; precipitation is influenced by climate cycles that can vary in length from decades to centuries. For the last 5,000 years, the southwest has experienced oscillations in its regional climate between wet and dry periods. These oscillations are highly uncertain but can be characterized by periods of wet and dry from 10 to 100 years in length. For the Colorado River, we have a written record that is only for the last 100 years, but we have been able to estimate past streamflows using tree ring records to estimate precipitation in past years. In this record, periods of drought as long as 35 years can be seen, but there is little evidence of a normal pattern of wet and dry periods. Even within these periods, high variability can occur. The southwest recently experienced a 15-year dry period from 1996 to 2011, but within this period, 2005 and 2006, respectively, were the driest and wettest years in the last 100 years. In other regions, this oscillation between wet and dry can be very slow, sometimes centuries long, thus there may be low variability in streamflow records. For some regions, a 500-year record of streamflow does not exist, thus the severity of dry years, like that which affected Texas and Georgia in 2011, seem like abnormal events, when actually they may be part of a climate profile that is longer than we have written records. Typically, surface water requires some level of treatment to be usable for potable purposes. How much treatment is required varies with the nature of the watershed and water source. Streams fed by mountain runoff that provides water supplies to Colorado Springs, Colorado and Portland, Oregon, require minimal treatment because the water has low suspended solids and organic material. Memphis, Tennessee, which uses the Mississippi River as a water source, must provide extensive treatment to remove suspended solids and organic material like bacteria that come from stormwater runoff and other sources.

From ancient times, groundwater has been a source of water for human settlements. But the technology limited the depth from which wells could draw water to the surface in any usable quantity. This limitation changed in the middle of the twentieth century when advances in drilling and turbine pump technology allowed large volumes of water to be pumped from aquifers thousands of feet below the surface. Today,

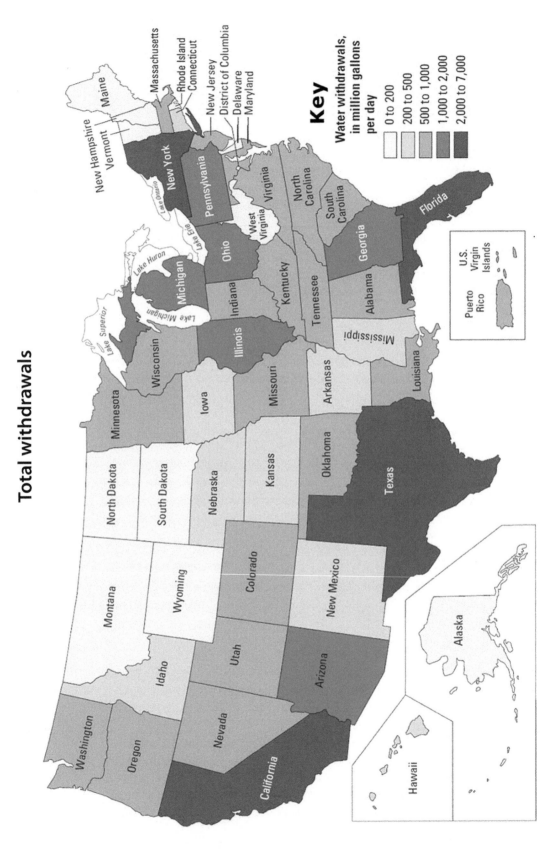

## Total withdrawals

**Key**

Water withdrawals, in million gallons per day

- 0 to 200
- 200 to 500
- 500 to 1,000
- 1,000 to 2,000
- 2,000 to 7,000

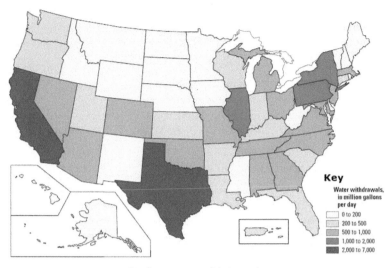

**Surface-water withdrawals**

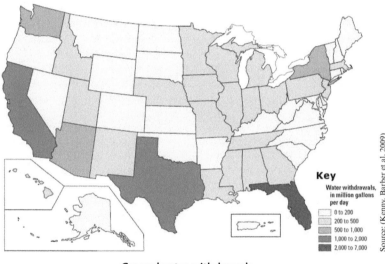

**Groundwater withdrawals**

Source: (Kenny, Barber et al. 2009)

groundwater is a major supply of water worldwide. Groundwater typically requires little, if any, treatment. Although the natural variability of groundwater supplies is not as high as that for surface waters, its variability is typically a function of the depth of the aquifer providing the supply. Shallow aquifers, where the time of surface water to recharge the aquifer can be measured in years, will be responsive to climate patterns of less than a decade. Thus, such groundwater can be susceptible to drought conditions. Deeper aquifers, where the recharge time can be measured in decades, will only be responsive to climate patterns that last for several decades or longer.

Groundwater is not an inexhaustible water supply. Withdrawal from aquifers at rates higher than they are recharged is a growing global problem. Aquifers in India and China are experiencing declining levels because of groundwater pumping. The Ogallala Aquifer, one of the largest in the United States, stretches under 174,000 square miles of the eight high plain states and has been the primary source of water for this region for the last 100 years. Unfortunately, it is being pumped so fast that estimates suggest it may be pumped dry in the next 25 to 30 years. The below image shows an estimate of global groundwater depletion in the year 2000. The aforementioned "Water use per residential customer" image shows the location by state of total water, surface water, and groundwater withdrawal in the United States.

Reclaimed water is water extracted from sanitary sewage. Today, only a small percentage of total freshwater comes from reclaimed water. In the United States, **wastewater treatment** plants generate effluent that is at or above the federal standards of the raw water source for drinking water supplies; however, federal and state regulations restrict use of this water to non-consumptive uses such as irrigation and cooling towers. Reclaimed water used in this manner is considered reuse because it is used once and then returned to the environment by percolation to groundwater or evaporation to the atmosphere. In the United States, some limited recycling of this water as a source for toilets has begun to emerge because of the Leadership in Energy and Environmental Design (LEED) building standards. Such reclaimed water is flushed down the toilet, eventually to be recycled back to the toilet. Other countries, such as Singapore, have now taken this idea to a new level where reclaimed water is used as a source for drinking water.

**Wastewater treatment** - the process of removing material from sewage that is harmful to humans or the environment.

# The Challenge of Water Resources Sustainability

The concept of water resources sustainability has been around a long time and has its roots in the concept of **sustainable yield** for renewable resources. Sustainable yield is the balance between the rate at which a resource is renewed and the rate at which it is harvested and consumed. At first glance, this seems to be a simple concept that would be simple to implement, that is, to identify the rate of renewal and manage demand so it does not exceed this renewal rate. If the social and environmental systems that generate demand for water and the natural cycle of water renewal were simple and stable, water sustainability could be easily achieved. Unfortunately, this is not the case. Social and environmental systems are highly **complex adaptive systems** that are constantly changing in response to a number of internal and external forces. Our ability to understand how these forces impact the complex relationships within these systems and our ability to predict the future of these forces and their impacts is very limited.

**Sustainable yield** - the balance between the rate in which a resource is renewed and the rate at which it is harvested.

**Complex adaptive systems** - systems that have complex internal dynamics and functionality that are costly changing in response to internal and external stresses.

This reliance on stationarity in natural-water supplies has been at the heart of sustainable yield for the last 100 years. "Stationarity—the idea that natural systems fluctuate within an unchanging envelope of variability—is a foundational concept that permeates training and practice in water-resource engineering."[10] Such a viewpoint suggests that a future yield can be predicted, and based on this prediction, a plan to allocate it can be developed. An example of the folly of this viewpoint is the 1926 **Colorado River Compact**. In 1926, the seven basin states of the Colorado River **watershed** (Upper Basin: Colorado, New Mexico, Utah, and Wyoming; Lower Basin: Arizona, California, and Nevada) agreed through the Compact to allocate to each state a share of the Colorado River. This allocation was based on an assumption that the last 20 years of instrument gauging (1906 to 1926) of the river's flow was representative of the normal pattern of wet-dry cycles for the river. This assumption of

**Colorado River Compact** - an agreement signed in 1926 that allocated to Wyoming, Colorado, Utah, Nevada, New Mexico, Arizona, California, and Mexico, different portions of the Colorado River's normal and stored river flow.

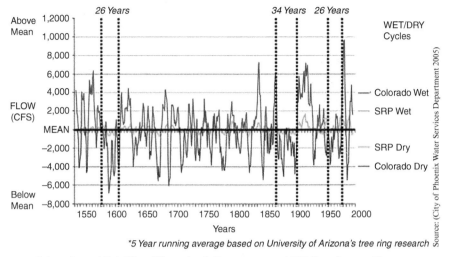

**Colorado and Salt River Watersheds Reconstructed 500 Year Stream Flows.**

stationarity yielded an average flow for the Colorado of 17.5 million acre feet per year. The Colorado and Salt River Watersheds demonstrate that stationarity does not even exist within past river flows and that this 20-year record was among the wettest periods over the last 500 years. The result was an over allocation of the river's resources, which are now estimated to be closer to an average of 15.5 million acre feet per year.

The impact of this misjudgment has been minor to date. The upper-basin states are not using their full allotment, and thus, river flows have been adequate to store sufficient water in the reservoirs to meet the lower-basin state allocations. The long-term effect will be that periods of flow less than 17.5 million acre feet per year will occur more often than above, and thus, over time, shortage conditions for the lower-basin states will happen sooner and more often than originally estimated. Since Arizona's and Nevada's rights are lower than California, these states will experience such shortages first.

Climate change introduces a new layer of uncertainty for water supplies. Current estimates of temperature resulting from climate change generally agree it will increase globally with only the magnitude of the change in question. However, exactly what impact this will have on water supplies and demand is less certain. The relationships between snowpack volumes, snowpack melting, and streamflows are quite complex. Rising temperatures may cause more rain and less snow, reducing the volume of water stored in snow packs and causing snowpacks to melt sooner. For areas that rely on snowpack for storage of water, such as Boston, California, Denver, Phoenix, Portland, and Seattle, this could create problems for existing systems of water storage and flood control. Temperature increases will also result in higher evapotranspiration rates, which may increase water demand for landscape irrigation, fountains, and pools. More air conditioning may be required, increasing demand for power and water for cooling towers.

Current estimates of the impact of climate change on, location and magnitude of precipitation are not as certain as temperature. Generally, in the United States, most of the 26 **global climate models (GCM)** included in the Intergovernmental Panel on Climate Change Fourth Assessment Report indicated higher levels of precipitation in

**Global climate models (GCM)** - models that simulate the complex functions of global climate systems over many years.

the northern parts of the country and decreases in precipitation in the southwest. Yet, some models indicate the opposite—less precipitation in the north and more in the southwest. Our ability to use GCMs to understand possible changes in extreme events and seasonality of precipitation is still limited. It is possible that a region may experience a decline in overall average precipitation but experience an increase in the severity of individual precipitation events. Temperature increases will affect how much snow falls in higher elevations and when it will melt.

Social systems are also subject to high uncertainty regarding their future. For the last two decades, regional growth has been considered a certainty, but the recent downturn in the economy and the collapse of the housing market has caused regional planners to pause and reconsider the future of growth in their regions. But even during the past periods of growth, there was a lot of uncertainty associated with what type and where growth would occur. These uncertainties make it difficult to estimate the future demand for water.

Financial resources are needed to fund water supply projects, but financial markets undergo cycles of bear and bull. Predicting the timing and magnitude of these cycles remains limited. Thus, the question of whether financial resources will be available when needed is uncertain.

The factors that affect demand are complex, and our understanding of them is limited. For example, how people will behave in response to increases in the price of water is not well established. We generally know that increases in price will result in declines in demand, but how much reduction and how fast it might happen are unclear because few regions have experienced rapid and significant changes in the cost of water. How technology will affect water use is also unclear. Is there a limit on how little water can be used to flush a toilet or wash a load of clothes? How increased temperatures will affect outdoor water use is unclear. Though we have experienced variations in temperature from one year to the next and can document the impact such changes have had on outdoor water use, these variations have been minor and our experience is over a small range of change. Is the affect linear, or will it decrease or increase over a larger range of change that may occur because of climate change?

Our experience with drought response to reduce demand is also limited. Normal water conservation activities focus on reducing people's water use without negatively impacting their quality of life. Such actions include improving the efficiency of water using appliances such as installing low-flow toilets and water-efficient clothes washers, changing habits to use water more wisely, and low-water use landscape design and maintenance. These actions can be implemented with little, if any, impact on a family's lifestyle. Drought response is when people are asked to take actions to reduce water use that will likely impact their quality of life or the economics of their business, hopefully for only a short period. Such actions include removing landscaping (grass, trees, and gardens) or allowing it to die, not filling a pool, taking fewer showers, not planting water-intensive crops, raising or lowering the thermostat, using water at off-peak periods, or reducing production of water-intensive products. Some utilities have had experience with managing a drought response from their customers for short periods of a year or two. What will the response and impact of drought response be over a decade? Will people or businesses leave the region for places with more water?

So, how do we achieve sustainability of water resources when there is so much uncertainty about the future? The answer does not lie in efforts to reduce uncertainty by better understanding social and environmental systems. That has not been our past experience where the more we understand about these systems, the more uncertainty we realize exists within them. The answer is within the complex adaptive systems themselves. **Resiliency**, the capacity of a system to absorb change or reorganize and retain essential functions, has emerged in the literature as a key concept for long-term sustainability of social-ecological systems. This is what happens within natural systems when they are stressed by external forces. The system changes to adapt to the external force and maintain essential functionality. Adaptability, the capacity of the actors in a social system to manage the system to successfully adapt to change, is one of the major components of resiliency. History shows many examples of where social systems were subject to some social or environmental forces such as drought and war. In some cases, the social systems were unable to adapt and a civilization collapsed. Others were able to anticipate change and effectuate a response, successfully adapting. These are two key factors of successful **adaptation**, anticipation and response. Unfortunately, even with the advancements in the science of systems modeling our ability to forecast the future is still significantly limited and our social-political systems seem lethargic in all but the most critical of situations. Thus, to achieve water-resource sustainability in an uncertain environment, we must create tools and methods that allow us to anticipate the future and develop flexible strategies that can be quickly implemented as the future slowly unfolds.

**Resiliency** - the capacity of a system to absorb change or reorganize and retain essential functions.

**Adaptation** - reorganization of a system in response to internal or external change, in a manner that still retains the essential functions of the system.

# Anticipatory Governance

A new model of planning and implementation called **anticipatory governance** is being used by water utilities to anticipate a range of futures, prepare a range of flexible strategies to respond to these futures, and then implement these strategies over time as anticipated. Anticipatory governance has three basic steps: 1) Futures analysis: Develop an ensemble of possible futures that represents the full range of futures that we can currently foresee for a particular issue. This can be based on expert opinion or can be developed using a model that forecasts future conditions across a range of values for one or more factors. Then, distill strategic concepts or trends across the entire ensemble that explores the sensitivity or risk of various factors and impacts. 2) Anticipate adaptation: Using the futures analysis, develop possible actions to adapt (react to change or effect change) to individual or groups of possible futures. Such actions may be important to preserve future options or respond to specific changes that may occur. 3) Monitor and adapt: On a regular basis, monitor the present to identify change that may indicate the realization or exclusion of one or more of the anticipated futures. Then, act to adapt as anticipated. The City of Phoenix is one of the communities that has embraced this anticipatory governance model.[11]

**Anticipatory governance** - the process of using foresight to anticipate a wide range of possible futures, plan adaptation strategies for these futures, monitor changes over time, and act to adapt to change as anticipated.

# Phoenix Water-Sustainability Planning Model

The City of Phoenix is located in central Arizona at the southern edge of the arid southwest United States with an average precipitation of eight inches per year. In 2008,

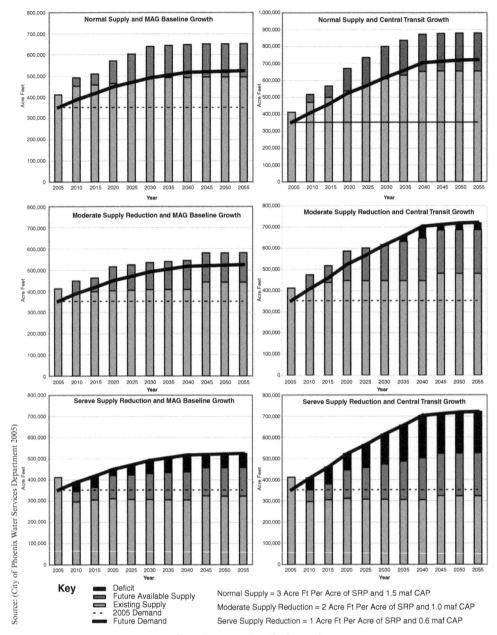

**Phoenix Water Supply Scenarios.**

Key
- Deficit
- Future Available Supply
- Existing Supply
- - - 2005 Demand
- Future Demand

Normal Supply = 3 Acre Ft Per Acre of SRP and 1.5 maf CAP

Moderate Supply Reduction = 2 Acre Ft Per Acre of SRP and 1.0 maf CAP

Serve Supply Reduction = 1 Acre Ft Per Acre of SRP and 0.6 maf CAP

Source: (City of Phoenix Water Services Department 2005)

Phoenix had an estimated population of 1.57 million people located in the center of a region of 3.5 million people. In 2008, Phoenix delivered just under an average of 300 million gallons per day to its customers, 184 gallons of water per capita per day. It has a robust water supply portfolio that consists of surface water, groundwater, and reclaimed water. Though Phoenix has substantial groundwater supplies (650 billion gallons, or 2 million acre feet of credits), it has chosen to rely primarily on its two surface-water supplies: the Colorado River delivered via the Central Arizona Project canal and the Salt and Verde rivers delivered via the Salt River Project reservoirs and canals. Phoenix is one of a few cities in the United States that reuses almost 100% of its effluent, 30% for agriculture and turf irrigation, 30% for power production, and 40% for environmental uses. Phoenix estimates it has enough water supplies to meet its needs today and growth for the next 100 years under normal conditions. But water supplies in the southwest are anything but normal.

Given these conditions, management of surface water supplies in Arizona over the last 100 years has been based on storage of water supplies during wetter years and delivery during dryer years. Reservoirs on the Colorado River provide this system of storage for California, Nevada, and Arizona, and reservoirs on the Salt and Verde rivers provide storage for central Arizona. During Phoenix's growth boom in the 1960s and 1970s, agricultural and urban uses were increasing their reliance on groundwater, which threatened to drain central Arizona's aquifers. Surface water delivered via the Central Arizona Project canal in the 1970s provided an opportunity to reverse this trend. In 1980, the state adopted the Groundwater Management Act (GMA), creating Maricopa **Active Management Areas** in the central part of the state where groundwater withdrawal was required to achieve sustainable yield by 2025. It is anticipated that the primary method for accomplishing this goal would be to switch groundwater use to surface-water use. This Act also requires all subdivisions to demonstrate that they have adequate water supplies (surface and groundwater) to meet the subdivision's water needs for 100 years. However, the GMA assumed that surface water supplies were stationary and did not account for climate variability or long-term droughts.

**Active Management Areas** - a regulatory term used in Arizona to identify regions of the state that must comply with the 1980 Groundwater Management Act goal of sustainable yield for the regions' ground-water resources.

In 2002, as the City of Phoenix began the update of its Water Resource Plan, it wanted to move away from the stationarity model of predicting and planning embedded in Arizona's standard requirements, and move to a model of anticipatory governance. This effort included elements of **foresight** and flexible adaptive strategies.

**Foresight** - the process of anticipating a possible future.

# Foresight

Phoenix began by identifying three key factors that had the most potential significance for water-resource planning and had high degrees of future uncertainty: 1) delivery of surface-water supplies (Salt River Project and Colorado River), 2) growth and development patterns, and 3) water conservation levels. Phoenix defined ranges of possible future conditions for each of these factors. Relying on tree-ring stream reconstructions to provide a wider range in variability in wet and dry periods for the Colorado and Salt/Verde river systems, Phoenix estimated allocations from these systems under normal, moderate, and severe drought conditions. Using a trends approach, Phoenix developed several spatial scenarios of growth, such as accelerated growth rate, changes in the type of economy, higher density in peripheral areas, higher densities in the core area, and a transit-influenced growth pattern. These scenarios were used to estimate demand based on residential and employment growth. Three levels of customer water use were anticipated based on past trends and possible future trends. These factors were combined to generate 144 scenarios of water supply and demand.

In developing its 2010 plan, Phoenix incorporated climate change as part of its foresight. Phoenix participated in a partnership of local, regional, and federal agencies with state universities (City of Phoenix, Salt River Project, Central Arizona Project, Bureau of Reclamation, University of Arizona, and Arizona State University) to regionally downscale scenarios of precipitation and temperature estimates from several global climate change models, estimate the impacts of these scenarios on the streamflow of the Salt/Verde river system, analyze impacts on reservoir management, and estimate impacts on local municipal water allocations. These new scenarios are being used to create new scenarios of surface-water supplies under average and extended drought conditions.

## Flexible Adaptive Strategies

As part of its 2005 Water Resource Plan, Phoenix identified two types of flexible strategies: robust short-term strategies and a worst-case infrastructure timeline for drought response. Robust strategies are those that can be implemented immediately and work well across a wide range of scenarios. For example, an analysis of all the scenarios showed that if no more growth or only little growth were to occur, adequate water supplies were available to meet existing demand even under the most severe surface-water shortage scenarios with moderate drought response to decrease water demand. However, if growth were to occur even at moderate rates, this growth would require infrastructure to deploy existing water supplies and, under conditions of water shortage, acquisition of supplemental supplies would be required. In response, the City placed the burden of financing new infrastructure and supplies for new growth under normal and shortage conditions on growth itself by increasing its water-acquisition impact fee, a fee required to be paid with the building permit of each new home or building. This strategy works well under normal and shortage conditions, and under conditions of slow or fast growth.

Water supplies are essential to a community, and the failure to meet demand can result in the community's economic failure. Various strategies can be used to aggressively reduce demand or enhance supply in critical water shortage conditions. Yet, if these strategies fail to meet a community's essential water needs, sustainability will be lost. One approach to minimize such failure is to anticipate a worst-case scenario and develop flexible strategies to implement incrementally as a worst-case situation unfolds. The basis for Phoenix's worst-case scenario was to assume that current trends were proceeding to the most severe water-shortage scenario that could be reasonably anticipated, a 35-year dry period. A timeline was developed that estimated the magnitude of water shortages and when they would occur over a 25-year time frame. (Phoenix was in its 10th consecutive dry year in 2005.) Using a worst-case projection of demand based on aggressive growth, a timeline of trigger points was developed that identified when new water resources or drought-demand reductions would have to be deployed to meet basic community water needs. Phoenix, like most utilities in the United States, has been experiencing substantial stress on its financial resources that will limit its ability to adapt to long-term drought and climate change in the near term. Using its infrastructure timeline as a just-time **decision tree** will be essential to minimize the investment needed to adapt over time. Each potential strategy can be assessed by water volume, certainty of availability, cost, and time to deploy. This assessment can be used to create a decision tree that indicates the latest point in time action would be required to preserve future options, plan future options, or fund and deploy future options. Using the decision tree, short-term plans of appropriate near-term actions can be created. Indicators of climate, drought,

**Decision tree** - for a specific problem, a diagram of questions (nodes) and answers (branches) that guide the decision maker to a recommended solution to the problem.

and certainty of supplies can be monitored, and the decision tree and short-term plans reassessed and updated as conditions change.

# Summary

The social and environmental systems that support water resources and water management are complex adaptive systems that are constantly changing in response to internal and external forces. Our limited ability to predict the future of these forces and their impact on these systems creates a high level of uncertainty about the future of water resources. This need not limit our ability to achieve a state of sustainable water resources. Using foresight to anticipate a range of possible futures and to plan flexible response strategies will increase the resiliency of our institutions, allowing us to successfully adapt as changes in environmental and social systems occur. Our view of sustainable water resources will need to extend beyond the concepts of sustainable yield. We will need flexible strategies that allow us to reduce our demand, enhance supplies, and finance and build the infrastructure needed to treat and deliver freshwater under a variety of possible future conditions.

## ■ LESSONS LEARNED FOR ACHIEVING SUSTAINABILITY

Planning under uncertainty—Natural and social systems are highly complex adaptive systems that are constantly changing in response to internal and external stresses to the system. Our ability to understand the future of these internal and external stresses, as well as adaptive changes that may emerge, is limited. Rather than trying to predict or control the future of these systems, we need to anticipate a range of changes that may occur and be prepared to respond and adapt to such changes. This is called resiliency and is a critical component of planning for sustainable communities in the long term.

Understanding tradeoffs—Managing our communities for sustainability will often require us to make decisions about tradeoffs between different sustainability objectives. Managing for water sustainability will require making decisions about allocating limited water supplies to various social, environmental, and economic demands. This will require an understanding of the costs and benefits of these demands so our society can value them and make tradeoff decisions about allocating water to them.

Understand the environment as consumer—As we focus on managing water supplies to meet human needs, we should not forget that natural environments also need water to be sustained. We need to better understand the ecosystem services that the environment provides to human settlements, and how much water is required to maintain these services. We must begin to include these demands within our frameworks of water-sustainability management.

## Supplemental Readings

Cronin, J., & Kennedy, R. F. Jr. (1997). *The riverkeepers: Two activists fight to reclaim our environment as a basic human right* (p. 304). Touchstone, NY: Simon & Schuster.

Gleick, P. H., Haasz, D., Jeck, C. H., Srinivasan, V., Wolff, G., Cushing, K. K., & Mann, A. (2003). *Waste Not, Want Not: The Potential for Urban Water Conservation in California* (p. 165). Oakland, CA: Pacific Institute for Studies in Development, Environment, and Security.

# DISCUSSION QUESTIONS

1. What are three dimensions of the global water crisis?

2. What are some factors that affect the rate of renewal and overall demand that determine achieving sustainable yield of water?

3. How does resiliency and adaptability play a role in the future of water sustainability?

4. How can foresight and anticipation affect water supplies and sustainability?

# Making Desert Cities Sustainable

*John Meunier*

## ■ WHY THIS CHAPTER IS IMPORTANT FOR UNDERSTANDING SUSTAINABILITY

Although it might seem contradictory for sustainable cities to exist in desert environments, as this chapter illustrates, several of the earliest cities were established and flourished in deserts. These cities were built in harmony with the desert, as opposed to the more recent view of the desert as a harsh environment that must be controlled and made comfortable for its residents through the use of air-conditioning and imported water. For instance, many cities in the American Southwest appear out of place with their desert surroundings: grass lawns and other water intensive land-scaping, an abundance of swimming pools, and numerous golf courses. Although many parts of the Southwest are in the midst of a several years long "drought," many scientists now believe that these are actually normal conditions, and predict that deserts will become even drier because of climate change.

So, can today's desert cities learn from the past and become sustainable? Part of the answer comes from employing valuable strategies from the past, coupled with the demands of the present, while ensuring that future generations can meet their needs. Ultimately, the sustainability of our desert cities depends on how we manage their scarce resources, especially water, as well as on policies that safeguard desert environments and help spur economic development that is compatible with the land.

## ■ KEY CONCEPTS AND TERMS

*After reading this chapter, you should be able to understand and discuss the following:*

compact urban form; compactness; cultural imperatives; indigenous cultural norms; pedestrian scale; population density; postindustrial technology; radiant heat; urban form; urbanism; and water harvesting.

# Introduction

Modern desert cities, such as Phoenix, Albuquerque, Tucson, Las Vegas, and even Riyadh and Dubai, are being made in ways that reflect the capacity of **postindustrial technology** to overwhelm the limitations that constrained the forms of older, pre-industrial, desert cities. This chapter questions whether both the technology and the living patterns that typify such modern desert cities are sustainable. It also looks at some older desert cities to see what they may have to teach us about how to live well in desert cities without an excessive dependence on nonrenewable resources, and without placing so much stress on the environment. At the same time, as some scholars have suggested, we must recognize that the forms in which cities are made respond as much, or more, to **cultural imperatives**, as to issues of climate and technology. We need to be cautious, therefore, as we derive these lessons and attempt to apply them. Nonethe-less, many of these older cities, such as Yazd in Iran, Shibam in Yemen, Jaisalmer in India, and Marrakesh in Morocco, have evolved in response to their desert contexts

**Postindustrial technology -** a period in the development of an economy or nation in which the relative importance of manufacturing lessens and that of services, information, and research grows; examples of postindustrial technologies include biotech, artificial general intelligence, intelligence amplification, and molecular technology.

**Cultural imperatives -** a belief or belief system that is unconsciously imposed on a group or individual by the greater society; the social norms that are found in all societies that presumably express the basic social needs of all people.

**City of Shibam in Yemen.**

**Compact urban form** - the physical layout, land use pattern, and design of a city; includes things such as land use mix and distribution, transit availability, infrastructure phasing, and resource management. It comprises a land use pattern that encourages efficient use of land, walkable neighborhoods, mixed land uses (residential, retail, workplace), proximity to transit, and the reduced need for infrastructure.

**Urbanism** - the characteristic way of life of city dwellers; the study of the physical needs of urban societies; used by archaeologists to describe the process that drives people to live in cities.

**Urban form** - the physical layout and design of a city. Growth management issues such as urban sprawl, growth patterns, and phasing of developments heavily influence urban form.

**Indigenous cultural norms** - agreed upon expectations, rules, or behaviors that are characteristic of a specific group living in a particular region.

over extended periods. Some have even survived significant cultural shifts, such as in Sana'a in Yemen, with the arrival of Islam after many centuries of growth. It is argued that they may provide valuable models, regarding **compact urban form**, alternative house forms, climate control and its optimization, water usage and its celebration, low energy construction materials and methods, even the nature of windows, in the making of modern desert cities.

Desert cities in the United States, such as Phoenix or El Paso, even Los Angeles and San Diego, face a unique responsibility as they provide models for what it means to live a "modern" life in a desert environment. Following these models can multiply by many times the stresses placed on other ecological and political systems as they are emulated, partially or wholly, throughout the world—first by the wealthy in their suburban villas, and then, over time, by others in the population—abandoning the old, dense city centers as they seek the benefits of a life that begins to match their images of twenty-first century **urbanism**.

This chapter aims to address a growing concern by many regarding the long-term prospects of cities, such as the rapidly growing cities of the American Southwest, with both an **urban form** and an array of building types that have largely ignored their desert settings. It also is a response by the author based on extensive travel to desert cities around the world, particularly, but not solely, to older cities whose cores were built in a preindustrial era, in search of lessons indicating more appropriate ways to live in the desert. This work is not informed by nostalgia or cultural conservatism, although these forces certainly stay the hands of those who would destroy, indeed in some places have already destroyed, the patrimony of ancient cultures in the name of "modernization," and in response to the ineluctable forces of the marketplace. It is informed by a deep commitment to what Vitruvius, an ancient Roman writer, called "propriety;" by a belief that the best way to live is not by dominating the context but by optimizing its benefits and gently ameliorating its challenges; and that the power of modern technology should be used only as a last resort when all other means cannot meet the demands of twenty-first century life.

# Background

The advent of twentieth-century technology has radically changed the nature of desert city living in many parts of the world. Widespread use of automobiles, increased access to large-scale urban water and sewage systems, almost universal access to electrical power and, in some cases, full climate control through air-conditioning have eroded the need for a careful relationship with both the social and physical environment. Satellite receivers, powered by that electricity, have infiltrated almost every household with images of ways of life that challenge **indigenous cultural norms** of both behavior and artifacts. This barrage of images, reinforced by the communications from international commerce, has promoted the uses of the new technologies as a means to "modern" life patterns.

There are still many desert settlements in the world where access to all of these modern technologies is very limited. Auto mobility is at best a motorcycle, and mini-buses or shared taxis enable much travel. Although electricity may be available via a tangle of overhead wires, water may be available only for a few hours a day or a few days a week, or must be brought in containers from communal taps or wells. The building of sewer systems often has been less than satisfactory in some desert cities, because leaking pipes have both polluted the ground and dissolved the foundations of older buildings. Further, effluent is often left untreated as it leaves the system. But these transitions to "modern" living, even when incomplete, have still been eroding ways of making desert cities that evolved over centuries and were adapted to the physical demands and opportunities of their physical and cultural contexts.

Is this process reversible? Some political and religious leaders have attempted to resist this tide of "modernization." Countries such as North Yemen had rulers who refused to let their community participate in twentieth-century developments throughout the first two-thirds of that century. The resistance to this western model of modernization may be reflected in some of the political turmoil in the world today among those who value the traditional ways of life and fear their destruction under the wheels of the juggernaut of western modernization. However, even in countries that profess a cultural hostility to the west, many of the forces of modernization seem to be irresistible. What is needed is an alternative model that retains much of what is valuable from the past but that also accommodates with a new sensibility the demands of the present.

# Modern Desert Cities

Greater Phoenix is a prototypical modern desert metropolis in the American Southwest. This city anticipates achieving its full realization as a major urban center in the twenty-first century and is accumulating the necessary elements of a metropolis. It is becoming a "major league" city more than simply in terms of sports. At the beginning of this century the population of the metropolitan area of Phoenix already had exceeded 3.5 million, with a land area of more

**Housing Expanding into the Desert in Scottsdale, Arizona.**

© John Meunier

than 1,200 square miles. By 2050, the population is projected to be between 9 and 28 million, depending on which previous growth trend is extrapolated. Phoenix has had most of its growth as an automobile city. As in other automobile-dependent cities, its **population density** has been low, averaging about 2,750 people per square mile.

**Population density** - the number of individuals occupying an area in relation to the size of that area (i.e., people per square mile); determined by dividing the number of people by the area they occupy.

What could be the model for a different urban density in a desert city? Older American cities such as Boston, New York, and San Francisco have much higher densities and more urbane lifestyles, and are among the most desirable places to live. But they are not desert cities.

What makes a city have a higher density? Typically, such factors include high-rise dwellings, closer proximity to goods and services, less driving, and more walking, biking, and the availability of public transport. The concept of urban density is important in understanding how cities function. Generally, it refers to the number of people living in an urban area, and it can affect that area's economics, health, innovation, psychology, geography, and sustainability. Many advocates of increasing urban density argue that higher-density cities are more sustainable than lower-density, dispersed cities that rely heavily on auto transport. In general, a compact and denser city is a more efficient city, in part, because many services such as schools, shops, and public transportation are within walking distance. Additionally, residents of compact cities with increased inner suburban density are less dependent on cars, resulting in a decrease in fossil fuel, thus improving air quality and decreasing greenhouse gas emissions. The use of undeveloped land and the costs of providing infrastructure, real estate development, and public services are all considerably less for managed and denser growth than for conventional sprawl development. School, road, and utility costs per residential unit vary depending on development density. Compared to denser urban development, sprawl costs are about 60 percent more. In fact, in recent years, planning strategies, especially in the United States, have focused on increasing urban densities; these strategies include New Urbanism (see Chapter 1), Transit Oriented Development (TOD) (see Chapter 7), and smart growth. These strategies rely on evidence that suggest that the lower a city's density, the more energy it consumes.

This chapter looks at lessons for making successful desert cities. It explores examples in Iran, Tunisia, Morocco, Rajasthan, Egypt, Yemen, Australia, Chile, and Peru. This is not a comprehensive array. Rather, it is a survey of a diverse set of long-enduring desert cities. Each has its own lessons, not only at the urban scale, but also at the scale of the building types. Within this survey, some shared characteristics are identified.

Among them are: shade, **pedestrian scale** and mass transit, courtyards, efficiency in water and energy use, natural ventilation and evaporative cooling, and enduring building materials; but most of all they share the characteristic of **compactness**. A brief description of these characteristics follows.

**Pedestrian scale** - an urban development pattern where walking is safe and efficient.

**Compactness** - high-density or monocentric development; some concentration of employment and housing, as well as some mixture of land uses.

© John Meunier

**Arcades onto the Main Plaza in Cuzco, Peru.**

## Shade

Shade is an essential component of desert living, particularly for the pedestrian. When one consults early photographs of the centers of cities like Phoenix, and of older Hispanic cities, porches and arcades (portales) are in front of almost every building, and awnings often shade the windows. In older cities in Australia, such as Adelaide, such portales are still to be found, somewhat like the cast-iron arcades of the French Quarter of New Orleans. In newer parts of cities such as Brisbane, high steel arcades have been constructed upon which shading plants climb. Major city streets are often lined with shade trees. Sometimes, as in Isfahan and Yazd in Iran, they are growing directly out of the irrigation ditches that flow alongside the sidewalks. In other North African desert cities, water is too scarce for all but the occasional street drinking fountain, often built as a philanthropic gift to the community by some well-to-do citizen. Here, the buildings themselves are the source of shade as they form the edges of the often narrow pedestrian alleyways. In cities such as Shibam in the Hadramawt of South Yemen, the tower houses that line the street are so high that they create a great deal of shade, and the narrow city streets are noticeably cooler than the surrounding countryside.

**Shade structures Brisbane, Australia.**

**Narrow shady street in Sana'a, Yemen.**

Shade is particularly difficult to achieve at the scale of the typical automobile dominated street. The roadway almost inevitably will be exposed to long-term solar radiation and will itself become a **radiant heat** source. This can be reduced by substantial shade trees along the sidewalks and in the medians, but such trees are rarely water conservative and would not meet the requirements for indigenous xeriscape plants often adopted by desert cities like Phoenix. This suggests that the higher-density, pedestrian dominated parts of the desert city should be served, not by streets predominantly conceived of as vehicular roadways with pedestrian sidewalks, but as relatively narrow, shaded pedestrian ways, with limited access for service

**Radiant heat** - heat transmitted by radiation as contrasted with that transmitted by conduction or convection.

and emergency vehicles as well as purely local traffic. This is the arrangement for many of the streets of older desert cities. Physical conditions limit vehicular traffic to small service and public safety vehicles, or two wheeled vehicles such as bicycles or mopeds. The widths of streets in the "medinas" of Morocco or Tunisia were often thought of in terms of the required number of laden donkeys or camels walking side-by-side. In a modern desert city, the dimensions could follow the minimums required for specially designed or selected essential vehicles, while recognizing the priority of the pedestrian, as do the malls on many of our university campuses.

## Pedestrian Scale

Pedestrian scale creates a very different built form than the scale of the automobile. Pedestrians need an intimacy of encounter with the environment, whether natural or human-made. They also need short-range destinations. This leads not only to a smaller scale environment but also to the possibility of a more varied geometry. Since 1785 when the Jeffersonian Land Ordinance established a neoclassical subdivision of land west of the Appalachians, the plans of most American cities have been dominated by the rectilinear mile square grid. The interest in the picturesque that emerged in the mid-nineteenth century introduced the curvilinear street pattern, originally in our cemeteries and parks and eventually in our suburbs. The desert city, however, in providing for pedestrians, will often have an even more complex geometry in its pattern of major and minor streets. A few examples appear in the history of desert cities planned for princes, such as Jaipur in Rajasthan, that are almost completely on a rectilinear grid, but the majority do not respond to a single dominant geometric concept. This is not to suggest that they are illogical, but that the logic is not that of simple geometry. Rather, as scholars have suggested, it is often the logic of religiously derived and legally enforced social relationships, and the creation of a hierarchy in street networks linking small communities to the larger city.

The dense network of intimate shady streets typically will lead to a major communal space. In the Hispanic colonial cities of South and North America, built under the influence of the Laws of the Indies, this will be a formal plaza, focused on a major fountain, flanked by arcades, and framed by the buildings of government and religion. In Isfahan in Iran, there is an enormous central square, or "maidan," whereas in cities such as Marrakesh in Morocco the major open space lacks such geometric clarity, but comes to life in the cooler evenings with food stalls and crowds clustering around storytellers, snake charmers, tribal bands, acrobats, and even dentists. In most Islamic countries, formal geometry is reserved for the paradise gardens of palaces or mosques, not for urban spaces. Nonetheless, the central plaza is the focus of the community. The major Friday Mosque also will be nearby, and at dusk, the air will be filled with the electronically amplified and distorted wail of the call to prayer from the loudspeakers mounted on its minaret. The vitality and identity of the city are relished by both its citizens and its visitors in such places. In the modern city similar public places are still necessary, and could relate to the transit systems that bring people from the further reaches of the city, thereby reducing the necessity for the major roads and parking garages that erode the intensity and thermal comfort of urban life in the desert.

In the ancient desert cities it is often from such places that the market, bazaar, or souk heads off as a shaded linear pedestrian passageway, burrowing its way through the fabric of the city. Typically, this linear market will be flanked by occasionally fountained service courts, workshops, and storerooms from which laden trolley carts head off to refill the emptying shelves of the small stores that line the pedestrian way, and also by the fondouks or inns that accommodate the visiting merchants. Bazaars or souks are often vaulted or domed, and illuminated and ventilated from round windows that let narrow

**Main Plaza Santiago, Chile.**

shafts of sunlight in and the heated air out. Such spaces, neither interior nor exterior, which are shaded but open to the fresh air, are crucial to the success of desert city buildings. Whether such a form of retail would work in the modern world may be questioned but it certainly has its parallels in cities such as Scottsdale in Arizona that has a naturally day lit, and in certain seasons, naturally ventilated, shopping mall a half mile long. The major difference is that the means of access via the automobile has isolated the modern mall from the rest of the city behind a moat of parking. With increased access provided by mass transit, and a higher density of residences within walking distance, such physical isolation of shopping from the surrounding community can be significantly reduced.

## Courtyards

Courtyards have been the focus of buildings in compact cities for millennia, but particularly in desert cities. The central courtyard allows the building to be constructed out to the very edges of its site, gaining most of the necessary light and air from within, rather than depending on a wasteful buffer around it of often relatively useless space. That courtyard becomes the focus of the building from which the major rooms are reached directly, and into which those rooms may open at cooler times of the day and depending on the season. In very hot desert cities, as in Fez or Marrakesh in Morocco, the courtyard will have provision to be shaded when necessary with sheets of fabric stretched on ropes, or by open-weave mats laid across a metal grille that protects the courtyard from the heat from above. Typically, within the courtyard there will be a fountain or pool and leafy plants that provide both physical and emotional cooling.

Buildings of this courtyard type were designed in the late 1950s for the campus of Arizona State University. The Farmer Education Building and the Social Science Building there have central fountains and planted courtyards around which the open to the air circulation of the building, both stairs and galleries, is located. These stairs and galleries share the shade of the light mesh canopy over the courtyard. Only on entering the rooms off that circulation does one experience full mechanical climate control. The courtyard also becomes the major social focus for the inhabitants of the building. In some courtyards in Iran, for example in the desert city of Yazd, the pool in the courtyard may have a wooden platform straddling it on which a family and friends

**Courtyard of Social Science Building at Arizona State University in Tempe, Arizona.**

**Wind tower and courtyard of the Lari house Yazd, Iran.**

may gather in the evening to eat and converse. The courtyard will have on its southern edge, facing north, an open porch or iwan for use in the summer, and on its northern edge, facing south, a winter space, that in the nineteenth century may have been furnished with moveable windows glazed with colored glass. The air movement through these courtyards and iwans is stimulated by windtowers, or baudgir, which climb above the rooftops and channel air from all directions down into the houses, iwans, and courtyards. In many older desert cities there is also space below ground to which people may retire in the heat of the day for rest, quiet, and contemplation.

Such below-ground space in Iran often surrounded a small pool through which the water from the qanats flowed. The qanats are underground channels hand tunneled from the base of the distant mountains to bring water to the city. The residents of major institutions and the important houses of the city were served directly by these qanats. Others had to go to a communal cistern into which water would flow from the qanats. This space is covered by a dome and ventilated by an array of windtowers. Qanats are also found in North Africa, although there they are called khettaras.

# Water

Water is obviously crucial to the survival of desert cities. Many were built on rivers that brought the water from far beyond the sparsely precipitated desert environment.

Cairo is the most extreme example of this, but many other desert cities—such as Lima in Peru, where the local rainfall is almost zero—are served by rivers fed from distant mountain watersheds. In the Chilean Atacama Desert, one of the driest in the world, there are richly vegetated fissures in the arid desert surface through which streams flow from the distant volcanic mountain ranges. Small oasis towns, such as Toconao, capture that water and guide it in narrow channels through their orchards, much as with the acequias in New Mexico and the great date palm groves of North Africa.

**Water in the Atacama Desert leading to the oasis town of Toconao in Chile.**

Another source of water has been groundwater in aquifers built up over millennia and replenished by seasonal rains (see Chapter 5). Surface water is the water that flows or is impounded on the surface of the Earth, such as that found in rivers and lakes. Some of this surface water percolates into the ground and into groundwater aquifers. Water in the aquifers moves underground eventually reemerging at springs that flow back to the oceans via streams and rivers. Unfortunately, the time it takes for recharged water to move into and through an aquifer can vary from decades to centuries. Compounding the problem is that the rate of pumping groundwater is much greater than the rate of recharge.

**A monsoon tank in Rajasthan, India.**

Sadly, in many ancient desert cities, such as Sana'a in North Yemen, the wells that almost every house had in its basement no longer reach the aquifer. This source of water has retreated beyond the reach of those wells because of profligate mechanical pumping caused by increased per capita use, multiplied by rapid population growth. Water is now piped into Sana'a, as is the case in most of the smaller towns and villages of Yemen where it is usually connected to communal taps in the street rather than directly to the houses.

In both ancient and contemporary desert cities, the modern technology of pumps and pipes, as well as canals that bring water from great distances, has changed patterns of water use as well as cultural attitudes toward water. The sense of water as a scarce and precious commodity, to be celebrated architecturally through noble fountains and the building of great cisterns and magnificent stepwells into which the monsoon rains are carefully channeled, can be seen in Yemen and Rajasthan. This sensibility has been displaced more recently by a purely utilitarian attitude that appears to have encouraged wastefulness. In beautiful old cities such as Jaisalmer in India, this newly excessive use of water overloads the inadequate drainage systems and erodes the foundations of older buildings that were not built to withstand the rising dampness.

In our modern desert cities there appears to be a growing consciousness of the need to be thoughtful about water. Many cities have adopted xeriscape as the standard for landscaping. Development also is constrained by the need to demonstrate the long-term availability of water, and an attempt is being made to avoid the exhaustion of the aquifers. In Phoenix, for example, the local press educates the public through articles about the loss of natural rivers because of the unconstrained increase in the number of wells within the watershed.

In fact, given the scarcity of water in deserts and the amount of time it takes depleting aquifers to recharge, some desert cities, such as Las Vegas, Nevada, have adopted water conservation measures. According to the Las Vegas Water District's website, southern Nevada has reduced its demand of gallons per capita per day by 29 percent in 2011.[1] Ultimately, their goal is a further reduction of 11 percent by 2035. Sadly, however, not all desert cities (such as Phoenix, Arizona) have yet adopted such sensible conservation measures.

What techniques and attitudes can then be learned from the history and recent experiences of these desert cities?

# Water Harvesting

**Water harvesting** is a term that needs to be understood and embraced. Desert cities throughout history have practiced it. The modern desert city may harvest water at the scale of the watershed and the region but, at the scale of the individual building and the small community, many still have lessons to be learned. For example, throughout Australia many older homes have under their eaves a great round steel cistern into which the rainwater drains. It is used to relieve dependence on the main water supply in old mining towns such as White Cliffs or Coober Pedy, where many live in underground houses converted from the opal mines and harvest water from the ground above.

**Water cisterns in White Cliffs, Australia.**

An older example is in the courtyard in the middle of the great mosque in Kairouan, Tunisia. Below the center of the courtyard sits a cistern into which the rainwater that falls on that courtyard is drained, and it is then available as a well for the ablutions required before prayer. At the center of the beautiful small town of Hababa, in Yemen, is the town cistern into which the winter rains are drained and stored; it is surrounded by a wall of houses and a small mosque. In India, water harvesting is now a requirement for all new developments. All other desert cities could benefit from such a fine grain attitude towards water conservation. The continuing use of water already used for ablutions is evident in Sana'a, the capital city of Yemen, as it irrigates gardens where fresh vegetables are grown. The Waqf, the local religious foundation, manages these gardens as well as the adjacent mosque.

**The town cistern in Hababa, Yemen.**

**Tower houses around a vegetable garden in Sana'a, Yemen.**

The celebration of water as a scarce and valuable commodity should be expressed in civic and private architecture, in urban form, and in management policies. As an example of what not to do, in a recent drought in Phoenix, the fountains were left dry to symbolize a commitment not to waste water, but this practice was actually misguided. The savings were negligible because the water used in the fountains is recirculated and the only slight loss would be through evaporation. Historically, fountains have been used to provide respite from the arid heat of the desert and to honor the cleansing and life-giving power of water. To keep the fountains flowing is to demonstrate the ability to continue life and civility in the desert. To turn them off is to admit defeat. The lesson here is in the appropriate use of civic architecture to celebrate the value of water as it is harvested and enjoyed.

## Earth

Earth is the material most used in the construction of many of the older desert cities. Adobe and rammed earth, or pise, often are dug from the immediately adjacent land. From the North African settlements of Morocco, Algeria, and Tunisia to most of the Middle East the communities are made of it. The towered city of Shibam in Yemen, for example, is built of mud brick from the great wash of the Hadramawt. Local stone also is used, as in Rajasthan, India, where the indigenous sandstone is extraordinarily versatile and can be used for columns, beams, floor slabs, as well as intricately carved screens and brackets. In Jerusalem, the city benefits from the continuing commitment to the use of its beautiful locally quarried Jerusalem stone on all of its buildings, giving a consistency and coherence lacking in many modern cities.

© John Meunier

**Rammed earth construction in Morocco.**

## Building Materials for the Desert

In contemporary desert cities, many architects of the Southwest have been exploring the use of rammed earth, adobe, and other more enduring materials and techniques that extend their palette to make a thoroughly modern architecture that fits their context as well as the contemporary needs of their clients. Eddie Jones in Phoenix and Rick Joy in Tucson are two of a rapidly growing school of regional architects whose work is being recognized far beyond the bounds of the region, and who have incorporated rammed earth as a valuable contribution to their architectural resources. Inorganic materials that will not deteriorate under the fierce attack of sunlight and dry air, such as earth and metals, have replaced wood as the primary raw material for the structure, or as cladding on the exteriors of buildings. Even the great wooden beams at Taliesin West, located in Scottsdale, Arizona and Frank Lloyd Wright's former winter home and school, have now been replaced by steel. In the arid air of the desert, steel often can be left unpainted in the knowledge that the rusting process will be extraordinarily slow. Will Bruder has been an architectural leader in exploring the use of metals, and his work at the Phoenix Central Library is sheathed in locally mined copper that has been corrugated by the same machines that mold the steel sheets that form the walls of agricultural silos.

# Air

Air in the desert has been one of its greatest assets. Many very talented people, such as New Mexico's great architect John Gaw Meem, as well as Frank Lloyd Wright, came to the desert to benefit from the clear dry air as a part of a treatment for their lung-based illnesses. For many months of the year, fresh desert air can be allowed to circulate freely through the buildings. The great mosques in the older desert cities of the Middle East are open to the air, without glazed windows. Indeed, one mosque type is little more than great arched porches, or iwans, on the four sides of an open fountained courtyard. In the older desert cities, many fresh air environments use architecture to create exterior microclimates rather than closed interior environments. These courtyards, kiosks, porches, shaded souks or bazaars, gardens, or naturally ventilated major rooms, often domed and even fountained, lend much of the quality and richness to the fabric of older desert cities, particularly those of ancient Persia, Egypt, and the Arab world.

Some modern desert based architects have understood the continuing value of these architectural elements as they build in Arizona, New Mexico, and other arid regions. Taliesin West, the winter home of Frank Lloyd Wright and his school, also had no glazed windows in its early years—just shutters that could be closed to keep out the wind or the cold night air. Similarly, older desert homes in Yemen also had shutters only in their lower windows, with the higher windows "glazed" with thin sheets of alabaster to diffuse light into the rooms. High-level ventilation through lantern vents, or simply holes in the roof similar to that of the Pantheon in Rome, have ensured the evacuation of hot air from both major halls and linear vaulted souks or bazaars throughout the history of architecture in arid lands.

In an Islamic city, because of Koranic laws against overlooking into the private courtyards of neighboring houses, there is a consistent height for all the houses. This permits a continuous stream of breezes above the rooftops. The wind towers of Iran, such as in the great desert city of Yazd, reach into that stream to play an important part in stimulating air movement within the courtyard houses, both through scooping air down on the positive pressure side of the tower and through drawing air out on the negative pressure side.

**Shutters below clerestory windows in Sana'a, Yemen.**

© John Meunier

# Compact Urban Form

What form should higher-density urban living take in a twenty-first century desert city? High and low-rise condominiums currently being built, particularly close to existing centers with an array of services available within walking distance, follow models established in San Diego and Dallas. For some people in the urban area, notably young professionals and older people without children, this may be an appropriate although relatively expensive housing type. Higher density traditional houses also are being built. The open space around many of these houses, though, has shrunk to a margin measured in feet rather than yards. This limits the use of the open-air space that is one of the rewards of desert living where, for much of the year, it is possible and enjoyable to be in appropriately positioned and shaded outdoor spaces connected to the house.

The older desert cities, built before the days of the automobile and air-conditioning, have much to teach us about ways to live comfortably and well at higher urban densities. The late Norbert Schoenauer wrote in "6,000 Years of Housing":

> In a world where no nation is wealthy enough to afford waste, the land-use efficiency of the oriental urban residential pattern is worthy of emulation in terms of both land use and energy conservation. This is not to say that the oriental urban environment should be duplicated, but merely that some of its urban design principles should be adopted, such as, for example, the hierarchical order in street networks that bring about a safer residential environment.

> Moreover, planning small precincts for residential neighborhoods without through traffic would afford a more intimate identity with the residential community. In addition, a compact urban development pattern with no waste space would result in reasonable walking distances to many community facilities and would create the population density required for efficient mass transportation systems. Finally, the courtyard concept could be applied successfully in the design of both single-family dwellings as well as multiple housing in which each dwelling would have some semblance of privacy and indeed also a "well of heaven."[2]

The following comparison illustrates the urban land use efficiency that Schoenauer analyzed. The typical North American suburb has 23 percent of its area devoted to public rights of way, 6 percent to driveways and garages, 17 percent to built-up areas, and 54 percent to private yard space, much of it just a buffer between the houses and the road. He compared this pattern to several other oriental urban patterns: Tunis, Medina, 9 percent public rights of way, 74 percent built-up areas, 17 percent private courtyard space; Ahmedabad, Kadwa Pol, 18 percent public rights of way, 69 percent built-up areas, 13 percent private courtyard space; Baghdad, Iraq, 16 percent public rights of way, 72 percent built-up areas, 12 percent private courtyard space. In the oriental examples, instead of only one-sixth of the land being used for dwelling, between two-thirds and three-quarters of the land is in residential use, and that does not count the private open space, nearly all in the form of central courtyards that are an intrinsic part of the home. This makes it possible to achieve much higher densities without building high or losing contact with the ground. It also allows the use of building and paving areas to collect the runoff from rains and support the plants that can flourish in its courtyards and along its pedestrian ways.

This comparison does not mention the great value of the roof surface of the desert house. Typically flat, it is accessible and usable. Residents use it at night, under the clear desert sky, as a cool place for sleeping. In the early morning, with the appropriate shade from the early morning sun, it can be a delightful place for breakfast. In the winter, the gentler sun can be enjoyed directly. In an Islamic city, due to the strict rules about overlooking, the neighboring houses will not block the distant views. This becomes a welcome contrast to the introversion of the rest of the house. Even without the rule of the Koran, such height limitations could be easily assured within the planning controls of the western world.

# Past and Future

Desert cities have been around since the beginnings of civilization thousands of years ago. Largely due to the extraordinary technological changes of the last century and a half, modern life has alienated us from much of the evolved wisdom of those millennia of urban desert living, even for those who grew up within such ancient patterns. For many contemporary desert dwellers, the term "sustainability" has attached to it a question mark. It would seem appropriate as we confront an uncertain future, where the optimism of modernity is being tempered by our growing concerns about the price it is exacting on our natural and social environments, for us to reconsider our heritage, not as something to be discarded, but as a source of valuable concepts. The past is not to be copied, but to be used as a reservoir of societal wisdom.

## ■ LESSONS LEARNED FOR ACHIEVING SUSTAINABILITY

As we have seen, there are many valuable lessons from the past that we can draw upon today to help increase our chances for an environmentally sustainable future in desert cities. Unfortunately, there are also different complexities and limitations to consider and evaluate when analyzing such unique and fragile environments. Two include limited (and ever diminishing) water supplies, and increased temperatures due to climate change, which scientists believe has a profound impact on desert regions.

However, employing successful past methods, and incorporating them into a framework for the present and future, helps ensure that we remain on the path to sustainability. Such a desert path should encompass both a sense of place and respect for its distinctive habitat, as well as learning to live harmoniously with, and benefitting from, indigenous knowledge and culture.

## Supplemental Readings

Ouroussoff, N. (2010, September 25). In Arabian Desert, a sustainable city rises. *New York Times*, p. A1. Retrieved from http://www.nytimes.com/2010/09/26/arts/design/26masdar.html?ref=nicolaiouroussoff

Biello, D. (2011, August 19). Can a sustainable city rise in the Middle Eastern Desert? [Special issue.] *Scientific American*, retrieved from http://www.scientificamerican.com/article.cfm?id=masdar-sustainable-city-in-desert

Alshuwaikhat, H. M., & Nkwenti, D. I. (2002). Developing sustainable cities in arid regions. *Cities, 19*(2), 85–94.

# DISCUSSION QUESTIONS

1. What are some examples of sustainability in early desert cities?

2. Why might desert cities be considered unsustainable?

3. How can compact urban form help make desert cities more sustainable?

# Sustainable Transportation

*Aaron Golub*

## ▉ WHY THIS CHAPTER IS IMPORTANT FOR UNDERSTANDING SUSTAINABILITY

Some of the world's most pressing problems result from how its urban systems operate. These systems consume huge amounts of energy and materials and create intense local "hotspots" for emissions, solid waste, water pollution, congestion, safety, and other challenges to livability. Of course, well-managed urban systems can be fairly efficient and effective at providing sustainable livelihoods for large numbers. Urban transportation systems, in this vein, can be both an asset and a liability to the development of sustainable cities. In the United States, a large share of energy consumption, carbon emissions, and preventable death and injury result from urban transportation systems. For example, because of enormous growth in urban travel, about half of Americans currently live in counties that fail the now four-decades-old National Ambient Air Quality standards, even after spending billions of dollars on technology to reduce emissions from automobiles.

In this chapter, we explore the sustainability challenges and solutions of urban transportation systems in three steps. First, we define the sustainability problem as a special class of urgent and harmful multi-scale and multi-sector problems. We can then clarify sustainability problems that United States urban transportation systems create.

Next, to move from defining a problem to solving it, we must understand the problem's drivers or sources. Looking at cars' exhaust pipes is just not enough to understand urban air pollution; we need to investigate all of the connections between the different factors to uncover the forces behind the pollution. If we could snap our fingers and eliminate the pollution, we would have solved the problem a long time ago. We need to recognize that some segments of society benefit from the air pollution, and that pollution is an outcome of a complex system of institutions with their own web of rewards and feedbacks.

Next, we can move toward solutions; understanding the causes allows us to uncover solutions. We can also develop intervention strategies, areas of policy and practice to focus efforts for change. We can uncover "low-hanging fruit," the easy changes in practice that yield large benefits, as well as the deeper underlying forces and values that may take decades to change.

This chapter will follow these three steps, first introducing and defining the special class of problems that are sustainability problems, and then exploring the various problems that stem from urban transportation systems in the United States. Then, it will explore the various drivers of those problems, which form barriers to moving forward toward solutions. Finally, examples and cases from places within both the United States and internationally show some promise toward solving these urgent and messy problems.

## ▉ KEY CONCEPTS AND TERMS

*After reading this chapter, you should understand and be able to discuss the following:*

bicycle space; Bus Rapid Transit; car-sharing; complexity; Critical Mass; greenfield; human-ecological systems; multiple sectors; vehicle miles traveled; and transit oriented development.

# Sustainability Problems and Solutions

**Human-ecological systems** - humans are dependent on natural systems, such as the water cycle or other nutrient cycles. On the other hand, humans alter these cycles by their effects on the natural environment. This combination of dependence and effects are characteristic of human-ecological systems.

**Complexity** - a characteristic of a system based on webs of interrelated and interdependent institutions and subcomponents. Complexity means that changes in certain inputs yield unforeseeable and unintended consequences.

**Multiple sectors** - urban systems are built on various sectors, such as housing, transportation, and the various systems that supply them with the resources they need, such as fuels, electricity, and other materials.

Not all problems we face are sustainability problems. Sustainability problems are a special class of problems that pose a particularly urgent threat to **human-ecological systems**. Their urgency is compounded by their **complexity** and their involvement of **multiple sectors** and actors across multiple scales. This complexity means that they are best tackled by using interdisciplinary approaches as diverse as the many systems that affect the problem or by applying new methods to these problems.

An example of a sustainability problem is urban air pollution. It poses significant harm to the health of many urban residents, and it causes billions of dollars in damage to infrastructure and crops, lost worker productivity, and additional burdens on the healthcare system. It is caused by a complex array of factors: emissions from electric power generation, exhaust from trucks and automobiles, and emissions from construction and industrial sites, among others. Obviously, to tackle such a problem would require understanding such diverse issues as household energy use, freight logistics, the demand for automobile and air travel, and the technological and regulatory factors governing automobile, freight, industrial, and construction site emissions. It gets even more complex when governments must set air pollution standards, implement strategies to meet these standards, and monitor them. Something as simple as clean air, as we can see, is not a simple matter, but requires a team approach involving efforts from across many different disciplines, such as urban planning, engineering, business, and public policy. Cultural and psychological factors may underlie certain household practices that result in pollution, and these need exploration as well.

We can now move to the focus of this chapter—sustainable urban transportation. We will explore the underlying sustainability problems current transportation practice poses, uncover the sources of problems in urban transportation systems, and then explore solutions.

## Urban Transportation and its Sustainability Problems

Following from such a definition of a sustainability problem, we can see that urban transportation is not a sustainability problem in and of itself, but it is a significant direct and indirect cause of several sustainability problems. This chain of causation means that focusing on urban transportation is an effective approach to solving those problems it causes. Here, we introduce some of these urgent problems that urban transportation systems cause, grouped into different realms; some, such as petroleum dependence, cause a set of other "indirect" problems.

Most urban travel in the United States is by automobile; thus, the urgent problems urban transportation systems create here derive from the particular issue of using automobiles for mass transportation. The problems from urban transportation in other countries may relate to different issues particular to systems there. In 2000, 88 percent of United States workers drove or were driven to work, and fewer than 5 percent took public transit.[1] For all trips, not just those to work, only about 6 percent are by human power (biking or walking). Compare this statistic with other industrialized countries like England, where 16 percent walk and bike, or Germany, where more than 34 percent bike or walk.[2] Thus, when we investigate the significant problems arising from our transportation system, they largely result from using the private automobile for mass transportation. Here, we review briefly some of these problems, grouped along social, economic, and environmental realms.

# Social Problems

## Social Disruption from Traffic Fatalities and Injuries

Around 3,000 people—roughly the same number that perished during the September 11 attacks—die *every month* on the nation's roadways from traffic crashes. Americans have been dying on our roadways at that rate for the past 700 months. On top of these fatalities are about 200,000 injuries from traffic crashes monthly, resulting in thousands of permanent disabilities and days,

Car Crash.

Image © Sergei Bachaikov, 2012. Used under license from Shutterstock, Inc.

weeks, or months of physical therapy and recovery and countless days lost from work or school.

## Social Inequality, Exclusion, and Isolation

Planning a transportation system around the need to own and operate a personal vehicle means that, for those who are unable to do so, the system will be poorly configured. In most metropolitan areas, around 25 percent of the population is too old to drive, too young to drive, or not able to afford an automobile. The dispersion and suburbanization of jobs and housing and the resulting automobile dependence means that those who cannot afford or cannot operate an automobile have greater difficulty finding work, and they can become isolated and excluded from the mainstream of society. A specific example of this issue is discussed in Chapter 4. In many central cities where low-income populations lack access to automobiles and decent transportation, a lack of access to healthy food and grocery options results in what is known as a "food desert." The reliance on cheaper but less healthy food options has been shown to create health problems, especially in inner-city neighborhoods.

## Sedentary Lifestyles and Detrimental Health Impacts

Studies have shown that transportation has a significant impact on how active people are, and in turn, on their health. The lack of "walkability" in many metropolitan areas leads to low rates of cycling and walking, and this inactivity is linked to higher body mass indexes and poorer health. Obesity and diabetes are at alarming rates in many segments of the population, including among children.

## Ethical Dilemmas of Petroleum Dependence

The strict reliance on petroleum for the operation of the economy is called "petroleum dependence." Today, U.S. demand for petroleum overwhelms the country's own

Bird killed in Gulf of Mexico oil.

domestic supply: more than half its petroleum needs are imported from other countries. Ethical problems arise because dependence on oil imports forces the United States to make political decisions that may often betray its own ethics. More fundamentally, however, dependence on oil means we are forced to use it, even if we don't want to. U.S. citizens in several cases were basically powerless to react by choosing alternatives, which were simply not available at any reasonable scale. Examples include the 2010 BP oil spill in the Gulf of Mexico, when the Exxon-Valdez oil tanker ran aground in 1989 off the coast of Alaska, and when the government of Nigeria executed indigenous activists in 1995 who were questioning its oil export practices. What is worse is that even these significant spills are dwarfed by the total amount of routine spills that result from the normal operation of the oil distribution system. Petroleum dependence poses a significant ethical dilemma for those urban residents hoping to choose freely how their lives affect the larger world.

## Economic Problems

### Costs of Traffic Fatalities and Injuries, Traffic Congestion, and Petroleum Dependence

Traffic fatalities and injuries impose large financial costs on our society. Some of these costs are borne by car insurance holders, and others fall on society at large. These "externalized" costs are estimated to be between $46 and $161 billion per year.[3] In good traffic conditions, driving is normally the fastest way to travel in U.S. cities, however, during rush-hour, the average traveler can suffer from long delays. At a value of $10 per hour, these delays are estimated to cost between $63 and $246 billion per year.[4] Petroleum dependence imposes several kinds of financial costs on the U.S. economy. Significant costs, estimated to total between $7 and $30 billion per year,[5] result from lack of flexibility in the economy to respond to changes in price. Additional costs result from the non-competitive structure of the oil industry, resulting in prices that are higher than what a competitive market would charge. The sum of these costs since 1970 is estimated to be over $8 trillion. Finally, the United States military incurs costs for its presence in locations of strategic importance to the oil industry, amounting to estimates of between $6 and $60 billion.[6]

## Local Air Pollution

The Clean Air Act, enacted in 1970 and enforced by the U.S. Environmental Protection Agency, has had a major impact on regulating and reducing pollution emissions from automobiles for more than 40 years. Most pollution is reduced to just a small percent of what it was before regulation. But, large increases in driving and worsening congestion in metropolitan areas means that although each vehicle is cleaner, local air pollution remains a national problem. More than 120 million Americans live in counties that fail at least one of the National Ambient Air Quality Standards that define what levels of pollution in the air are safe to breathe.[7]

## Infrastructure Barrier Effects

Infrastructure for automobiles, such as freeways and arterial roads, are large, intrusive, and can separate neighborhoods from each other and cause barriers to mobility. Studies show that these "barrier effects" exacerbate automobile dependence because they can deter residents from walking or cycling for even short trips.

## Greenhouse Gas Emissions

Greenhouse gasses in the atmosphere manage the planet's greenhouse process, whereby temperatures are regulated. Overwhelming evidence suggests that the significant additional greenhouse gas emissions created by human activity, rivaling the amount of gases produced by natural ecological systems, are influencing the planet's normal climate. Reducing greenhouse gas emissions is essential to avoid the worst effects of climate change. Unfortunately, because human-induced climate change has already begun, we are already too late in avoiding some significant climate change effects. Transportation systems burn fossil fuels, which create greenhouse gas emissions such as carbon dioxide and methane, either in the vehicle's own engine or in power plants that make electricity for electric vehicles' batteries. Transportation is responsible for about one-third of our country's greenhouse gas emissions. About 70 percent of that is for cars, light trucks, and SUVs.[8]

## Production and Disposal of Vehicles

Cars and lights trucks use a large amount of non-renewable steel, glass, rubber, and other materials. Data from 1990 showed that automobile production consumed 13 percent of the total national consumption of steel, 16 percent of its aluminum, 69 percent of its lead, 36 percent of its iron, 36 percent of its platinum, and 58 percent of its rubber. Around 10 million automobiles are disposed of every year.[9]

## Environmental Impacts of Petroleum Extraction, Transport, and Refining

Negative environmental effects occur throughout the supply chain—from spills and flares at

**A lot of used cars in the junk yard.**

**Gulf Shores Alabama.**

the local sites of oil extraction, to spills and toxic pollution emissions at ports and refineries, to local service stations where fuels can cause groundwater contamination. Oil spills, large and small, are part of our transportation system, which is so reliant on international extraction, transportation, and refining of oil. Roughly 10 million gallons are spilled into U.S. waters every year.[10] This does not include the large spills such as the 2010 BP oil spill of around 170 million gallons, or the 1989 Exxon Valdez spill of 11 million gallons. Worldwide, more than 3 billion gallons have been spilled into waters since 1970.

# Agents of Automobile Dependence

Urban transportation systems in the United States are driven by a complex set of historical and institutional factors giving current practices great momentum and resistance to change. Its complexity results from the combination of numerous histories, cultural norms, expectations, and practices. Urban transportation is shaped and reshaped, produced, and consumed across several groups of actors. Entering into a discussion about fundamentally changing urban transportation systems in the United States means one must consider the needs of these various actors, how they interact with each other, and how they respond to demands for change. We must understand that a web of actors *benefits* from the current system. In this section, we briefly consider these different actors and how they interact. This discussion will then lead us into our final section, where we discuss strategies for change.

## The Individual and the Household

The individual and household sit at the most micro level of activity, making daily decisions about how to travel and less regular decisions about home location or vehicle ownership. These decisions are made mostly on rationally minimizing travel times and maximizing convenience. As work and home became more decentralized in most cities, the automobile was a clear choice for travel: the automobile system delivers significantly higher performance than public transit systems. This is due entirely to the government's much greater attention and resources placed on guaranteeing the performance of driving. It is not a result of any technical or "natural" advantage that cars have over public transit.

What is more, however, is that individuals and households engage with larger cultural forces. For instance, car ownership in general and specific vehicles in particular are often powerful tools of an individual's identity formation in our society. Automobile ownership is seen as a symbol of status, patriotism, and of belonging to and supporting mainstream (referred to as Fordism) society. These cultural contexts can become significant shapers of decisions regarding automobiles.

## Planners and Developers

Urban planning emerged as an important force in the process of urban development in the United States. Early last century, planners felt that suburban areas offered a better quality of life compared to the crowded and dirty industrial cities of the time. To this day, much professionalized urban planning practice merely reproduces the suburban,

**Modern Surburban Neighborhood.**

automobile-oriented models. Since this is often what the public and governments request, this is what planners deliver.

Developers reproduce the suburban model, not out of a particular preference, but mostly because that is what seems to be the least risky endeavor. Banks are more likely to lend construction loans to build traditional suburban developments, and developers will find it easier to develop fresh "**greenfield**" sites on the edge of cities, compared to dealing with potential neighborhood conflict and higher or unpredictable construction costs in urban infill sites.

**Greenfield** - urban growth that happens on previously undeveloped "green" land, such as agricultural or forested areas. This is in contrast with urban growth, which happens by reusing previously developed land within the city's areas.

## The State and Federal Government

State governments have a special role in urban transportation systems because they are tasked with overseeing the design and construction of the interstate highway system. Most states also collect their own gasoline taxes, mostly used for investment in roads and freeways. The federal government has an important role for supporting automobile use and urban development around automobile dependence, as well as regulating it and supporting alternatives to the automobile. Federal funds have long been used to support automobile use. Federal funds were first used to build roads in significant amounts during the 1920s and the 1930s New Deal stimulus package. The 1956 Interstate Highway Act solidified support into a set of financing systems, based on the national gasoline tax and federal planning support, to build the national network of interstate highways we have today. Furthermore, U.S. foreign policy is heavily tied to the stability of oil supply in order to keep gasoline prices low and predictable. Urban historians point to two federal policies that spurred suburban development after World War II—the Interstate Highway Act and federal support for home mortgages.

Federal policies have also been important in managing automobile use. These include regulations to control safety, pollution from automobiles, and fuel economy standards that all automobile companies must follow. Federal funds also support public transportation systems, though in small amounts compared to the monies spent for roads.

## Industrial Structures: Oil and Automobiles

The oil and automobile sectors are some of most heavily concentrated in the entire United States economy—relatively few companies account for nearly all of their industry's production. (Fordist society is built around large companies that can direct the mass production and consumption process more efficiently.) This concentration means that they can together easily coordinate their concerns, influence public policy, and shape consumer demands through organized action. Thus, we must see urban transportation systems' use and dependence on petroleum and automobiles as being tied directly into the needs of the oil and automobile-related industrial pillars.

Automobile manufacturers became the focus of the emerging Fordist economy, riding the wave of public investments in freeways and suburbia, and overcoming competition from transportation alternatives, such as streetcars, in most cities. The 1956 Interstate Highway Act, passed by a federal commission with ample automobile-related representatives, solidified the course toward automobile dependence, guaranteeing financing and planning support for freeways. Though homebuilding in the suburbs pre-dated the Highway Act, the pace of suburbanization exploded after its passage.

Surrounding larger pillar industrial sectors sit countless small companies—automobile parts suppliers, independently owned car dealers, service stations, repair shops, along with other related sectors such as automobile insurance companies, drive-through restaurants, and suburban homebuilders. In the 1970s, one study found that all together, the automobile-related industries contributed one-seventh of the total U.S. economy.

## Sustainability Solutions: Toward Sustainable Transportation in the United States

Thus far, the chapter has explored the particular sustainability problems urban transportation systems produce and then discussed some of the most powerful drivers of the current transportation system. Now, we can envision sustainability solutions to particular problems by appreciating the drivers of those problems. Understanding the drivers will help us formulate specific strategies. Because we have emphasized the social nature of these problems, we will emphasize a social approach to their solution by looking at examples of social change and social movements that work toward advancing sustainable transportation. This approach generally involves challenging and reducing automobile dependence, which, in turn, would reduce driving, which would reduce fatalities, emissions, costs, among other things. Challenging the broader role of driving in society would yield compounding benefits across different problem areas.

**Car-sharing** - a system that allows members to use cars on a short-term rental basis. The car-sharing system owns and maintains the cars, and allows members to access and use them at any time of the day, for as little as 30 minutes, removing the hassle of going to a rental car facility. The cars are placed in public parking facilities or on streets to facilitate easy access. As of 2012, there are an estimated 500,000 car-sharing members in North America.

As we saw earlier, the social production and maintenance of automobile dependence occurs at various scales and institutions. In this section, we explore several solutions that build on the social context of transportation systems across those various scales and institutions. The first is an urban planning approach that reorients the city away from traditional automobile planning. We look at the cases of Curitiba, Brazil, and Portland, Oregon, as inspiring examples where social change and social movements led to the rejection of the automobile-dependence model. Then, we look at the international movement in **car-sharing**, and how technology has been used to facilitate automobile sharing. Rather than redesigning the automobile, these systems redesign how people use the automobile, replacing ownership with short-term usage.

Finally, we consider the social movement around bicycling in the United States, looking at the specific example of San Francisco. Here, we can see glimpses of challenges to Fordist society by challenging dominant paradigms about urban efficiency and the use of road space.

## Proactive Urban Planning Paradigms

Research shows that urban planning, and reflecting variations in the mix of land use and transportation systems in a region, can have profound effects on automobile dependence and the accompanying problems that automobile use produces. Travelers in urban areas are always faced with the choice of different modes of travel—between walking, bicycling, public transportation, and driving. The relative convenience and costs of the different options dictate how travelers decide to travel. Some modes become more or less convenient depending on the arrangement of land uses and the prices of using those modes, such as gasoline, parking, and bus fares. Strategies to reduce automobile use then rely on a range of land use and price changes. For instance, the density of jobs or houses in an area dictates how proximate origins and destinations are in space. When jobs, houses, and other uses are close together, it makes walking or bicycling relatively more convenient and a more likely option for a greater number of travelers. If land uses are spread out, then the average distances between places is much farther, making travelers rely on faster modes such as driving or public transportation. Making land uses closer together is a key strategy to reduce the reliance on automobiles. It can also help to improve the walkability of a place.

More specifically, there is a strategy of integrating the location of public transportation and land uses such as job and housing centers; the strategy is called **transit oriented development (TOD)**. TODs combine the idea of density, with the convenience of being located at a public transportation facility such as a light rail or **Bus Rapid Transit (BRT)** station. Evidence shows that compact development approaches such as TODs reduce the need for driving by around 20 to 35 percent, depending on the specific design.[11] In fact, residents in one TOD area in Atlanta drive only one-third as much as the average Atlanta resident.[12] Combining land use strategies such as TOD with measures such as increasing the supply of public transportation, reducing the rate of highway construction, and increasing fuel prices (whether by raising taxes or through the natural increase in petroleum prices) have been estimated to reduce total driving by about 38 percent.[13]

It is clear that the arrangement of land use and transportation in a region dictate how people travel. Knowing this fact, however, does not get us any closer to solutions—implementing alternative land use and transportation systems is not easy, considering the array of institutions listed earlier in this chapter. We proceed with two cases showing how citizens and elected officials worked to change their land use and transportation planning in an effort to reduce automobile dependence.

**Transit Oriented Development (TOD)** - the practice of mixing land uses, such as retail and housing, and increasing the density of urban development near public transit stations. This enables more residents and workers to use public transit for their travel.

**Bus Rapid Transit (BRT)** - using buses to offer rail-like public transit services. BRT systems are based on using normal buses in exclusive, dedicated lanes that allow them to avoid traffic. BRT also relies on passengers prepaying their fares at kiosks or stations like rail systems to speed up passenger boarding.

### Curitiba, Brazil

Curitiba is generally considered an example of best practices in terms of urban transport planning in the world. The city's history shows the importance of the relationship between investment in public transport improvements and urban development.

An important element of its success was a master plan adopted in 1966 to direct the city's growth and development.[14] It was decided at this early stage that the city's growth would be directed along certain corridors and that these corridors would be focused around public transit, not automobiles. This was, in effect, a rejection of the U.S.-originated model of automobile-based urban development being exported around the world, especially in Brazil, during the post-war period. In fact, at around the same time Curitiba was growing, Brazilian planners had just completed Brasilia, the capital city, based on a decentralized, automobile-oriented model. It has since needed retrofitting with heavy and light rail systems to improve its functioning.

The relationship between land use planning and public transport was solidified when higher densities were enforced along the bus corridors through a strict zoning code. This makes public transit very attractive to most residents of the city, since most live close to the various bus routes and most destinations are also close to the bus system. In addition, these plans were made before there were residents—the proactive planning channeled development with explicit goals rather than having to respond to ad hoc development after problems arose.

Jaime Lerner, mayor of Curitiba during this period, favored a bus-based system over the often-proposed rail systems because of its relative lower cost and ability for flexible and fast deployment. In 1974, a hierarchical bus system was developed with the introduction of express and local buses and the single ticket. A "trinary road system" was developed wherein an exclusive bus way (lanes only for buses) and slower travel lanes make up the main axis of the system. Buses in the bus way, sometimes called Bus Rapid Transit, act like light rail—they use mini-stations with platforms that help speed boarding. The exclusive bus lane speeds the buses up ahead of crowded local streets. The rail-like boarding system makes boarding much faster since passengers have already paid to get into the bus stop, thus eliminating the need to pay the driver.

Lerner's proposals were not always accepted by the car-owning public in Curitiba. He engaged in several political battles with proponents of the automobile model, and was forced at times to use drastic measures to protect the public spaces he was trying to remove from the automobile network. In one instance, car drivers threatened to drive through a pedestrian plaza he had created by closing several downtown streets; in response, Lerner brought hundreds of schoolchildren to play in the plaza.[15] Curitiba's comprehensive and proactive planning, in contrast to more typical piecemeal and reactive planning in U.S. cities, makes it an inspiring example. Curitiba's thinking has gone on to influence urban planning and sustainability thinking around the world. Bogota, Colombia, recently implemented a city-wide BRT system to inexpensively add significant capacity to its public transit systems.

A recent national study showed that these new planning approaches linking land use and public transportation will be essential for the United States to reach carbon dioxide targets (60–80 percent below 1990 levels) required for climate stabilization.[16] Though nothing as sweeping as Curitiba's approach can be found in the United States, there is an increasing awareness of the interaction between transportation, land use, energy, and emissions. Dozens of new transit-oriented developments are appearing in public transit station areas across the country. New-Urbanist principles are being increasingly used in what would have been more conventional suburban master planned communities. Moreover, Curitiba's BRT innovations are now being built in dozens of cities across the country with funding and planning support from the Federal Transit Administration.

## Portland, Oregon

During the 1950s and 1960s, when many U.S. cities were being retrofitted for automobile use, communities in Portland, Oregon rejected a significant part of freeway plans developed for it by the State of Oregon's Department of Transportation. The Mt. Hood freeway was slated to connect downtown Portland to the southeast, running through established neighborhoods as it made its way to connect to an outer interstate running north-south. The Mt. Hood, as a designated interstate, was to be funded by the federal gas tax—only 8 percent of the funds would need to come from local sources. Regardless, neighborhoods in the area organized themselves to challenge the freeway using new regulations in the National Environmental Protection Act of 1969 and the Clean Air Act of 1970. These acts required environmental impact analyses for infrastructure projects—tests never required before for freeways. Using these procedures and growing support from local political bodies, the community and city government got the freeway cancelled in 1974. New rules in the 1973 renewal of the 1956 Interstate Highway Act allowed the use of federal highway funds for mass transit, and the $180 million planned for the Mt. Hood freeway was redirected to build light rail in Portland.

Dozens of other communities across the United States successfully fought freeway plans in their communities. The most famous cases include San Francisco's cancelling of the planned Embarcadero Freeway connection to the Golden Gate Bridge, and Boston-area residents' stoppage of the "inner beltway" around Boston. For more on the history of freeway revolts, see "Stop the Road: Freeway Revolts in American Cities," written by Raymond Mohl in 2004.[17]

# Rethinking Automobile Ownership

At first glance, trading the convenience of one's personal, private car for the occasional use of a shared car, owned and maintained by others and located somewhere out in the public realm seems supremely countercultural in the United States. It appears that there are places all over the nation, however, where this idea makes sense and has increased in popularity. Car-sharing is a system that allows members to use cars on a short-term rental basis—for as short as 30 minutes in some systems. The cars are placed in public areas in cities, rather than in car rental agencies. Then, members can use them by swiping a smartcard any time of the day. Though no car-sharing programs existed before 1994, in mid-2009, there were roughly 280,000 car-share members sharing about 5,800 vehicles in the United States,[18] with these numbers growing roughly 20 percent per year.

Car-sharing dates back to the 1940s in Northern Europe, and most notably, with the electric car-sharing system in central Amsterdam during the 1970s and 1980s.[19] San Francisco saw an early experiment in car-sharing in its Short-Term Auto Rental program, though it only lasted from 1983 to 1985. Eventually, with improvements in communications technologies, modern car-sharing took off with systems introduced in Europe and Canada in the early 1990s. Portland, Oregon, was the site of the first car-sharing system in the United States, with its CarSharing-PDX opening in 1998.

Car-sharing takes place when a member makes a reservation online or by phone through a voice-operated menu some time before he or she needs it (though the reservation can be made instantly, so long as the car is available). The system shows, based on the person's location, where vehicles are available for the reservation period requested. The user can specify the kind of vehicle they want or do searches anywhere in the system—even in other cities, for members of a multi-city network like Zipcar. The car is available to the user once the reservation is made; a cardkey activates the car. Reservations can be extended on-the-go as long as the car is still available.

**Car-share car in Berkeley, California.**

**Car-share car in San Francisco, California.**

**The windshield-located card reader on a car-share vehicle in Berkeley, California.**

Numerous studies have been made of the transportation impacts of car-sharing. Car-sharing can have effects on several aspects of transportation systems, such as household car ownership and parking demand, car use, and demand for "alternative" transportation such as public transportation, cycling, and walking.[20] Research across North America shows extremely significant effects: after joining car-sharing groups, households went from owning an average of 0.47 vehicles (already somewhat lower than typical North American households) to 0.24 vehicles. Put another way: in the group of about 6,000 surveyed households that joined car-sharing, almost 1,400 vehicles were "shed"— equal to almost half of the vehicles the group owned. Even more vehicles were reduced because car-sharing households avoided planned purchases of vehicles.

# The Rise of Bicycle Activism in the United States

Bicycling makes up a very small share of daily travel in the United States, with only about 1 percent of all trips. But, with increased gasoline prices and traffic congestion, growing concern about climate change, and interests in physical activity, bicycling has experienced a boom in many U.S. cities.[21] Chicago, New York, Portland, Seattle, and many smaller university cities have experienced significant increases in utilitarian bicycling. In San Francisco, it is estimated that 5 percent of adults use bicycles as their main mode of transportation (up from 2 percent in 2001), and 16 percent ride a bike at least twice a week.[22]

Bicycling is poised to be a substitute for many short-range automobile trips and has enormous potential to contribute to reductions in **vehicle miles traveled** (a measure of the total distance in vehicle travel). Nationally, roughly 72 percent of all trips less than three miles in length are by car, a spatial range that an average cyclist can cover easily.[23] Bicycles do not require expensive, long-term capital investment or operating costs like that of transit and so can be deployed quickly. And, in many respects, bicycling is among the most equitable forms of transportation because it is affordable and accessible to almost everyone.[24] **Bicycle space**, or an interconnected, coordinated, multifaceted set of safe bicycle lanes, paths, parking racks, and accompanying laws and regulations to protect and promote cycling, has been extremely difficult to implement in the United States. Lack of political will to develop bicycle space has been a major barrier. There is no strong national bicycle policy with dedicated funding programs as there are for automobiles. Advocacy for bicycling has been a largely local, fragmented, and isolated effort. Therefore, the few cities, such as San Francisco, that have established a political will to promote bicycling—and that have seen significant increases in bicycling—are worth considering.

## San Francisco, California

In San Francisco, an 11,000-member bicycle organization has lobbied hard for the production of bicycle space, and the city has experienced a rapid upsurge in bicycling. Between 2005 and 2009, bicycling increased 53 percent, accounting for 6 percent of all trips in 2009 and amounting to 128,000 daily trips.[25] In some inner neighborhoods of San Francisco, the mode share of bicycling is above 10 percent for all trips. This is despite the fact that much of the city terrain is quite hilly. How did this happen, when so few people bicycled there in 1990?

Through the early and mid-1990s, despite a growing and vocal San Francisco Bicycle Coalition (SFBC), the City of San Francisco's unspoken priority was to ensure that bike lanes did not impact car space. It was a lonely and sometimes daunting existence for San Francisco cyclists in those days. The frustration over the lack of political will to create bicycle space led bicyclists to create their own spaces. These were the spaces of **Critical Mass** bicycle rides which, beginning in 1992, occurred on the last Friday of every month in downtown San Francisco. Similar Critical Mass rides eventually spread to New York City, Chicago, and globally to cities like Rome and Vancouver. The name Critical Mass is as implied: a critical mass of cyclists that once reached, can recapture urban space from the automobile, enabling the mass to progress through streets unimpeded, and forcing motorists to have to wait for its passage.[26] Critical Mass helped reframe the questions about urban sustainability, pushed open the debate about the use of street space, and showed the possibilities of a humane city.[27]

**Vehicle miles traveled** - a measure of total travel by all vehicles. If 100 vehicles travel each 100 miles, the total vehicle miles traveled is 10,000.

**Bicycle space** - coined by Jason Henderson, the well-connected set of bicycle-related infrastructure, such as bike lanes and paths, as well as bicycle storage facilities like bike racks and larger storage facilities at public transit stations.

**Critical Mass** - a number or amount large enough to produce a particular result; in this case, the number of bicyclists that can recapture urban space from the automobile, enabling the mass to progress through streets unimpeded, forcing motorists to have to wait for its passage. As such, critical mass is an act of civil disobedience meant to illustrate what a city might be like without automobiles and if street space were used for bicycle travel.

Image © anderm, 2012. Used under license from Shutterstock, Inc.

**Bicycle demonstration in Budapest.**

Eventually, struggles between Critical Mass and the City's mayor led to a particularly violent clash in the fall of 1997. In response, the mayor directed his traffic department to hold hearings around the city in 1997 and 1998. Hundreds of cyclists attended these meetings, and the SFBC took a more aggressive position in its lobbying efforts. Although the SFBC made pains to differentiate itself from Critical Mass, the outfall from Critical Mass strengthened the SFBC, which had 1,700 members by 1998 and was gaining allies with some members of the city's board of supervisors.

Some key streets were made more welcoming to cyclists. When bicycle lanes were added to Valencia Street in 1999, bicycling increased by 144 percent. The success of the Valencia Street project further emboldened activists and proved that, with adequate infrastructure, more people would choose to bicycle. By 2004, 16 percent of all trips on the street were by bicycle. By the mid-2000s, and with almost 5,000 members, the SFBC had almost every local elected official concerned about the "bicycle vote" and very few elected officials spoke against bicycling, although ambiguity about how to implement bicycle space was widespread among many politicians. In 2005, with a clear pro-bicycle majority on the city's board, the SFBC pushed through a bicycle plan that is now adding 34 new bike lanes to the existing 45 miles.

## Conclusions

Taking a social view of the problems leads us to a social view of the solutions. The social arrangement of industry, government, along with individual choices for convenience and identity formation create a complex web built around automobile dependence. Challenging this process will require profound and difficult social changes. Although there are few good examples of these changes, those examples assembled in this chapter give us a flavor of what social change can look like.

The public-transit oriented example from Curitiba showed a clear departure from standard models at the time. This model was developed and supported by a team of active citizens, planners, architects, and elected officials.[28] Finding similar examples of such sweeping efforts will be difficult, but the efforts of Portland communities are inspiring nonetheless. Their rejection of transportation planning paradigms integral to the Fordist model was in effect a rejection of that model. The need for high-performance driving to serve an ever-expanding suburban fringe was traded for less traffic congestion, lower automobile use, and improved public transit capacity. Trade-offs also may have occurred, such as lower economic performance and growth from the diversion of investments to other regions.

Similarly, the explosion of car-sharing illustrates that, indeed, many communities are willing to sacrifice convenience for other goals. Of course, for many, car-sharing is a rational approach to high parking or automobile ownership costs. But, those costs are integral to the Fordist model—they are the costs of identity because the automobile becomes part of how a person is valued. Rejecting car ownership on purely rational grounds is still irrational according to the model. We must wait and see how large of a dent car-sharing can make into the dominant model—right now, it appears that in places where the finances make sense, there is a willingness to reject Fordist roles.

Finally, in a similar vein, we find bicycle activists challenging the dominant urban management of roadways for automobiles, asserting an alternative vision for urban streets filled with bicycles rather than cars. That is, filled with things not extracted, produced, nor distributed by the international oil conglomerates or international automobile conglomerates. Producing bicycles is a minor part of the national economy, yet it can provide a significant amount of our mobility if that possibility were made real. Urban streets were used for thousands of years by humans, horses, bicycles, and streetcars before automobiles came along. There is nothing natural about any one of their roles in the streets—it is purely a social decision. Thus, moving forward with the understanding that our problems and our current state is socially produced, we can see more clearly how our solutions will require social changes involving a constellation of actors across multiple scales and approaches.

## ■ LESSONS LEARNED FOR ACHIEVING SUSTAINABILITY

Several important lessons are found in the efforts of cities and citizens attempting to reduce their automobile dependence. The larger lesson is that urban practices, such as automobile dependence, water or energy use, and pollution, are results of webs of institutions, from citizens and neighborhoods to city and state governments, to federal policies. Effective action for achieving sustainability begins with understanding these institutions and how they respond to and resist change. We saw how important the Fordist framework of mass consumption was to the overall production and maintenance of automobile dependence.

Effective cases of reducing automobile dependency can be found across all of these scales and institutions. We examined how at the regional scale, proactive citizens, neighborhoods, and city governments led movements against the expected city planning paradigm. They emphasized goals of walkability and public transportation over the typical reliance on roads and automobiles.

Other citizens have implemented visions for reduced reliance on automobiles by proposing reasonable alternatives. Groups around the world have implemented car-sharing services that reduce the need to own an automobile. The impacts on urban travel have been shown to be profound. Likewise, groups around the world have used the civil disobedience of Critical Mass to illustrate what cities more reliant on bicycles would look like. These acts of theater have successfully translated into real policy changes at the city and regional scales.

This chapter emphasized the role of citizens and activists together at a variety of scales to show that it is not enough to have a "right answer"—that with such technology or such a density we can reduce automobile use by such an amount. The importance is in how citizens and governments implement these solutions. Thus, we can see that sustainability is achieved when we join with others with similar visions and create the social change needed to challenge the dominant urban planning and practice of automobile dependence.

## Supplemental Readings

Urban Land Institute. (2010). *Growing Cooler—the Evidence on Urban Development and Climate Change*. Retrieved from http://www.smartgrowthamerica.org/documents/growingcoolerCH1.pdf

Wray, Harry J. (2008). *Pedal power: The quiet rise of the bicycle in american public life*. Boulder, CO: Paradigm Publishers.

Schiller, L. (2010). *An introduction to sustainable transportation: Policy, planning and implementation*. Ontario, Canada: Routledge.

# DISCUSSION QUESTIONS

1. How do social and economic issues affect sustainability problems relating to urban transportation?

2. How does automobile ownership affect urban transportation and its sustainability?

3. What are effective ways cities can positively influence sustainability in urban transportation?

## BOX 1: OIL AND UNITED STATES—A Short History

Oil was initially used in the United States to produce kerosene for illumination. It was discovered in large quantities first in Pennsylvania in the 1850s, though it would not be until the 1890s when demand for it rose because internal combustion engines were becoming more commonplace in industry and transportation. Oil was discovered in California and Texas around 1900, during which time a single company dominated the system for distributing and refining it—Rockefeller's Standard Oil Company. After 1900, the demand for oil products exploded—and so did Standard's wealth, along with threats from new competitors and government displeasure with Rockefeller's ruthless anti-competitive behavior. In 1911, Standard was broken up into more than a dozen independent companies, many of which still exist today, such as Chevron, Exxon, Mobil, Amoco, ARCO, and Conoco, among others. The international system of oil production and distribution also began during the last years of the 1800s, with tight competition between Standard Oil and Royal Dutch Petroleum Company (now Shell) in Indonesia. Soon after, Mexico, Venezuela, Iraq, and Iran became locations of significant oil extraction.

While in 1900 only about 25 percent of the few thousand existing automobiles ran on gasoline—most were steam or electric—in a short time, gasoline would emerge as the dominant fueling technology. Significantly as well, military prowess became linked to petroleum as World War I (1914 to 1918) showed for the first time how important planes and tanks would become to the future of warfare. After 1920, the demand for gasoline in the United States would explode and the number of automobiles reached 27 million in 1939.[29] Thus, the die was set—our economy would become increasingly dependent on petroleum, and those firms who could supply it would become increasingly powerful. On the eve of World War II, the United States contained over 80 percent of the world's automobiles and consumed 65 percent of the world's oil produced.[29]

Between the late 1930s and 1950, large oil deposits were discovered in the Gulf countries of Saudi Arabia, Iran, Iraq, and Kuwait, completely rearranging the world oil map. Initial dominance of the British in the Middle East followed from their colonial administration of it after the fall of the Turkish Empire during World War I. During and after World War II, diplomacy was increasingly used to support oil production by U.S.-based companies in the Middle East and to edge out British competition. By the 1950s, five U.S. oil companies, together with two European firms, controlled nearly all of the Middle Eastern oil resources. These "Seven Sisters" include British Petroleum, Royal Dutch–Shell, Gulf Oil, Chevron, Exxon, Mobil, and Texaco.

This close relationship between the U.S. government, private oil companies, and the governments in the Middle East would become problematic. Rapidly rising demand for oil in the United States following the full shift to Fordist consumption after World War II would put pressure on the U.S. government to preserve these special relationships in the name of oil supply stability. (The U.S. demand for oil would outstrip its own internal production in the 1960s.) The power struggle over oil, while complicated by the tension caused by the presence of the Soviet Union in the Middle East, forced the United States to support many anti-democratic regimes over the years. The relationship between the United States and Saudi Arabia is particularly close—it provides the United States with access to some of the largest known oil reserves on the planet in exchange for guaranteed revenues and protection of the Saudi government against external or internal aggressors. In another example, the United States supported a coup against Iran's Mossadeq government after it nationalized (converted from private to public ownership) the Anglo-Iranian Oil Company in 1951 (ironically, the Anglo-Iranian Oil Company was itself a national company of the British government). This coup installed the pro-U.S. Shah as ruler. A similar coup was supported in Iraq when it too threatened to nationalize its oil system, leading eventually to the rise of Saddam Hussein. His desires to restrict oil production to raise prices were, in part, responsible for the 1991 U.S. invasion. While Hussein had always cooperated with the United States, his new activism did not follow U.S. plans. U.S. strategy in the region also forced the United States to overlook Iraq's attack on the Kurds in 1973 and forced it to arm groups such as the Mujahedeen in Afghanistan.

The United States and Europe became so dependent on Middle East oil that changes in oil production policies among Middle East oil producers had profound effects on their economies. In late 1973, responding to U.S. and European support for Israel during its war with Egypt and Syria, several countries in the region restricted or completely halted oil production. This quickly quadrupled the world price and caused shortages throughout the United States. World prices would soon stabilize, but spike again during the 1979 Iranian revolution over the U.S.-backed Shah. To this day, oil prices continue to rise and fall with changes in production and policy in the few oil producing countries. The United States has reduced some of its dependence on Middle East oil by improving its energy efficiency and moving to alternative sources for oil, such as Mexico, Venezuela, and Nigeria. Still, it remains in a highly vulnerable position in the world system: in 2008, it imported 57 percent of its petroleum needs, about one-third of that from the Persian Gulf.

For more information on the history of oil and the development of U.S. policy, see *The Political Economy of International Oil* by George Philip (1994) and *The Prize* by Daniel Yergin (2008).

## BOX 2: FORDISM: The Marriage of Mass Production and Mass Consumption

Throughout human history, a dynamic interaction has existed between social organization and its technologies and techniques. New ideas about the organization of work and production lead to technological innovations, which in turn reveal even new ways of organizing work and production. A complex series of changes to the U.S. economy during the late 1800s led to a shift from small-scale to industrial production and to a corporate form of private investment management. Large companies' capacities for investment and further innovations in mass production during the early 1900s led to incredible improvements in industrial productivity. The limited capacity for the society to absorb all of the outputs of mass production,

*Continued*

along with other factors, led to the crash of the U.S. economy and the Great Depression of the 1930s.

The response to the Depression was a new way of thinking about the interaction between the economy and society and between production and consumption. Through the theories of British economist Keynes and the political negotiations between industry, organized labor, and the government through the New Deal, a plan to stabilize the economy was developed. This plan, sometimes called Keynesianism, would emphasize government intervention in the economy to stimulate consumption to solve the crisis of the Great Depression. The government would borrow and tax to play a more significant role in building infrastructure, regulating business and finance, subsidizing and insuring credit, and stabilizing the overall size of the economy. Together with wartime spending and an employment boom during World War II, the plan succeeded, causing relatively stable and sustained growth for the 30 years following the end of the war.

This new form of society is known as Fordism—named after one of the originators of the assembly line, Henry Ford. Government intervention in infrastructure and credit meant that highly productive and well-paid workers could afford to purchase much more of the goods they produced, such as automobiles and houses, and even become investors themselves. The suburb and the single-family home, the freeway and the automobile, along with the oil and other resources needed to power them all, became the centerpieces of the Fordist society. Indeed, many of these processes remain alive today, though conditions have changed. Fordism was linked to the incredible manufacturing capacity of the U.S. economy, along with the existence of inexpensive oil, conditions which have changed drastically over the past 40 years.

Today, the Fordist links between worker productivity, production, and consumption are weakening. An increasingly global production system supplies ever cheaper goods for the U.S. economy, while the role of domestic workers has changed from production to service for this new "Post-Fordist" arrangement. The implications for urban development, automobile ownership, and suburban growth are only weakly understood.

For more information on the history and inner workings of Fordism, see *The Public and Its Possibilities* by John Fairfield (2010), *A Consumers' Republic* by Lizabeth Cohen (2003), and *The Condition of Postmodernity* by David Harvey (1991).

# Coping with Global Climate Change

*Bjoern Hagen*

## ▪ WHY THIS CHAPTER IS IMPORTANT FOR UNDERSTANDING SUSTAINABILITY

Coping with global climate change is important to ensure long-term sustainability on the global and local scale. Climate change threats will affect future generations more than today's population. Measurements taken today to improve sustainability in various areas will help reduce the causes of global climate change and the severity of future impact. Moreover, improving sustainability today will improve the capability of future generations to cope with negative consequences that cannot be avoided any longer.

It will take local and global efforts to address possible future effects of global climate change to sustain and improve today's quality of life for us and future generations. Place-specific strategies as well as international cooperation will play a crucial role in addressing the challenges that global climate change will present over the next decades.

## ▪ KEY CONCEPTS AND TERMS

*After reading this chapter, you should be able to understand and discuss the following:*

adaptation; advanced scenario planning; albedo; anticipatory governance framework; climate change; climate change action plans; climate forcing agents; climate models; fossil fuel combustion; global warming; greenhouse effect; greenhouse gas emissions; heat-trapping gases; high levels of uncertainty; institutional capacity; Kyoto Protocol; mitigation; National Academy of Sciences; Palmer Drought Severity Index; radiative forcing; resiliency; rise of the sea-level; scenarios; and thermal expansion.

# Introduction

Global **climate change** is one of the most important science and societal issues of the twenty-first century. Although climate change is often perceived as a global issue, impacts can already be observed at both the national and local scales. The majority of the scientific community agrees that human behavior and current urban patterns are key drivers of the rapid increase of the average global temperature in recent decades. Cities cover less than one percent of the earth's surface, but are disproportionately responsible for causing **greenhouse gas emissions**. Currently, more than 50 percent of the world's population lives in cities and it is projected that the number of city dwellers will rise to 5 billion by the year 2030. Cities and urban areas consume 75 percent of the world's energy and are responsible for up to 75 percent of greenhouse gas emissions, which cause climate change. Thus, a majority of the world's energy consumption either occurs in cities or is a direct result of the way in which cities function.

Cities, however, not only are a major contributor to climate change, but they also play a major part in solving current and future challenges stemming from climate change.

**Climate change** - statistically significant changes over long time scales of the global average temperature.

**Greenhouse gas emissions** - gases in the atmosphere that absorb and re-emit solar radiation back to the earth's surface; the four most common greenhouse gases released by humans are carbon dioxide ($CO_2$), methane ($CH_4$), halocarbons, and nitrous oxide ($N_2O$).

Urban sustainability plays a key role in the discussion about the causes, impacts, and solutions of climate change. In recent years, there is growing acknowledgement among scientists and policymakers that the challenges of climate change can be met through the design, development, and redesign of urban spaces. Making our cities more sustainable will not only reduce the causes of climate change, but also will improve our **resiliency** toward the effects of climate change that cannot be avoided. Therefore, this chapter not only presents the issues and science behind climate change, but also emphasizes the importance of urban sustainability through **mitigation** and **adaptation** applications as well as building **institutional capacity** to make more effective decisions under **high levels of uncertainty**. The chapter also examines the role of public perceptions in developing sustainable public policies and local climate action planning.

# Climate Change

Climate is a significant component of the world as we know it. The landscape, plants, and animals are greatly influenced by long-term climate conditions and urban areas are often affected by short-term climate fluctuations. Prior to the introduction of irrigation and the start of industrialization, climate determined food supplies, trade, trade routes, and where people could live. In general, the term "climate" stands for the typical range of weather and its variability experienced at a particular place. People speak of "climate variability" to describe the irregularities of weather at a particular location from one year or decade to another. Changes over longer time scales are referred to as "climate change." Although modern technology now allows people to live in places where it was impossible to live earlier, local climate is still a key factor for choosing an appropriate design for buildings and urban areas.

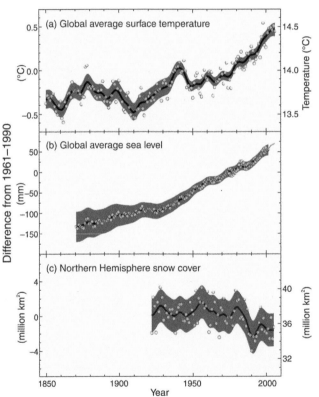

Climate Change 2007: Synthesis Report. Contribution of Working Groups I, II, and III to the Fourth Climate Change 2007: The Physical Science Basis. Working Group I Contribution to the Fourth Assessment Report of the Intergovernmental Panel on Climate Change, Figure 3.39; FAQ 3.2, Figure 1. Cambridge University Press.Assessment Report of the Intergovernmental Panel on Climate Change: Figure SPM.1; SPM.4.IPCC, Geneva, Switzerland. Climate Change 2007: Impacts, Adaptation and Vulnerability. Working Group II Contribution to the Fourth Assessment Report of the Intergovernmental Panel on Climate Change, Figure 3.8. Cambridge University Press.

**Impacts of global climate change on the average global temperature, sea-level, and northern hemisphere snow cover.**

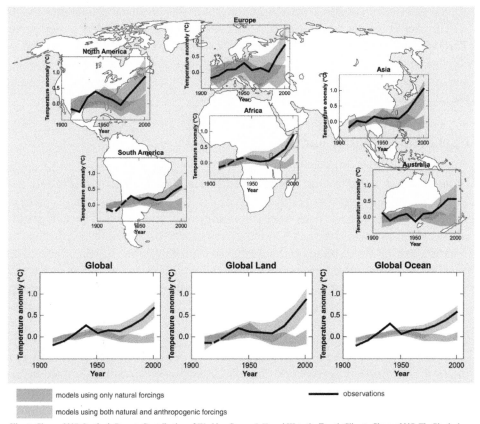

models using only natural forcings

models using both natural and anthropogenic forcings

observations

Climate Change 2007: Synthesis Report. Contribution of Working Groups I, II, and III to the Fourth Climate Change 2007: The Physical Science Basis. Working Group I Contribution to the Fourth Assessment Report of the Intergovernmental Panel on Climate Change, Figure 3.39; FAQ 3.2, Figure 1. Cambridge University Press.Assessment Report of the Intergovernmental Panel on Climate Change: Figure SPM.1; SPM.4.IPCC, Geneva, Switzerland. Climate Change 2007: Impacts, Adaptation and Vulnerability. Working Group II Contribution to the Fourth Assessment Report of the Intergovernmental Panel on Climate Change, Figure 3.8. Cambridge University Press.

**Temperature trends by continent over the past century. The black lines show the actual measured temperatures. The blue band shows the expected temperatures if climate would only be influenced by natural causes. The pink band show possible trends of temperatures if human actions are acknowledged as causes for climate change.**

Climate change is becoming recognized as one of the major challenges of the twenty-first century.[1, 2, 3] Aside from some natural variations, scientists concur that the rapid changes experienced in climate during the last several decades are mostly caused by human activity or are anthropogenic, i.e., resulting from the influence of human beings on nature.[4] Overall, it is not new that climate can change over time. Yet, what is distressing is both the acceleration of the rate of change and the observability of the **global warming** trend recorded in the last few decades. As shown in the figure above, the average global surface temperature has risen by 0.7 degrees Celsius since the beginning of the twentieth century. The total sea-level rise is estimated to be 17 cm and the snow cover in the northern hemisphere decreased from about 37 million km² to 35 million km² over the same period of time[5] due to rising global temperatures and changes in precipitation patterns.

More detailed data of the temperature rise in the twentieth century is shown in the maps above.[6] The map illustrates the temperature trends by continent over the century and shows that the average temperature has indeed increased in the past three

**Global warming** - the rapid increase of the global temperature in recent decades caused by natural factors, natural processes, and human activities.

decades in every continent. Overall, from 1950 to 2000, the warming trend was around 0.13 degrees Celsius per decade, almost twice as much as in the 100-year period before. This trend continued into the beginning of the twenty-first century and is expected to accelerate even further in the future. Worldwide, the years between 2000 and 2009 have been the warmest decade ever measured, and the year 2009 is the all-time warmest year in the southern hemisphere.[7]

## Causes of Climate Change

The basic principle of the earth's climate is that the energy entering the atmosphere from the sun is reflective and has to go out again. The sun's energy is mostly submitted by sunlight, either as visible or ultraviolet light. A great fraction of incoming radiation is then reflected back to space by snow, ice, and clouds. The sunlight that is reflected away from the earth is referred to as the earth's **albedo**, and it does not "deposit" energy. If this steady exchange between incoming and outgoing energy is out of balance, meaning that less energy is being reflected back to space than in the past, then the temperature from the earth's surface and atmosphere changes. The lower the albedo, the greater is the heat absorption on earth. Various factors can change the earth's temperature and these are called **climate forcing agents**, and the strength of these factors is **radiative forcing**.

The human-caused emissions of greenhouse gases play a key role in the changes in the earth's temperature in recent decades. This phenomenon is called the **greenhouse effect**. Greenhouse gases, such as $CO_2$, function as **heat-trapping gases**, preventing the earth's albedo from reflecting the sun's energy back into space. Instead, those gases trap the energy inside the earth's atmosphere and send parts of it back to the surface. As a result, over time, the atmosphere and the earth's surfaces warm up more and cool down less.

### Greenhouse Gas Emissions

The four most common greenhouse gases (GHG) released by humans are carbon dioxide ($CO_2$), methane ($CH_4$), halocarbons, and nitrous oxide ($N_2O$). Overall, GHG emissions have increased 70 percent between 1970 and 2004 with carbon dioxide being the largest contributor to GHG.[8] In addition to its high percentage in the earth's atmosphere, $CO_2$ has a longer lifetime than many other gasses emitted by humans. Systematic measurements of the concentration of carbon dioxide in the earth's atmosphere began in the 1950s. Since then, the concentration of $CO_2$ has been rising at an accelerating rate. For example, the concentration of $CO_2$ rose 20 percent faster between the years 2000 to 2004 compared to the 1990s.

Greater $CO_2$ concentration largely is due to an increase in human-caused $CO_2$ emissions from **fossil fuel combustion**, deforestation, and cement manufacture. Burning of fossil fuels, mostly by private automobiles, is the largest single source of $CO_2$ emissions with about 57 percent of all $CO_2$ emissions. Another source of significant $CO_2$ emissions is the building sector. In the United States, buildings account for 39 percent of the total $CO_2$ emissions. This large amount of emissions by the building sector is due to their high electricity consumption and the fact that much of that energy is created by the burning of fossil fuels, such as coal or natural gas. Deforestation causes

**Albedo** - a measurement used to determine the reflectivity of the earth's surface; it states how much solar energy is reflected from earth back into space.

**Climate forcing agents** - the various factors that can alter the energy balance of the climate system.

**Radiative forcing** - the strength of climate forcing agents in changing the earth's temperature.

**Greenhouse effect** - the phenomenon of increasing global temperatures; greenhouse gases prevent the earth's albedo from reflecting the sun's energy back into space, thus, over time, the atmosphere and the earth's surfaces warm up more and cool down less.

**Heat-trapping gases** - gases that prevent the earth's albedo from reflecting the sun's energy back into space; these gases trap the energy inside the earth's atmosphere and sends parts of it back to the surface.

**Fossil fuel combustion** - refers to the process of burning coal, oil, or natural gas to generate energy, in the way that most automobiles are powered by fossil fuel combustion engines burning gas.

high $CO_2$ emissions from burning or decomposing of trees and soil carbon. In the case of cement manufacturing, carbon monoxide is an unavoidable byproduct of the process. The production of cement requires temperatures up to 1,700 degrees Celsius which, with today's technology, can only be achieved by the combustion of fuel.

Based on measurements taken from ice cores, methane concentration has doubled in the atmosphere compared to the year 1750. Methane is the second most frequent greenhouse gas found. Compared to a molecule of $CO_2$, the radiative forcing from a molecule of methane is about 30 times stronger. However, with a current lifetime of about eight years, methane molecules' lifespan is much shorter than its $CO_2$ counterparts' lifespans. Another difference with $CO_2$ is that the concentration of methane in the atmosphere has not increased since 1993. Natural and artificial wetlands, as well as oil wells, are the largest sources of methane emissions. Although methane concentrations are currently stable, methane sources are expected to increase due to thawing permafrost, a climate change impact area. Halocarbons and nitrous oxide have a significantly smaller impact on climate change than carbon oxide and methane. The concentrations of halocarbons in the atmosphere, however, are declining as a result of international efforts to protect the ozone layer. International agreements such as the Montreal Protocol regulate the emission of these gases, which are used in appliances such as refrigerators and air conditioners. Nevertheless, the concentrations of halocarbons are only declining at a very slow pace due to their long lifetime of 50 to 100 years. Nitrous oxide has an even longer lifespan of about 150 years.

## Natural Causes of Climate Change

Besides the human-made causes discussed above, there are also different climate change forces that are of natural origin, such as variations in solar intensity and volcanic eruptions. Solar intensity varies naturally over time and depends on the number of dark sports on the surface of the sun. Observations suggest that there is an 11-year sunspot cycle with up to 100 dark spots during the maximum of the cycle.[9] Accurate measurements of the solar intensity have only been available since the 1970s. The data shows that the sunspot cycle only changes the intensity of the sun by 0.08 percent, which is a very small number compared to the radiative forcing of greenhouse gases. Volcanoes also influence the earth's climate by releasing sulfate aerosols into the atmosphere. This can lead to a strong, but short-term, cooling. At the regional scale, past eruptions have led to increases in temperature in the stratosphere and decreases on the earth's surface.

# Current Impacts of Global Climate Change

An average temperature increase of 0.7 degrees Celsius since the beginning of the twentieth century might not sound like much. Impacts of climate change, however, are already visible in the United States and at a global level. Measurable increases in air and water temperature, reduced frost days, a higher rate and magnitude of heavy rainfall, a rise in sea-level, reduced snow cover, glaciers, permafrost, and sea ice, can be seen today. These changes will likely affect human health, water supply, agriculture, coastal areas, and numerous other aspects of society and the natural environment. The latest observation leads to the conclusion that in many areas of the world, global climate change effects are occurring faster than once expected.[10]

# Sea-level Rise and Ice Sheets

**Rise of the sea-level** - refers to the fact that the mean high tide levels have increased constantly over the past decades.

**Thermal expansion** - the process of the water in the oceans expanding in volume due to increasing temperatures leading to measurable sea-level rise.

The expansion of the ocean as its temperature rises and the melting of ice sheets are both direct results of global climate change and the main contributors to the **rise of the sea-level** observed since the beginning of the twentieth century. The process of the water in the oceans expanding as it gets warmer is called "**thermal expansion**" and has a relatively small effect. Nonetheless, considering that the oceans are on average 3,800 meters deep, even an average expansion of one hundredths of one percent would result in the ocean rising by 38 centimeters.

The possible melting of ice sheets is a far bigger issue. If **all** ice sheets melted entirely, the sea-level could rise by as much as 70 meters, changing the world's coastal landscapes forever, and impacting the coastal environments of all continents. Currently, however, the ice sheets are in relatively stable condition and are not melting too much. Nevertheless, scientific studies show that the sea-level is rising by 3.5 millimeters per year and in total 17 centimeters since the beginning of the twentieth century.[11] The two ice sheets with potentially the greatest impact on sea-level rise are Greenland and Antarctica. The melting of the ice sheet of Greenland alone could raise the sea-level by 7 meters. Measurements in Greenland show that the ice closest to the sea is already melting on the surface, creating meltwater ponds and water streams toward the open sea. On the other hand, the Antarctic ice sheet is currently more stable. Since the temperature is much colder there, no surface melting has occurred yet. The only way that Antarctica is losing ice currently is by entire icebergs breaking off the main ice sheet and melting in warmer waters. If temperatures continue to rise, however, it could only be a matter of decades before the ice sheets of Greenland are melted completely and the Antarctic ice sheets become unstable. Sea-level rise is not the only outcome of melting ice. Another consequence is the loss of surfaces that reflect sunlight back into space, decreasing the earth's surface albedo and adding more heat to the earth's surface.

Compared to ice sheets, mountain glaciers and ice caps contain significantly less water, but this water melts much more quickly under increasing temperatures. Glaciers have been retreating since the eighteenth century, but only since the 1970s has the speed of the melting increased. This trend can be seen in the above pictures. The four pictures were taken at four different times of the Muir Glacier in Alaska, or what is left of that glacier. The two pictures on the left were taken in August 1941 and September 2004. The pictures on the right were taken in September 1976 and 2003. Over a timespan of 65 years, the glacier retreated more than 7 miles and the resulting runoff created a mountain lake. This illustrates what dramatic impact an increase in temperature can have on the landscape when the glacier retreats substantially over time. Mountain glaciers and snowpacks store winter precipitation and release it slowly over the summer, providing a freshwater source just when it is needed for agricultural irrigation. With galciers retreating and snowpacks declining, freshwater from mountain streams could cause decreases in downstream storage of water supplies. (See Chapter 5.) The melting of permafrost soils is another problem that has the effect of increasing the concentration of greenhouse gases in the atmosphere. Arctic permafrost underlies almost one-fifth of the planet's land surface and usually contains methane hydrate. As long as it is frozen, methane hydrate does not present any danger for the environment, but when the ice thaws due to climate change, the methane converts to a very effective heat-trapping gas.

Field, William Osgood. 1941, Muir Glacier. Glacier Photograph Collection. Boulder, Colorado USA: National Snow and Ice Data Center/World Data Center for Glaciology. Digital media.

Molnia, Bruce F. 1976, Muir Glacier. Glacier Photograph Collection. Boulder, Colorado USA: National Snow and Ice Data Center/World Data Center for Glaciology. Digital media.

Molnia, Bruce F. 2004, Muir Glacier. Glacier Photograph Collection. Boulder, Colorado USA: National Snow and Ice Data Center/World Data Center for Glaciology. Digital media.

Molnia, Bruce F. 2003, Muir Glacier. Glacier Photograph Collection. Boulder, Colorado USA: National Snow and Ice Data Center/World Data Center for Glaciology. Digital media.

**Retreat of the Muir Glacier in Alaska from 1941 to 2004. Clockwise from the top left: August 1941, September 2004, September 1976, September 2003.**

## Precipitation and Drought

Despite increasing global temperatures, climate change also impacts precipitation patterns. Unlike temperature, which has increased almost everywhere on the planet, precipitation is increasing in some parts of the world and decreasing in others. The warmer the air becomes, the more water it can store and then release it during wet days. This can lead to storm floods and heavy damage in areas where the infrastructure is not able to handle the release of large amounts of water in short amounts of time. This map shows the areas where heavy rainfall increased or decreased.

For example, heavy rainfall increased on the east coast of the United States, but decreased in Africa where food shortages and hunger are already a major concern. In 2011, Hurricane Irene caused heavy rainfalls on the east coast causing floods, heavy damages, and even human casualties. In the New England states, for example, rivers flooded several towns in Vermont destroying roads and forcing emergency evacuations.

In addition to the increases in frequency and magnitude of heavy rainfall, seasonal changes of precipitation are occurring as well. These changes are especially important to land ecosystems and the agricultural sector. Farmers are concerned that seasonal changes of rainfall will affect their growing and harvesting seasons. Heavy rainfalls have delayed spring planting in some areas of the United States, jeopardizing the livelihoods of farmers. The resulting flooding of the fields during the growing season

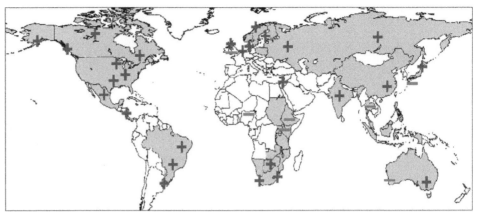

Climate Change 2007: Synthesis Report. Contribution of Working Groups I, II, and III to the Fourth Climate Change 2007: The Physical Science Basis. Working Group I Contribution to the Fourth Assessment Report of the Intergovernmental Panel on Climate Change, Figure 3.39; FAQ 3.2, Figure 1. Cambridge University Press. Assessment Report of the Intergovernmental Panel on Climate Change: Figure SPM.1; SPM.4.IPCC, Geneva, Switzerland. Climate Change 2007: Impacts, Adaptation and Vulnerability. Working Group II Contribution to the Fourth Assessment Report of the Intergovernmental Panel on Climate Change, Figure 3.8. Cambridge University Press.

**Changes in heavy rainfall around the world both increases (+) and declines (−).**

Image © Petrov Stanislav Eduardovich, 2012. Used under license from Shutterstock, Inc.

**Flooded neighborhood in Little Falls, N.J. after Hurricane Irene.**

causes low oxygen levels in the soil, which destroys crops and increases the likelihood of root diseases. In addition, research suggests that increasing temperatures will most likely reduce livestock production during the summer season.

Without causing any changes in the annual average rainfall, in some regions, precipitation has decreased in the summer but increased in the winter, resulting in increasing risks of flooding during the winter and drought in the summer, with potentially devastating results for the agricultural sector. Seasonal changes may also impact areas that rely heavily on tourism and winter sports. In some areas, precipitation that used to fall as snow during the winter is now falling as rain. Consequently, the reduction in the snowpack not only shortens the winter sports season, but also reduces the water runoff during the summer when water is most needed. We find this occurrence in Arizona, which causes concerns about a long-lasting drought condition in the Phoenix area.

Droughts are another major result of changes in precipitation. There are different ways to define and measure the severity of droughts. The most common measurement used is the **Palmer Drought Severity Index (PDSI)**, which considers not only the monthly amount of precipitation, but also the regional average temperatures. According to the PDSI, droughts have increased and became more severe between 1990 and

**Palmer Drought Severity Index (PDSI)**- the most common measurement used to define and measure the severity of droughts, by considering not only the monthly amount of precipitation, but also the regional average temperatures.

2002. In this index, the severity of the drought is shown in terms of minus numbers and excess rain is reflected by plus numbers. Although heavy rainfall has increased, the risk of droughts has only decreased in very few regions of the world. Instead, the amount of dry areas has more than doubled in size since the 1970s.[12]

## Human Health

The impact of climate change on human health is a relatively new research field and at this point not much data are available.[13] However, existing research does indicate a strong correlation between heat waves and increased mortality rates. In 2003, the European heat wave was responsible for more than 70,000 deaths in Europe, many of them in highly industrialized countries that were considered less vulnerable to weather extremes compared to developing countries in Africa or South America. Furthermore, data indicate that ticks spreading Lyme disease and the anopheles mosquito carrying Malaria and other viruses are spreading northward. An increase of pollen allergies is another impact of climate change, since the increase in temperature causes the pollen season to start earlier in the year. For those interested in this area please see the following Internet sites:

- World Health Organization: http://www.who.int/globalchange/en/
- Environmental Protection Agency: http://epa.gov/climatechange/effects/health.html
- United States Global Change Research Program: http://www.globalchange.gov/

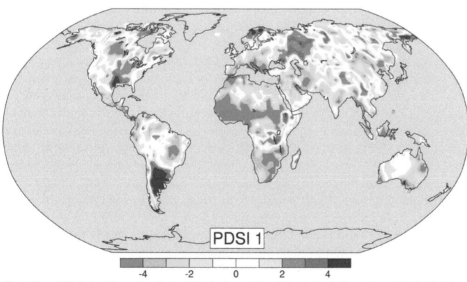

PDSI 1

-4    -2    0    2    4

Climate Change 2007: Synthesis Report. Contribution of Working Groups I, II, and III to the Fourth Climate Change 2007: The Physical Science Basis. Working Group I Contribution to the Fourth Assessment Report of the Intergovernmental Panel on Climate Change, Figure 3.39; FAQ 3.2, Figure 1. Cambridge University Press.Assessment Report of the Intergovernmental Panel on Climate Change: Figure SPM.1; SPM.4.IPCC, Geneva, Switzerland. Climate Change 2007: Impacts, Adaptation and Vulnerability. Working Group II Contribution to the Fourth Assessment Report of the Intergovernmental Panel on Climate Change, Figure 3.8. Cambridge University Press.

**Drought severity from 1990 to 2002 according to the Palmer Drought Severity Index. In this index the severity of the drought is shown in terms of minus numbers and excess rain is reflected by plus numbers.**

# Science Behind Global Climate Change: The Intergovernmental Panel on Climate Change

Since 1979, when the **National Academy of Sciences** first raised concerns about global warming, the body of knowledge and the amount of scientific data observing this phenomenon has grown. The year 1988 marked the start of the Intergovernmental Panel on Climate Change (IPCC), founded by the World Meteorological Organization (WMO) and the United Nations Environment Programme (UNEP). Today the IPCC is considered to be the leading institution for the assessment of climate change. Its mission is to monitor the scientific work done worldwide regarding climate change.

With the help of thousands of scientists, the IPCC assesses regularly the available scientific information relevant for improving the understanding of climate change and its possible environmental and socioeconomic impacts. The participating scientists are divided into three "Working Groups": 1) the scientific assessment of today's research regarding global climate change;[14] 2) examination of the potential impacts of climate change to socioeconomic and natural systems, and how they can be reduced;[15] and, 3) evaluation of options for avoiding the causes of global climate change.[16] The results are summarized and published in specific chapters for the "Assessment Reports of the Intergovernmental Panel on Climate Change."

## IPCC Assessment Reports

Since 1988, the IPCC has released four Climate Change Assessment Reports. The first report was released in 1990 and did not find sufficient scientific proof to demonstrate a relationship between human behavior and global climate change. Nevertheless, the report concluded that by 2000, the connection between human actions, such as the emission of greenhouse gases, and global climate change would likely be measurable. The second report released in 1995, however, concluded that evidence of human-induced climate change had already been found, five years earlier than the first report projected. The third report in 2001 supported this claim and provided more evidence that the increase in temperature over the past 50 years could be linked to human behavior. The fourth and latest report released in 2007 finally stated that (with a likelihood of 90-99 percent) global climate change is driven by human emissions of heat-trapping gases and opined that greater environmental damages can be expected in the future. The fifth assessment report is currently underway and is scheduled for release in 2014 or 2015. In addition to the main reports, the IPCC also releases summaries for policy makers and the public. The full reports are very extensive and for most people who are not scientists in the field of climate change, they are often hard to understand. By releasing the summaries, the IPCC hopes that more of its findings are considered by policy leaders and decision makers, decreasing the causes of climate change and increasing the capacity to deal with the impacts that cannot be avoided.

## Climate Models and Scenarios

Future climate change is already built into the system by past greenhouse gas emissions that will take decades to disappear from our atmosphere. Thus, impacts will occur even if we act today and reduce GHG emissions. In fact, the first **Kyoto Protocol** had as its goal to reduce GHG emissions by 5.2 percent below the 1990 emission levels by 2012. Nevertheless, the amount of worldwide GHG emissions is still increasing. The research supports the increased likelihood that extreme weather events and sea-level rise will increase and droughts will become longer and more severe. Additional impacts in the future might be major alterations in oceans, ice, or storms, as well as massive dislocations of species or pest outbreaks, or even major shifts in wealth, technology, and societal priorities.[17] A wide range of **climate models** are available, ranging from relatively basic models that focus on the aspects of the earth's heat balance to very complex and detailed simulations that aim to show possible future impacts of global climate change under a variety of different assumptions.

The models compute different outcomes or **scenarios** based on different assumptions regarding possible future amounts of GHG emissions, policy selections, behavioral actions, and other aspects that might impact future climate trends. It is important to understand that these models do not predict the future. Instead, they simply offer possible future scenarios. The future depends to a large degree on human behavior, which is impossible to predict. However, the scenarios do provide important data to decision-makers, which allow them to make better informed long-term decisions that impact the future. Based on different scenarios, several impacts of climate change by sector will be discussed in more detail in the following paragraphs.

**Kyoto Protocol** - an international treaty initially adopted in December 1997 with the goal of reducing greenhouse gas emissions to prevent further increases in the global temperature. Today, more than 190 countries have signed the treaty.

**Climate models** - a wide range of models, ranging from relatively basic models that focus on the basic aspects of the earth's heat balance to very complex and detailed simulations, that aim to show possible future impacts of global climate change under various different assumptions.

**Scenarios** - possible future circumstances computed by climate models, based on different assumptions regarding possible future amounts of greenhouse gas emissions, policy selections, behavioral actions, and other aspects that might impact future climate trends.

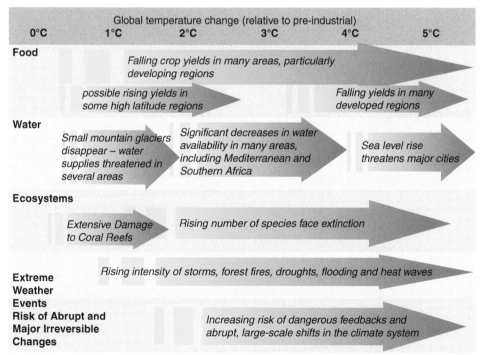

From The Economics of Climate Change: The Stern Review-Executive Summary by Nicholas Stern, Cabinet Office-HM Treasury. Copyright © 2006 by Cambridge University Press. Reprinted by permission.

**Projected impacts of climate change according to specific rises in temperature.**

## Future Global Temperatures

According to the Fourth IPCC Assessment Report from 2007, the scenario with the lowest increases in GHG emissions still suggests a rise in global temperature from 1.1 to 2.9 degrees Celsius between 1990 and 2095. The scenario is based on the highest amount of future emissions and predicts an increase of temperature between 2.4 and 6.4 degrees Celsius for the same time period. Looking only at the global average, however, can be misleading because the temperature does not change in the same way in every location across the globe.

## Future Precipitation Patterns

In addition to rising temperatures, changes in precipitation will also impact society and the natural environment. A secure water supply is fundamental for our food supply and for the livelihood of plants and animals. Yet, a possible future change in precipitation is much harder to predict than other features of climate change. Current climate models operate on a large spatial scale, thus making it very difficult to capture important regional differences in rainfall. Therefore, since precipitation can vary on a small regional scale, the uncertainties regarding possible future trends of rainfall extremes or droughts are quite large.

Despite the uncertainty in terms of the severity of the precipitation changes, all models anticipate future droughts, heavy rain falls, and floods.[18] The different scenarios indicate that land areas impacted by extreme droughts could increase from the current 1 percent to 30 percent by the end of the twenty-first century. Some of the findings suggest that extreme rates of precipitation will most likely increase in northern Europe, South Asia, East Asia, Australia, and New Zealand. Risks of droughts, on the other hand, are also forecasted to amplify in Australia, the eastern parts of New Zealand, as well as in the Mediterranean, Central Europe, and Central America. In terms of snowfall, likely decreases in the length of the snow season can be expected in most of Europe and North America.

## Future Decline in Ice Sheets and Sea-level Rise

As discussed earlier, ice sheets are shrinking and climate models predict that this trend will continue and may in fact accelerate in the future. Some models even suggest that by the end of the century, the Arctic ice cover could become seasonal. In that case, the ice sheet would become open water during the arctic summer and freeze again in the winter. Since the ice acts like a mirror reflecting sunlight back into space, this would further reduce the earth's albedo.

Sea-level rise is happening today. What remains unclear is what changes to the sea-level can be expected in the future due to the melting of the large ice sheets of Greenland and Antarctica. Those ice sheets have the biggest potential to raise sea-levels in the future. As a result of these uncertainties, the projected scenarios for sea-level rise range from 18 to 59 centimeters by the end of the twenty-first century. These global averages, however, can be misleading because sea-level rise will not be the same everywhere. Instead, there will be regional differences that will differ from the global average. Recent studies along the Pacific and north Atlantic coast of the United States show that in the last decades, sea-level has risen even more than the global average. Furthermore, these studies also project future sea-level increases by up to 167 cm by the year 2100 in some regions along the west coast, and emphasize the increase of vulnerability for coastal cities to flooding, storm surges, and loss of wetlands due to sea-level rise.

## Future Impacts on Water Security

One of the most significant impacts of climate change on human society in the future is its possible effects on water security.[19] Regions in the Mediterranean, southern Africa, Western Australia, and in the southwest United States will face serious future droughts. According to the 2007 IPCC report, by the year 2050 one to two billion people could suffer from droughts and decreasing water quality. Moreover, water stress will increase, affecting up to two-thirds of the global land area. In turn, this will affect food security and water quality, and adversely impact human health.

## Uncertainty in Climate Change Projections

All future climate change impact scenarios are characterized by uncertainties. The uncertainty arises from the very complex climate science itself, from possible future behaviors and decisions by humans, and from internal processes in the climate system. Future human behavior is very unpredictable and is influenced by attitudes toward quality of life and wealth. Future emission trends will depend heavily on the development and availability of new technologies, the implementation of different policies, and by their level of acceptance and support by the public. Internal processes in the climate system might involve changes in vegetation, variations in the earth's orbit around the sun, or volcanic eruptions. Given these large uncertainties, it is very difficult to choose the appropriate adaptation strategies to ameliorate future climate change impacts. Traditional approaches such as making decisions based on worst-case scenarios do not apply to the highly complex and uncertain issue of climate change. Instead, a more flexible framework is required that allows decision makers to develop strategies based on many different possible scenarios. This approach is referred to as **advanced scenario planning** and is a key component of the **anticipatory governance framework**.[20] The concept of "anticipatory governance" can be described as "a system of institutions, rules and norms that provide a way to use foresight for the purpose of reducing risk, and to increase capacity to respond to events at early rather than later stages of their development".[21] It presents a new model for decision making while dealing with high uncertainties and consists of the anticipatory future steps and feedback creation of flexible adaptation strategies, monitoring, and action. Anticipation and future analysis is based on advanced scenario planning and includes methods such as aggregated averages, risk assessments, sensitivity analysis of factors or decisions driving the scenarios, identification of unacceptable or worst-case outcomes, and assessment of common and different impacts among the scenarios. Due to the uncertainties surrounding climate change and the changing impacts over time, the final steps of "monitoring and action" demand that policymakers and decision-makers revise adaptation strategies on a regular basis.

Overall, the knowledge to make accurate projections has increased over the past two decades. As long as the uncertainties are acknowledged, the results from climate models already allow decision-makers to evaluate policies and take actions depending on the future consequences of global climate change.

**Advanced scenario planning** - a flexible framework that allows decision-makers to develop long-term strategies based on many different possible scenarios, and includes methods such as aggregated averages, risk assessments, sensitivity analysis of factors or decisions driving the scenarios, identification of unacceptable or worst-case outcomes, and assessment of common and different impacts among the scenarios.

**Anticipatory governance framework** - an approach that relies on the development and analysis of a range of possible scenarios, rather than a forecast or selection of a single scenario. It presents a new model for decision-making while dealing with high uncertainties and consists of the anticipatory future steps and feedback creation of flexible adaptation strategies, monitoring, and action.

# Climate Change Strategies

A great amount of political intervention, public behavioral change, and support for climate strategies and policies will be necessary in the next decade to fight the causes of climate change and reduce the negative potential consequences (mitigation). Comprehensive changes in numerous aspects of society and the built environment are required to cope with the effects of global climate change impacts that are already unavoidable (adaptation). Adaptation and mitigation strategies are considered the two main policy responses to global climate change. However, they are not independent; in fact, mitigation and adaptation are driven by the same set of problems and the more mitigation that takes place, the less adaptation that will be needed, and vice versa. Improving the resiliency of urbanized areas and their inhabitants through successful implementation of mitigation and adaption strategies will be one of the major challenges resulting from global climate change.

## Mitigation

Mitigation addresses the core cause of human-induced climate change, namely the large amount of energy consumption and the resulting GHG emissions. The concept of mitigation is clearly understood by scientists and decision-makers. As a result, various international treaties exist such as the Kyoto Protocol (1997) and the Copenhagen Accord (2009), which were signed by many countries setting GHG reduction goals and strengthening the international cooperation in the fight against climate change. The fact that GHG emissions are easy to assess and can be monitored quantitatively has led to the development and implementation of numerous mitigation strategies.

Overall, cities and urban areas consume about 75 percent of the world's energy and are responsible for up to 75 percent of GHG emissions. The burning of fossil fuels, mostly by private automobiles, is the largest single source of $CO_2$ emissions, representing approximately 57 percent. However, cities are not only part of the climate problem, but their development can also be part of the solution. The following paragraphs address three major sectors of energy consumption, especially in urban environments, and discuss how mitigation strategies can reduce their GHG emissions.

### Transportation Sector

The transportation sector is among the fastest growing areas of energy use. The heavy reliance on combustion engines fueled by oil has led to a significant increase in GHG emissions over the past several decades. Although gas prices are increasing, many consumers still seem to prefer big vehicles with powerful engines that rely on fossil fuel. Thus, the free market with its seemingly unpredictable price swings for oil has little impact on people's travel behavior and the mode of transportation they choose. In contrast, mandatory regulation regarding fuel economy has been much more effective in reducing GHG emissions while also encouraging research toward higher fuel efficiency.[22] As a result, new technologies have emerged that already make automobiles up to 40 percent more efficient compared to cars relying entirely on fossil fuels. These technologies, such as hybrid vehicles, turbo diesels, and biofuels, will decrease GHG emissions even further as new technologies become available for the mass market in the near future.

Strategies that provide a technological alternative for the use of fossil fuels in the transportation sector, however, are not the only steps available to mitigate climate change. Current research also suggests that GHG emissions from the transportation sector can be reduced by establishing specific settlement structures and densities that reduce the necessity to drive and decrease the overall amount of vehicle miles traveled. The underlying strategies include the mixing of land uses, implementation of compact development patterns, creation of walkable environments, and allocation of transportation alternatives such as public buses or light rail systems. The possible reduction in vehicle miles traveled by implementing these strategies is still heavily debated among scientists. The existing literature suggests that, in the best case, a reduction of 25 percent in vehicle miles traveled[23] can be achieved utilizing all of the strategies mentioned above.

## Building Sector

Changing the energy use of buildings can also reduce GHG emissions significantly. The building sector provides low-cost opportunities to reduce $CO_2$ emissions. Many energy saving efficiency measures regarding the heating, cooling, or lighting of buildings are currently being implemented. Energy efficiency can be improved and heating costs reduced by improving the insulation of buildings, sealing leaks, and using energy efficient windows. Depending on the climate, these measures alone have the potential to decrease heating costs by up to 90 percent.

Reducing emissions from air conditioning and decreasing cooling costs is also relatively simple. These goals can be achieved through architectural designs such as orienting the long axis of a house on an east-west axis, so that wall areas receiving hot morning and afternoon sun are minimized. Another possibility to save energy is by using reflective materials and light colored surfaces, which reflect most of the heat away from the house. Providing shade through specific landscaping is also an effective way to cool buildings and reduce cooling costs by up to 40 percent.

## Industry Sector

The industrial sector is the third major source of energy use and significant contributor to global climate change. It is responsible for roughly 8.4 Gton $CO_2$ being emitted into the atmosphere. In 2007, total world $CO_2$ emissions from the use of fossil fuels added totaled 26.4 Gton, of which 8.4 Gton (31.8%) came from the U.S. (One Gton equals 7 billion metric tons of carbon.) Compared to the transportation and housing sectors, however, the annual increase in emissions from the industrial sector is relatively low with only 0.6 percent. Within the industrial sector, the metal and chemical production industries are the most energy intensive and account for 85 percent of the sector's total GHG emissions. The highest potential for reducing emissions from the steel, cement, and petroleum industries is through investments focusing on the use of cleaner industrial processes and stricter environmental laws. The latest IPCC report argues that emission cuts of up to 40 percent are possible if the responsible company were to be charged $20 for each ton of $CO_2$ or any other GHG emitted into the atmosphere.

## Adaptation

Adaptation strategies focus on avoiding negative impacts caused by global climate change. They are essentially adjustments with the aim to increase resilience or decrease vulnerability to current or expected impacts of climate change. Even if current mitigation measurements prove to be successful in reducing GHG emissions, global climate change is already occurring. Moreover, further climate change is already built into the system by past emissions. This development makes the design and implementation of adaptation strategies a necessity to deal with the impacts that cannot be prevented and to prepare for possible future threats.

Compared to mitigation strategies that focus on the global and national scales and require international cooperation, adaptation is more of a regional and local challenge. Unlike mitigation strategies, the effectiveness of adaptation strategies is influenced by high uncertainties because they depend on the accuracy of regional climate and impact projections. Moreover, many governments agreed on GHG emission targets and time frames to reach that goal. On the contrary, there are no targets and schedules for adaptation. Most importantly, compared to adaptation, mitigation has a legal instrument in the form of the Kyoto Protocol, which was initially adopted in December 1997 in Kyoto, Japan and was subsequently signed by more than 187 countries.

## Strategies and Their Impact

Reducing GHG emissions will take time, and benefits will not be fully experienced for decades. Adaptation measurements on the other hand have a much shorter lead time. Due to the strong links with development initiatives and the fact that implementation occurs mostly on the local or regional scale, adaptation efforts and their results are much faster and visibly seen compared to mitigation measures. Furthermore, the efficiency of adaptation strategies is less dependent on the actions of others and does not need international agreements.

Since adaptation is primarily a local and regional problem, the appropriate strategy has to be evaluated on site. In general, without the successful implementation of adaptation strategies, it will be impossible to minimize the economic costs of climate change impacts, protect human health and welfare, and limit harm to infrastructure, ecosystems, and biodiversity. Adaption measurements are required to either protect settlements threatened by sea-level rise, floods, and droughts, or to enable the affected populations to relocate. In the case of water shortage, development of new supplies or the implementation of conservation measures will become necessary. Adaptation measures also play an important role in the agricultural sector. Farmers and ranchers might need to react to the impacts of climate change by changing crops, raising different livestock, or by relocating. Furthermore, vulnerable settlements need protection from increasing heat-related events. Already occurring shifts in disease and insect pattern also emphasize the need for adaptation measures for the public health sector.

Real-world examples of implemented adaptation measurements include coastal defense planning, flood gates, and early warning systems to prepare for sea-level rise and storm floods. Furthermore, different regions are starting to prepare for water shortages by implementing water storage, implementing conservation measures, and by building seawater desalination plants. In addition, land management plans and zoning laws are being updated to help prevent soil erosion. Regions depending on winter tourism are shifting ski slopes to higher altitudes and cities are preparing emergency plans to deal with future heat waves or other extreme weather events.

Unfortunately, well-designed adaptation and mitigation strategies do not guarantee success in the fight against global climate change. Aspects such as individual and organizational deviance, unintended consequences, legal problems, and changing political or administrative priorities can make their implementation difficult.

## Local Climate Change Action Planning

Cities cover less than one percent of the earth's surface, but are disproportionately responsible for causing climate change. A majority of the world's energy consumption either occurs in cities or as a direct result of the way that cities function (e.g., through transportation of goods to points of consumption in cities). Nevertheless, the concentration of resources in cities can be a useful weapon in fighting climate change. Cities are often centers of new thinking and policy innovation and are in a great position to lead the way for others to follow.

As a result, many cities and states have developed in recent years "**Climate change action plans**" to mitigate and adapt to climate change. Climate change action plans help states and cities to identify and evaluate feasible and effective policies to reduce their GHGs emissions through a combination of public and private sector policies and programs.

The first generation of climate change action plans focused mainly on improving municipal operations in terms of energy use and GHG emissions with the most prominent strategies consisting of the following:

- Creating building codes and standards that include practical, affordable changes that make buildings cleaner and more energy efficient.

- Conducting energy audits and implementing retrofit programs to improve energy efficiency in municipal and private buildings.

- Installing more energy-efficient traffic and street lightning.

- Implementing localized, cleaner electricity generation systems.

- Developing bus rapid transit and non-motorized transport systems.

- Using clean fuels and hybrid technologies for city buses, rubbish trucks, and other vehicles.

- Implementing schemes to reduce traffic, such as congestion charges.

- Creating waste-to-energy systems at landfills.

- Improving water distribution systems and leak management.

Today, these plans are also addressing adaptation strategies and jurisdiction-wide policies such as land use planning.[24] By the end of 2009, at least 141 local jurisdictions had developed climate change action plans in the United States. Climate change action plans and their recommendations present a great opportunity; they provide a framework to change current development patterns and establish a sustainable way of living in the future, which reduces the vulnerability to climate change and increases the adaptive capacity of communities.

A very good example of a Climate Action Plan that considers mitigation and adaptation strategies is the plan developed by the City of Chicago. The city published the plan in 2008 after consulting with dozens of experts, an internationally recognized research

**Climate change action plans** - plans that help states and cities to identify and evaluate feasible and effective policies to reduce their greenhouse gas emissions through a combination of public and private sector policies and programs. In addition, these plans provide a framework to change current development patterns and establish a sustainable way of living in the future, which reduces the vulnerability to climate change and increases the adaptive capacity of communities.

advisory committee, and numerous business, labor, civic and environmental leaders from Chicago. The overarching goals of the plan are to achieve a 25 percent reduction of 1990 level GHG emissions by the year 2020, an 80 percent reduction of 1990 level GHG emissions by 2050, and to prepare the city for the affects of global climate change.[25]

Therefore, Chicago's Climate Action Plan outlines five main strategies, which are broken into 26 actions for mitigating GHG emissions and nine actions to prepare for climate change. The plan identifies key opportunities to meet the emission goals by improving the energy efficiency of residential, commercial and industrial buildings, or upgrading power plants and improving their efficiency. Furthermore, the plan emphasizes the need to reduce GHG emissions by decreasing the amount people drive and improving vehicle fuel efficiency. The different strategies include supporting principles of transit-oriented development and policies encouraging car-sharing and carpooling, improving fleet efficiency, and achieving higher fuel efficiency standards. In terms of adaptation, the nine strategies focus on the management of possible heat waves, the protection of air quality, the preservation of plants and trees, the engagement of the public and local businesses, green urban design, and innovative cooling techniques. In addition to the environmental benefits of these actions, the Climate Action Plan also points to other benefits, such as the potential for thousands of new jobs once the policies are implemented.

Several good examples of climate change action plans developed by U.S. cities can be found at:

- Chicago: http://www.chicagoclimateaction.org/
- New York: www.nyc.gov/planyc
- San Francisco: http://www.sfenvironment.org/index.html
- Denver: http://www.greenprintdenver.org/

## Public Behavior

There are numerous ways for the public to reduce GHG emissions through behavioral changes. For example, people could use public transit for most of their travel or install solar panels on their home. Other sustainable options include buying mainly locally produced goods, using mainly recycled paper, or purchasing only energy saving appliances.

However, despite the robust and convincing body of research addressing human-induced global climate change, there is still a significant gap between the recommendations provided by the scientific community and the actual actions by the public. In the effort to mitigate and adapt to global climate change, the public plays a critical role, not only in terms of its direct energy consumption and resulting GHG emissions, but also through its support for climate change policies developed by the government.

The way the public processes information, how it perceives threats, and other perceptional issues have a significant effect on how and to what degree mitigation and adaptation strategies are supported. Existing research suggests that many people do not have a full understanding of the issues inherent in global climate change. A significant portion of the public is not aware of the precise nature, causes, and possible negative impacts of global climate change. Despite its widespread media coverage, average individuals have many misconceptions about global climate change.[26] Misconceptions, such as that GHG emissions are just a form of air pollution, result in the public support for the wrong policies. For example, many people support traditional pollution controls as the solution to decreasing GHG emissions. However, actions such as filters and strengthening pollution controls alone do not stop global climate change.

# Conclusion

It is important that not only scientists and policymakers, but also everyday people, have a good understanding of the causes and impacts of global climate change. Only then will people support the appropriate mitigation and adaptation strategies and make the necessary behavioral changes to reduce the causes of global climate change. However, it is important to acknowledge that the key challenge of effective communication is not just the presentation of information or knowledge.[27] Instead, global climate change must be communicated in a way that motivates the public to change their behavior and support adaptation or mitigation policies.

## ■ LESSONS LEARNED FOR ACHIEVING SUSTAINABILITY

In terms of achieving sustainability in the context of global climate change, various aspects need to be considered. The issue of global climate change is very complex and uncertainties remain in terms of how severe the future impacts will be. Global climate change is a long-term problem and although impacts might not be experienced for many people in the near future, actions need to be taken today.

Mitigation strategies are well known and implemented in many places worldwide. Without global cooperation and public support, however, GHG reduction targets are often not met, with the result that future impacts of climate change cannot be avoided any longer. Adaptation strategies need to consider the wide range of different possible scenarios of future impacts due to the remaining uncertainties during the climate modeling process. Thus, adaptation measures need to be flexible to react effectively to unexpected changes in the global temperature and the resulting new potential negative impacts. Overall, to cope with global climate change and improve sustainability, long-term commitments and long-term strategies are required on different spatial scales by various institutions, governments, and the private sector.

Despite the importance of international institutions and federal governments to take action, global climate change also illustrates the importance of personal behavior to face the issue and achieve sustainability. Personal lifestyle choices regarding transportation, household energy consumption, and the degree of support for adaptation and mitigation policies have a great impact on the fight against global climate change.

## Supplemental Readings

Pittock, B. A. (2009). *Climate change: The science, impacts and solutions*. London, UK: Earthscan.

Bulkeley, H., & Betsill, M. (2003). *Cities and climate change: Urban sustainability and global environmental governance*. New York, NY: Routledge.

Davoudi, S., Crawford J., & Mehmood, A. (Eds.). (2010). *Planning for climate change: Strategies for mitigation and adaptation for spatial planners*. Washington DC: Earthscan.

# DISCUSSION QUESTIONS

1. Are adaptation and mitigation strategies equally important or can we focus only on one of these strategies?

2. Why should we take actions against climate change today even though major impacts might not be experienced in the near future?

3. What do you think you or your community could do to mitigate or adapt to climate change?

# The Urban Heat Island Effect and Sustainability Science: Causes, Impacts, and Solutions

*Darren Ruddell*

*Anthony Brazel*

*Winston Chow*

## ▨ WHY THIS CHAPTER IS IMPORTANT FOR UNDERSTANDING SUSTAINABILITY

The urban heat island (UHI) effect offers many critical insights into urban sustainability. The creation, manifestation, and extent of an UHI is driven by human development of the natural environment. Consequently, the choices regarding building materials and codes, transportation systems, waste management systems, and energy sources, among many other urban support systems, play a critical role in the long-term viability, resilience, and equity of a city. As the global population simultaneously increases and urbanizes, sustainable development principles play a vital role in providing city planners and others with the tools and diagnostics necessary to create and promote vibrant and integrated cities that utilize low-impact development practices that effectively lessen the intensity and extent of urban heat islands. The policies and development strategies this chapter discusses offer concurrent benefits to environmental and social systems.

## ▨ KEY CONCEPTS AND TERMS

*After reading this chapter, you should be able to understand and discuss the following:*

adaptation; albedo; anthropocentric worldview; anthropogenic waste heat; carbon sequestration; central business district; flux; health co-benefits; heat wave; intergenerational; intragenerational; land use and land cover; megacities; misery days; mitigation; morphology; park cool island; shortwave and longwave radiation; sky view factor; social dimensions; spatial equity; spatial scales; sustainability science; thermal admittance; thresholds; urban canyons; urban heat island intensity; urban heat island subtypes; and urbanization.

# Introduction

As Chapter 3 described, the urban experiment began approximately 10,000 years ago when people first began organizing into small enclaves. While people initially used local and organic materials to meet residential and community needs, advances in science, technology, and transportation systems now support urban centers that utilize distant resources to produce engineered surfaces and synthetic materials. This process of **urbanization**, which is manifest in the growth of cities in terms of both population and spatial extent, has increased over the course of human history. For instance, according to the 2010 U.S. Census, the global population has rapidly increased from one billion people in 1804 to 6.8 billion in 2010. During the same period, the percent of the global population living in urban centers grew from 3 to over 50 percent by 2010.

**Urbanization** - the process whereby native landscapes are converted to urban land uses, such as commercial and residential development. Urbanization is also defined as rural migration to urban centers.

**Megacities** - urban agglomerations with a population exceeding 10 million residents.

**Spatial scales** - the extent or coverage of a given area, such as a county, state, or nation.

**Morphology** - the study of the form, structure, process, and transformation of the urban heat island.

**Urban Heat Island Intensity (UHI)**- a global phenomenon generally seen as being caused by a reduction in latent heat flux and an increase in sensible heat in urban areas as vegetated and evaporating soil surfaces are replaced by relatively low impervious, low albedo paving and building materials.

**Mitigation** - strategies to reduce greenhouse gas emissions and increase carbon sequestration in order to slow the rate of climate change.

**Adaptation** - adjustment strategies to increase a system's ability to adjust and reduce vulnerability to the effects of climate change.

**Land Use and Land Cover (LULC)** - land use refers to the syndromes of human activities (e.g., agriculture, urbanization) on lands. Land cover refers to the physical and biological cover of the surface of land. The vegetation, water, natural surface, and cultural features on the land surface.

**Anthropogenic waste heat** - human-induced environmental change, such as emissions from factories and transportation systems, among other sources.

**Urban Heat Island (UHI) subtypes** -

1. subsurface: below the surface of the earth

2. surface: the skin of the surface of the earth

3. urban canopy layer: the atmospheric air layer between the ground surface and average building roof height

4. urban boundary layer: the lowest portion of a planetary atmospheric boundary layer that is directly influenced by an underlying urban area

As previously stated, the number of cities is also rapidly growing. For example, in 1950, there were 86 cities in the world with a population of more than 1 million. Today, 400 cities fit this criteria, and by 2015, it is projected that at least 550 cities will have more than 1 million residents.[1] **Megacities** (urban agglomerations with populations greater than 10 million) have also become commonplace throughout the world. Megacities in developed countries include Tokyo, New York, Los Angeles, and London; however, the highest rates of urbanization and most megacities are in the developing world, particularly in South America (i.e., Sao Paulo, Buenos Aires, Rio de Janeiro), Asia (i.e., Mumbai, Shanghai, Dhaka), and Africa (Cairo, Lagos).

One common thread that links all cities, regardless of population size and urban extent, is that urbanization inadvertently alters the local climate system. Although impacts vary at different **spatial scales**—such as at the scale of an individual building, neighborhood, city, or urban region, clear differences occur in climate between urban and rural areas, such as with precipitation (rainfall and snowfall), humidity, particulate matter, and wind speed.[2] In this chapter, we examine the best-known, urban-induced alteration of climate: the UHI effect. By the end of this chapter, you will understand:

- The **morphology** (i.e., form and structure) of UHIs, as well as different UHI types
- Factors causing or modifying **UHI intensity**
- The impacts of the UHI on residents
- Linkages between the UHI effect and urban sustainability
- Various **mitigation** and **adaptation** strategies to reduce the UHI effect

# The Urban Heat Island Effect

Formal scientific study of the UHI first began with the English meteorologist Luke Howard, who noted that temperatures within the City of London were different from the surrounding climate of the countryside:

> "The temperature of the *city* is not to be considered as that of the *climate*; it partakes too much of an artificial warmth, induced by its structure, by a crowded population, and the consumption of great quantities of fuel in fires."

He hypothesized that **land use and land cover** (LULC) change (the conversion of the earth's natural surfaces (e.g., grasses, shrubs, trees, bare soil) into urban surface (e.g., asphalt, concrete, buildings, glass)) for human socio-economic activities, and the generation of **anthropogenic waste heat** (such as emissions from factories and transportation systems, among other sources) were key factors in causing the UHI. As it turns out, Howard wasn't far off!

The UHI effect quantifies the temperature gradient between urban and nearby rural areas, which often depicts a given urban area as an "island of heat" amid the native landscape (as illustrated in the Louisville Metro UHI image below). This pattern is similar to the geomorphic land/sea interface of an island, with a notable "cliff" separating the urban and rural temperature fields. There are four distinct **UHI subtypes**: 1) subsurface, 2) surface, 3) urban canopy layer (the atmospheric air layer between the ground surface and average building roof height), and 4) urban boundary layer (the lowest portion of a planetary atmospheric boundary layer that is directly influenced by an underlying urban area).[3] Observation of each UHI subtype has distinct methodological platforms. For example, urban canopy layer studies use data either obtained from point measurements taken at weather stations or taken during mobile traverses.[4] Surface and subsurface UHI studies often utilize data from handheld, infrared thermometers, or from instruments mounted on remotely sensed platforms such as airplanes, helicopters, or satellites. Lastly, the urban boundary layer UHI can be investigated through radiosonde data collected by weather balloons that travel up to the top of the lower atmosphere.

Typically, scientists measure the UHI size either by the increase of minimum temperatures ($T_{min}$) of a weather station as its surrounding environment "urbanizes" over time (image below), or by the difference in temperatures between urban and rural areas ($\Delta T_{u-r}$).[5] Maximum magnitudes of $\Delta T_{u-r}$ are generally found at the urban core (e.g., downtown). A "plateau" of elevated temperatures can also be found in other areas that have distinct urban land-use categories (e.g., commercial, residential, and industrial). Parks, lakes, and open areas within cities generally observe lower temperatures than the surrounding urban area and can disrupt urban temperature peaks; these are sometimes called a **park cool island (PCI)** (image of Daytime Surface Air Temperature). Knowledge about the cooling influence of PCIs within cities is important in discussing ways to sustainably mitigate the UHI, as we shall see later in this chapter.

The UHI is also a dynamic phenomenon that arises from different urban and rural temperature cooling rates. Under clear and calm weather conditions for a hypothetical city, $\Delta T_{u-r}$ usually varies in a consistent manner during a 24-hour period (UHI development image). Canopy layer temperatures generally start cooling in the late afternoon

**Park cool island (PCI)** - zones in the urban landscape reporting relatively cooler temperature conditions, which are often associated with parks, lakes, or open areas.

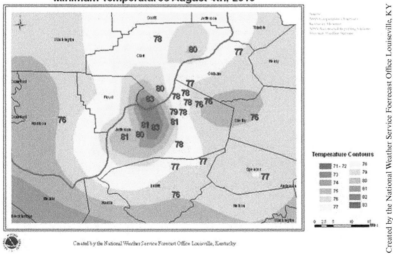

**The spatial form of the Metropolitan Louisville UHI in August 2010, as measured by minimum temperatures ($T_{min}$) taken from several weather stations. $T_{min}$ is considered a good indicator of UHI as the urban influence on temperatures is significantly stronger during nocturnal periods as opposed to daytime conditions (Source: National Weather Service).**

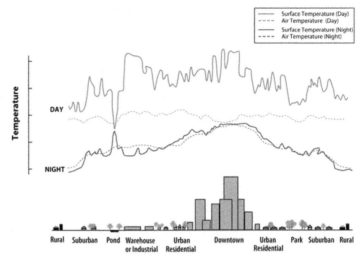

Daytime surface and air temperature UHI for a city (Source: EPA
-http://www.epa.gov/heatisland/about/index.htm)

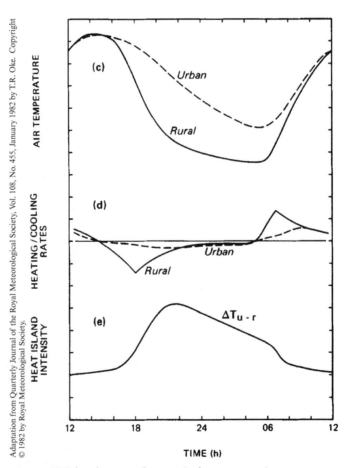

Adaptation from Quarterly Journal of the Royal Meteorological Society, Vol. 108, No. 455, January 1982 by T.R. Oke. Copyright
© 1982 by Royal Meteorological Society.

UHI development for a typical temperate city as seen
through: (a) air temperature changes, (b) heating/cooling
rates, and (c) heat island intensity (Oke, 1987).

and evening, with urban areas cooling at slower rates than rural areas. This difference results in the growth of $\Delta T_{u-r}$ reaching a maximum about three to five hours after sunset.[6]

It is important to understand the physical factors that cause the UHI (and modify its maximum intensity) when modeling its occurrence and development within different cities and at different scales. Atmospheric models can range from relatively simple statistic-based regression models based on observed data to highly complex, physics-based numerical models that require enormous computational power.[7] Results from both observation and modeled studies have great potential in urban planning and policy toward alleviating the negative impacts of the UHI.

## What Factors Cause the UHI?

The key to understanding how a UHI is caused is to examine alterations to the urban surface-energy balance, which is expressed in equations 1 and 2.

$$Q^* = K_\downarrow - K_\uparrow + L_\downarrow - L_\uparrow = K^* + L^* \qquad \text{(eq.1)}$$

$$Q^* + Q_F = Q_H + Q_E + \Delta QS \qquad \text{(eq.2)}$$

This balance accounts for all energy exchanges within a city that affect net radiation ($Q^*$). $Q^*$ is the sum of total radiation arriving at ($\downarrow$) or exiting from ($\uparrow$) a surface. $Q^*$ includes radiative **fluxes** (both incoming shortwave (K) and outgoing longwave (L) radiation), and also describes turbulent atmospheric sensible ($Q_H$) and latent ($Q_E$) fluxes, as well as energy stored or withdrawn from the surface substrate ($\Delta Q_S$). Heat fluxes represent the movement of energy for a given area at a fixed unit of time. An additional term included for cities is the heat added by anthropogenic waste heat ($Q_F$). (See eq. 2 above.) Examples of $Q_F$ include heat emissions from vehicles, industrial plants, and air conditioners, among other sources. In most cities, however, anthropogenic waste heat is a relatively small component of the urban-energy balance when compared to $Q_H$ or $\Delta Q_S$.

**Flux** - rate of flow of some quantity.

**Causes of the UHI through alteration of the urban energy balance and urban features associated with the changes**

| Surface-energy balance equation symbol | Surface-energy balance variable | Typical associated urban features | Direct urban climate effects |
|---|---|---|---|
| Increased K* | Shortwave radiation | Canyon geometry | Increased surface area and multiple reflection |
| Decreased L* | Longwave radiation | Air pollution | Greater absorption and reemission |
| Increased $L_\downarrow$ | Longwave radiation | Canyon geometry | Reduced sky view factor increases heat |
| Addition of $Q_F$ | Anthropogenic waste heat | Buildings and traffic | Direct addition of heat |
| Increased $\Delta Q_S$ | Storage heat flux | Construction materials | Increased thermal admittance |
| Decreased $Q_E$ | Latent heat flux | Construction materials | Decreased surface infiltration |
| Decreased ($Q_H + Q_E$) | Sensible and latent heat fluxes | Canyon geometry | Reduced wind speed |

The previous table demonstrates how various factors influence the urban surface-energy budget and therefore the UHI. The UHI is essentially caused through alterations of the urban surface-energy balance and impacted by specific urban factors. For example, changes in land uses or land cover, say in terms of the amount and extent of asphalt applied over areas, will affect the amount of storage heat flux and have the tendency to increase heat. Understanding typical city features and how they vary within urban areas is critical in explaining how the UHI is caused. Increases in construction materials, such as in the use of concrete, glass, asphalt, and steel, reduce the potential for evapotranspiration and increase **thermal admittance**. Thermal admittance is the ability of a surface to store and release heat. This term explains why materials like concrete and asphalt store, and later radiate, more heat to the environment over a longer period, especially when compared to vegetated surfaces such as urban parks. Even greater levels of traffic within confined areas and other sources of waste heat contribute to the UHI. Increased urban air pollution through the creation of smog, for instance, can also reduce the rate of surface radiative loss and reemit **longwave radiation** back toward the urban surface, creating more surface heat.

We mention two other urban features that influence UHI—**urban canyons** and the **sky view factor**. (See dense urban canyon image, below.) Urban canyons are characterized by tall buildings on either side of long, narrow streets typical of most **central business districts**. These artificial canyons increase the total urban surface area for energy storage and reduce urban wind speed. They can also reduce the sky view factor. This term illustrates how much of the sky is seen from a surface, and lower magnitudes reduce surface radiative loss, especially at night.

Understanding the influence of **albedo** is important in **sustainability science** for two reasons. The first reason is that surfaces with low albedo values absorb large quantities of solar energy, while high albedo surfaces reflect sunlight back into the atmosphere. Second, albedo values associated with various building materials and land

**Thermal admittance** - a surface thermal property that quantifies the rate at which a material stores or releases heat. It is the square root of the product of thermal conductivity and heat capacity.

**Urban canyons** - an artificial "canyon" formed by two vertical walls of buildings with a horizontal street or pavement surface.

**Sky view factor** - the ratio of the amount of sky "seen" from a point on the ground that is potentially available. It ranges from 0 (completely obscured) to 1 (completely visible).

**Central business district** - the commercial and often geographic center of a city.

**Albedo** - the fraction of earth's incoming solar radiation that is reflected back to space.

**Sustainability science** - a field of research dealing with the interactions between natural and social systems, and with how those interactions affects the challenge of sustainability.

Source: Author - WTLC

**A dense urban canyon (i.e., two walls and street) of downtown Singapore that is typical of most central business districts (left), and a fish-eye lens picture that represents the low sky view factor seen at the surface of the street (right) (Source: Author's personal image (Chow).**

uses, and land covers are critical when introducing or replacing features in urban environments. For instance, converting an asphalt parking lot (a low albedo surface material) to a park or open green space (a moderate albedo surface material) will increase the solar reflectance of that parcel of land and thus reduce local heat-storage capacity. The absorption of **shortwave radiation** heats up the earth, and thus, the earth's surface transfers energy from it toward space to make for an overall earth energy balance.

## Additional Factors Influencing UHI Intensity

$\Delta T_{u-r}$ is strongly affected by the prevailing regional climate over a city. Higher wind speeds, increased cloud cover, and lower cloud heights have been shown to reduce magnitudes of $\Delta T_{u-r}$.[8] These meteorological factors disrupt surface cooling in different ways. Higher wind speeds increase near-surface turbulent mixing, which decreases the efficiency of surface radiative cooling. Increased cloud cover limits surface longwave radiation loss, with low-level clouds (e.g., stratus and cumulus) having greater impact compared to high-level clouds (e.g., cirrus and cirrostratus). Maximum UHI intensities are thus generally associated with periods having clear and calm weather.

The size and geographic location of cities also affects the maximum magnitude of $\Delta T_{u-r}$. Generally, the bigger the urban population, the larger the maximum UHI intensity.[9] Cities located in temperate climates typically have higher maximum $\Delta T_{u-r}$ compared to tropical, subtropical, and highland cities, with population size held constant. Of interest is that tropical cities experiencing more precipitation appear to have lower observed maximum $\Delta T_{u-r}$ compared to tropical cities with pronounced dry seasons, which suggests a strong impact of surface moisture on attenuating UHI intensity.[10]

Water bodies and topographic features located next to a city can also affect the UHI's shape and intensity. Cities located by the coast are subject to a regular daily cycle of land and sea breezes. Typically, moister and cooler air masses over the ocean are advected into warmer urban areas in the early evening, resulting in a distinct temperature gradient seen in cities such as Vancouver, British Columbia.[11] Similarly, cities located in valleys may be subject to daily cold air drainage flow patterns. These flows—also known as katabatic flows—are usually strongest at night and can directly affect urban temperatures in complex topography.

The temperature of the surface of the earth is controlled by energy transfers from the sun. Energy enters the earth's atmosphere from the sun in the form of shortwave radiation where the energy is either absorbed or reflected back into the atmosphere. The energy reflected from the earth out to space is called longwave or infrared radiation. Solar energy accounts for approximately 99.97 percent of energy entering the earth's atmosphere (other energy sources include geothermal, tidal, and anthropogenic waste heat). Albedo refers to the percent of incoming solar radiation that is reflected back to space. Albedo values vary depending upon surface materials and are expressed as a percentage ranging from zero (no reflection) to 100 (complete reflection). Light surfaces such as snow and ice are highly reflective and report albedo values in the range of 80–95 percent. In contrast, dark-colored materials such as asphalt have low levels of solar reflectance and report albedo values in the range of 5–10 percent. This effect happens in three ways: 1) longwave earth emission of radiation; 2) heating of the lower atmosphere or conduction/convection; and 3) transfer of energy through latent heat. The interactions in the long wavelengths of radiation to and from the earth are

**Shortwave and longwave radiation** - energy enters the earth's atmosphere from the sun in the form of shortwave radiation, which is either absorbed or reflected back into the atmosphere; energy reflected from the earth back out to space is called longwave radiation.

critical to the planet's sustainability, because the atmosphere acts as a greenhouse to keep the planet warm. Scientists have calculated that without this greenhouse effect, earth's temperatures would be some 30 ° Celsius (C) cooler than present.

## Impacts of the UHI on Cities

While the UHI effect is a near-universal phenomenon in cities, its resulting impacts—and whether such impacts are "good" or "bad" for urban residents' quality of life—depend on factors such as geographic location and season. Increased urban warmth can be beneficial for residents in high-latitude cities (e.g., Moscow) with cold winters, but detrimental to city dwellers in hot subtropical cities (e.g., Las Vegas) with hot summers. This section discusses three UHI-derived impacts on urban residents, which are: 1) thermal discomfort and vulnerability to increased heat stress; 2) changes to urban energy and water use; and, (3) impacts on urban economic output.[12] .

**Heat wave** - a prolonged period of excessively warm weather.

The UHI effect, coupled with naturally occurring summer **heat waves**, is linked to negative impacts on human health and well-being, such as morbidity (illness) and mortality (death).[13] The UHI increases thermal discomfort and is particularly hazardous to human health and well-being when summer temperatures are elevated and sustained over multiple consecutive days. Excessive exposure to heat already accounts for more deaths in the United States than any other weather-related phenomenon.[14, 15] Research shows that mortality rates and hospital admissions for cardiovascular, respiratory, and other preexisting illnesses increase in conditions of very hot weather.[16] The dangerous impacts of excessive exposure to extreme heat are evident from two recent heat waves: 1) the Chicago, Illinois heat wave in July 1995 that claimed over 700 lives,[17, 18] and 2) the 2003 heat wave that gripped Western Europe resulting in between 22,000 and 52,000 deaths, many of them in large cities.[19]

A warmer urban climate could also translate into increased demands on natural resources, such as on urban energy and water use. These increased demands are very likely to occur in cities subject to seasonal high temperatures in summer or located in equatorial climates with relatively hot temperatures year-round. Increases in the UHI intensity in metropolitan Phoenix, Arizona have coincided with increased total and peak-energy demand for residential and commercial cooling from the period between 1950 and 2000.[20] Energy demands increase because of more residents using air-conditioning units at higher demands and for longer periods to provide thermal comfort during the warm summer season. Although air-conditioning systems provide relief from summer temperatures, they also release large quantities of anthropogenic waste heat (and produce greater emissions of air pollutants, thus worsening urban air quality) into the surrounding environment. Warmer temperatures in metropolitan Phoenix are also likely to increase demands on local water systems. For instance, demand on local water resources is greatest during summer months when residents irrigate outdoor vegetation and fill their pools to provide relief from intense summer temperatures.[21, 22] A secondary demand on the water system relates to energy production and consumption. Higher energy demands translate to increased demand on water resources because large quantities of water are consumed when producing electricity. **Note: in other words, coal-fired and nuclear power plants use a lot of water to produce a single watt of energy.

Despite the extensive environmental and human benefits associated with the mitigation strategies outlined in the Causes of the UHI through Alteration table, there are several challenges with successfully implementing these tactics. For example, implementing any mitigation or adaptation strategy requires an initial financial investment, which many individual homeowners and city officials may be reluctant to make, particularly in a depressed economy.

A second challenge is the issue of sovereignty. For instance, the choices of individual homeowners are often limited by the covenants, codes, and restrictions (CCRs) governing a community or neighborhood that are enforced by Homeowners Associations. In some instances, homeowners would like to install solar panels on their roof or install a solar hot-water heater, but these actions may violate the CCRs and thus individuals are unable to implement the adaptation or mitigation strategy that would simultaneously reduce fossil-fuel energy demands, and improve local air quality, while providing an economic incentive to the homeowner.

Another challenge is the suitability of a given mitigation/adaptation strategy in a local geographic context. A perfect UHI mitigation strategy for Portland, Oregon may be inefficient for Phoenix, Arizona. Thus, mitigation and adaptation strategies must be considered by individual cities based on the resources and natural advantages of a given city. Perhaps the biggest challenge to implementing a given UHI mitigation or adaption strategy is conducting a cost-benefit analysis. The many benefits of expanding an urban forest need to be evaluated against the costs: increased pollen (allergies), tree maintenance services, and a greater demand on water resources, which is highly problematic in arid environments.[23, 24] The use of alternative energy systems, such as solar thermal energy (STE) systems, is an increasingly popular method for meeting residential and commercial energy needs with reduced greenhouse gas emissions, but the current systems are highly water-intensive, which must be considered when siting STE plants and allocating water resources.[25]

## CASE STUDY: The Phoenix, Arizona UHI

The Phoenix metropolitan area is an ideal city to investigate the physical and **social dimensions** of the UHI effect due to its hot subtropical climate coupled with the rapid increase in population and land use land cover. In this case study, the physical characteristics of the Phoenix UHI are examined temporally and spatially. The case study then investigates the social dimensions of the Phoenix UHI.

The case study on the Phoenix urban heat island is examined from two perspectives. The first method utilizes historical temperature readings from the National Weather Service regional weather station from 1900–2008. The second perspective examines the spatial signature of the Phoenix UHI by employing temperature readings from a network of weather stations throughout metropolitan Phoenix.

### Temporal Pattern

A common method for investigating temperature change in an urban area is to examine mean annual temperatures. The Mean Annual Temperature chart shows maximum and minimum annual temperature for the Phoenix regional weather station from 1900–2008. Note the natural variability in annual temperatures for both maximum and minimum temperatures. For instance, the mean annual maximum

*Continued*

**Social dimensions** - the impacts of urban heat islands on the quality of life of individuals and their families living in a given city.

temperature varied from a low of 81.4 ° Fahrenheit (F) around 1915 to a high of 89.8 °F around 1985; the range is 8.4 °F. Mean annual minimum temperatures

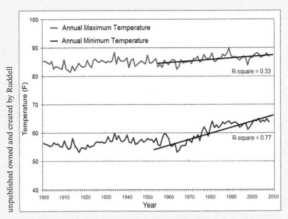

**Mean Annual Temperature for Phoenix, AZ Regional Weather Station from 1900–2008.**

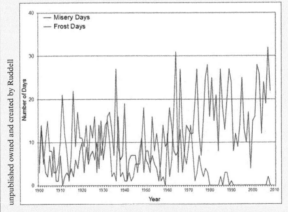

**Annual Number of Threshold Temperatures for Phoenix, AZ Regional Weather Stations from 1900–2008.**

also varied from year to year. For example, the lowest mean annual minimum temperature was 53.3 °F while the high was 65.0 °F; the range is 11.7 °F. In contrast to the natural variability observed among mean annual maximum temperature and mean annual minimum temperature shows a strong deviation from natural variability, which begins in the mid-1960s when the mean annual minimum temperature rises sharply in the last 50 years.

In addition to examining mean annual minimum and maximum temperature trends, the distribution of two temperature **thresholds** were investigated from 1900–2008 for the Phoenix regional weather station.[26] Results are shown in the chart below. "Frost days" is the first temperature threshold measurement that is defined as daily minimum temperature of less than

0 °C or 32 °F. The second temperature threshold is "**misery days**," a local measure of excess heat, which is defined as a daily maximum temperature greater than or equal to 43.3 °C or 110 °F. During the 109-year period of analysis, there were a total of 670 frost days, with annual counts varying from a minimum of 0 to a maximum of 31. The average annual number of frost days from 1900–2008 was 6.1. In contrast to frost days, there were a total of 1,212 misery days during this period. The annual number of misery days reported a minimum of 0 (in 1900) and a maximum of 32 (in 2008). The average annual number of misery days from 1900–2008 was 11.1. This chart also shows a major regime shift in the annual number of frost and misery days. Note the fluctuation in both frost days and misery days from 1900–1970, but beginning around 1970, there is a strong departure from historical

trends. We observe a steady rise in the annual number of misery days (Phoenix is getting hotter) and a rapid decline in the annual number of frost days.

## Spatial Signal

Examining the spatial distribution of temperatures within the same urban area is a second method for investigating the UHI effect in a given city. The Annual Number of Threshold Temperatures graph shows the metropolitan Phoenix UHI effect at three time-steps: 1) 1990–1994; 2) 1995–1999; and 3) 2000–2004. Air temperature data were collected at discrete locations by the network of weather stations throughout metropolitan Phoenix, and then a statistical procedure was used in Geographic Information Systems (GIS) to provide a continuous surface of the distribution of temperatures throughout the study area. When comparing the results of the three periods of investigation, distinct patterns emerge. The first pattern is that the UHI effect is becoming more intense. We find a rise in mean minimum air temperatures from 22 °C or 71.6 °F in the 1990–1994 time-step up to 24 °C or 75.2 °F in the 2000–2004 time-step. Second, the Phoenix UHI is expanding with the majority of temperature change occurring on the urban fringe where suburbanization replaces desert landscapes. For instance, the area reporting temperatures of 22 °C during the period from 1990–1994 is merely a fraction of the area reporting temperatures of 22 °C (or even 23 °C) in the 2000–2004 period of analysis.

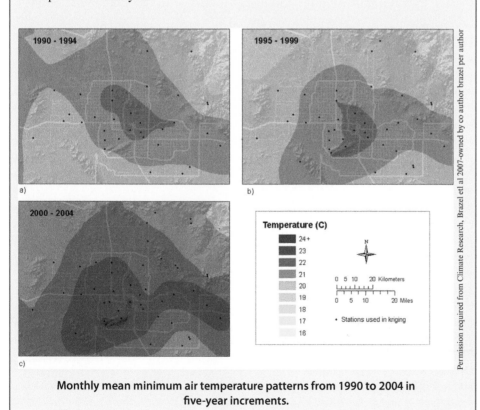

**Monthly mean minimum air temperature patterns from 1990 to 2004 in five-year increments.**

*Continued*

## The Social Landscape

Sustainability scientists have only recently begun to explore social dimensions of UHIs. This section explores exposure to temperatures among different social groups within metropolitan Phoenix and its implications in the area of **spatial equity**, a fundamental concept in sustainability. The second part investigates temperature variability with predominant land use land cover type. Temperature exposure among different social groups in Phoenix was investigated by using a sophisticated atmospheric model to simulate air temperature throughout metropolitan Phoenix. The Weather Research and Forecast climate model was used to estimate air temperature at hourly time intervals at a spatial resolution of 1-square kilometer for a four-day heat wave that occurred on July 15–19, 2005. The data provides insight on temperature variability across metropolitan Phoenix.

Census block group data for year 2000 combined with output from the model were used to correlate between exposure to air temperature and the social characteristics of people living in the warmest/coolest places within metropolitan Phoenix. The model was used to create a Heat Intensity Index to compare exposure to extreme heat among 40 neighborhoods during the four-day heat wave. The heat index was divided into three classes: low exposure, medium exposure, and high exposure. Four census block group variables were examined—density, income, ethnicity, and age—and all four were highly correlated to the Heat Intensity Index. The population per square mile of the high-heat intensity class is almost double the population density of the low and medium intensity classes. Median household income is considerably higher in the low- and medium-heat intensity classes compared to the high-heat intensity class. The percentage of ethnic minorities is significantly larger in the high-heat intensity class relative to the low and medium classes. Finally, the medium- and high-heat intensity classes reported relatively large percentages of elderly residents, which is a concern due to the fact that physiologically, the elderly are one of the most vulnerable groups to extreme temperatures. In short, extreme heat is not evenly distributed among all social groups within the urban environment. Residents exposed to the worst environmental conditions tend to be low-income, minority, and elderly.

**Spatial equity** - the concept of spatially equitable living conditions within a given urban area.

**Population characteristics of neighborhoods by heat intensity class**[27]

| Demographics | Heat Intensity Class | | |
| --- | --- | --- | --- |
| | Low | Medium | High |
| Neighborhoods | 15 | 10 | 15 |
| *Density* | | | |
| Population per sq. mile | 3,569 | 3,757 | 7,550 |
| *Socioeconomic Status* | | | |
| Household income | $71,903 | $62,669 | $38,621 |

| Demographics | Heat Intensity Class | | |
|---|---|---|---|
| | Low | Medium | High |
| *Ethnicity* | | | |
| Percent minority | 20.7 | 25.9 | 44.7 |
| *Age* | | | |
| Percent ages 65 and over | 9.8 | 20.4 | 17.5 |

Source: 2000 U.S. Census, Summary Files 1 and 3

# Mitigation and Adaptation Strategies

Several mitigation and adaptation strategies are designed to reduce the UHI effect. Mitigation strategies refer to initiatives that slow the rate of the UHI effect, such as reducing greenhouse gas emissions or increasing **carbon sequestration**. Long-term UHI mitigation strategies available to cities include policies to reduce energy use among commercial, residential, and transportation systems through programs such as Leadership in Energy and Environmental (LEED), LEED for Neighborhood Development, and investments in public transportation. Green design is a proven instrument to substantially reduce energy and water demands in commercial and residential sectors. Adaptations introduce new systems or adjust existing urban features within the urban infrastructure to both reduce the intensity of the UHI and human vulnerability to the adverse impacts of UHI effects.

**Carbon sequestration-** the capture of carbon dioxide from the atmosphere.

The Illustration of Mitigation and Adaptation Strategies to Reduce the Urban Heat Island Effect with Health Co-Benefits chart provides a list of various mitigation and adaptation strategies that cities and individuals have employed to combat the urban heat island effect. UHI mitigation strategies include the creation of urban forests that offer a number of environmental benefits, such as sequestering or storing carbon, retaining storm water during rain events, and improving air quality. Urban forests also provide a number of benefits to local residents; these benefits are described as **health co-benefits**, such as providing shade and increasing thermal comfort, as well as creating green spaces for recreation and relaxation. Improved air quality from urban forests, increased green spaces, and reduced fossil fuel consumption will help restore ecosystems and provide a healthier living environment, which has been found to stimulate physical activity among residents. A more active lifestyle translates into lower rates of obesity and reduced cardiovascular disease, as well as improved mental health.[28, 29, 30] In addition to direct benefits of a particular mitigation or adaptation strategy, there are a number of wide-ranging co-benefits among urban residents. This concept of redesigning cities to reduce or mitigate UHIs through the understanding of sustainability science needs to be broadened. Advancing sustainable solutions for one problem area may be utilized to support other benefits through a wider articulation of goals. For example, reducing the UHI through additional vegetative cover in cities can also support urban wildlife corridors, rainfall runoff management, and urban farming, thus making for healthier cities.

**Health co-benefits** - multiple benefits of a program whereby one of the domains benefits the public health sector, such as providing shade and increasing thermal comfort.

Illustration of mitigation and adaptation strategies to reduce the urban heat island effect with health co-benefits. Modified from Harlan and Ruddell, 2011.

| Mitigation/ Adaptation Strategy | Environmental Outcome | Human Health Co-Benefit | City Example |
|---|---|---|---|
| *UHI Mitigation Strategies* | | | |
| Urban Forest | Sequester carbon, storm water retention, improve air quality | Increase shade and thermal comfort, reduce heat-related illnesses, provide recreational green spaces | Chicago, IL has implemented an urban forest to improve air quality while reducing the UHI effect. |
| Community Garden | Sequester carbon, retain storm water, improve air quality | Improve nutrition, increase community engagement | Boston, MA is using community gardens to capture carbon, increase green space throughout the city, and provide fresh fruits and vegetables locally. |
| Alternative Energy Systems | Reduce greenhouse gas emissions, harvest natural and sustainable energy sources, improve air quality | Reduce heat-related illnesses and respiratory illnesses | London (England) is experimenting with biofuels, wind turbines, and photovoltaic and solar thermal arrays to promote renewable energy generation and economic development, while reducing dependency on fossil fuels. |
| Green Roofs | Sequester carbon, retain storm water, reduce energy consumption, improve air quality | Reduce heat-related illnesses | Toronto (Canada) utilizes green roofs to help reduce local outdoor temperature while providing insulation and cooling capacity inside buildings. |
| LEED Compliance | Increase energy efficiency of buildings, reduce energy consumption and greenhouse gas emissions | Reduce heat-related illnesses and respiratory infections | Cape Town (South Africa) utilizes LEED certification standards to recognize and reward the impact of environmental building design. |
| Public Transportation and Pedestrian Friendly Transit | Reduce greenhouse gas emissions, reduce extraction of fossil fuels | Increase exercise, increase community engagement | Copenhagen (Denmark) reduces fossil fuel dependency by increasing public transportation systems. |

## ■ LESSONS LEARNED FOR ACHIEVING SUSTAINABILITY

The urban heat island effect is an artifact of the current relationship between humans and nature. The philosophy of human domination over the land, which has emerged over the last 400 years through major changes in science, technology, and culture, is described as a human-centered or **anthropocentric worldview**. While human ingenuity has successfully engineered and constructed urban centers consisting of various transportation systems, dams, and reservoirs, as well as commercial and residential districts, these efforts have also resulted in significant modifications in the local climate system. Changes in the local climate system are a major concern due to the associated impacts on human health and quality of life, energy and water use, and economic development.

The field of sustainability science offers valuable tools and insight to help address social and environmental concerns associated with the urban heat island effect. Although there are numerous

**Anthropocentric worldview** - the philosophy of a human-centered domination over the natural environment.

definitions for the terms *sustainability* and *sustainable development*, it is generally agreed upon that there are three components of sustainability, which are: 1) environmental conservation; 2) equity (inter and **intragenerational**); and 3) economic development. An anthropocentric paradigm often exploits one sector for the benefit of another, such as harvesting a resource beyond its natural rate of production for economic gain. Sustainable development initiatives aim to simultaneously maximize all three values.

Why was the UHI concept important from the larger framework of sustainability and the idea of maximizing the three values of sustainability—environment, equity, and economics? How we design cities, the materials used for construction and infrastructure, the extent of vegetative open space, and the nature of public transportation systems will affect the intensity of the UHI. But we also learned that we can redesign neighborhoods and individual buildings and establish mitigation policies to reduce the impacts of the UHI. In the case study section on Phoenix, the natural environment has been significantly altered, producing a well-defined, urban heat island as a result of urbanization. Land use and land cover change transformed the native Sonoran Desert into an urban concentration; however, the resulting alterations in the local urban climate system present new challenges and vulnerabilities to local residents. The degree of change in the intensity and spatial coverage of the UHI will depend on the ways in which a given city is built (or rebuilt) and the materials that are used to construct various features within the urban environment.

The variability of temperatures within a given city represents issues of both inter and intragenerational equity. For instance, **intergenerational** equity refers to longitudinal access of a given resource, in this case, climate. The increase of minimum temperatures in the urban environment compromises the ability of future generations to enjoy a comparable climate. Intragenerational involves variability within the same generation. In the case of UHIs, some parts of a city are much warmer compared to other neighborhoods or areas of the city. The distribution of temperatures within a given city is often concerning because the burden of temperatures is not evenly distributed among social groups. Research shows that minority and low-income populations are often exposed to the worst environmental conditions, yet they possess the fewest resources to cope with extreme heat.

**Intergenerational** - fair or just access to a given resource across multiple generations.

The economic sector is also intimately related with UHIs. Suburbanization is a significant contributor to UHI formation, and the expansion of urban areas into sprawling megacities is largely driven by economics. Rather than introduce a growth boundary, redevelop an existing lot, or increase density (through vertical development), residential development often occurs on the urban fringe where land is relatively cheap. Although economics has contributed to the development of UHIs, this sector also offers opportunities to increase the efficiency of cities. For instance, city efforts to introduce or enhance public transportation systems would provide local employment opportunities, commuting options for residents and visitors, and reduce dependency on automobiles and fossil fuel consumption, in addition to improving air quality. There are also wide-ranging opportunities for the private sector to provide services for sustainable development, such as solar technologies.

## Supplemental Readings

Rosenzweig, C., Solecki, W.D., Parshall, L., Chopping, M., Pope, G. and Goldberg. R. (2005). Characterizing the urban heat island in current and future climates in new jersey, Global Environmental Change Part B: *Environmental Hazards*, 6(1):51–62. DOI: 10.1016/j.hazards.2004.12.001.

Environmental Protection Agency, United States (EPA): Basic Information—Urban Heat Island Effect. http://www.epa.gov/heatisland/about/index.htm.

Grimmond, S. (2007). Urbanization and global environmental change: Local Effects of Urban Warming, *The Geographical Journal, 173*, 83–88.

# DISCUSSION QUESTIONS

1. How does urbanization alter the local climate system?

2. What health implications occur due to the urban heat island effect?

3. What are some ways to mitigate the UHI effects?

# Sustainable Agricultural Systems for Cities

*Rimjhim M. Aggarwal*
*Carissa Taylor*

## ▓ WHY THIS CHAPTER IS IMPORTANT FOR UNDERSTANDING SUSTAINABILITY

The key take-away lesson from this chapter is to think critically about the type of food system that we foster within an urban area. Does it provide sustainable livelihoods to the farmers and farm workers who participate in it? Does it offer affordable food for low-income populations? Does it make sense environmentally, in terms of energy, water, and other resources, to grow the food here rather than somewhere else? Does it truly add to ecosystem services such as waste recycling and biodiversity, or does it rely on distant, nonrenewable sources of fertilizer, and exist primarily as chemical monoculture—providing little in terms of wildlife habitat? These are the questions that we, as sustainability scholars, must struggle with as we work to inform policy and decision-making to shape our food system and our urban environments in a way that truly embodies the principles of sustainability.

## ▓ KEY CONCEPTS AND TERMS

*After reading this chapter, you should understand and be able to discuss the following:*

accessibility of healthy food; acute pesticide poisonings; agribusiness; aquaculture ponds; biodiversity; defensive localism; economies of scale; ecosystem services; embodied energy; eutrophication; food accessibility; food deserts; food insecure; food security; food supply chain; food systems; food mile; global food system; globalization of the food system; Green Revolution; industrial agriculture; industrial food system; industrial organics; inter-cropped polyculture; life-cycle approach; lifecycle assessment; local food; local food systems; metabolism; nitrogen-fixing cover crops; organic; phases of the food system; and urban and peri-urban agriculture.

# Introduction: The Challenge of Feeding Cities

As the world becomes increasingly urbanized, with cities moving to former agricultural land and farmers moving to cities, the question of who will feed the cities and how has become critical. The world today is very different from nineteenth-century Europe when productivity in agriculture was rising. This meant that as people moved to cities, they could be fed by the shrinking number of farmers in rural areas, but the rate of production in farmlands had to continue to increase. In the twentieth century, farming in cities was discouraged or ignored as urban planners drew a clear distinction between rural areas as primarily agricultural and urban areas as primarily industrial and residential. The same model was carried to other regions of the world by the colonial rulers, and it was believed that farming had no place in the building of modern cities. Despite this objective, several cities in Europe continued to have significant urban land devoted to urban farming.

**Accessibility of healthy food** - limited availability to purchase healthy food normally seen in low-income neighborhoods.

**Food systems** - the infrastructure and process needed in feeding a population (growing, harvesting, processing, packaging, consumption, etc.).

**Global food system** - decisions made by countries and companies regarding who produces food, what food is produced and when, and where and how the food is produced creates social, economical, and political impacts on everyone.

Now, we live in a world where the majority of people live in cities, far from the primary sources of food production. The whole process, from growing the food to bringing it to consumers, has become highly energy intensive, and there are large ecological impacts associated with each step of the lifecycle process, from the local to the global scale. Rising rates of food deprivation and obesity within neighborhoods of even relatively rich cities have raised concerns about the **accessibility of healthy food** within cities. As our **food systems** become highly integrated globally, questions about food safety are regularly raised, and we seem to be less and less in control of what gets into our plate. In the United States and Western Europe, in particular, this feeling of disconnect and loss of control over something as intimate as the food we eat has motivated people to look for alternative ways of securing their food. In some cities in Africa and Asia, where the rate of migration into urban areas is very high, widespread poverty and unemployment has driven residents to find ways of growing their own food in cities to survive.

Given the centrality of food in our lives and the dominant role played by the **global food system** in shaping resource use on this planet, it is clear that we cannot achieve sustainability without fundamentally restructuring our food system. By 2050, the world population is expected to increase to 9.1 billion, with around 70% of people living in cities. Feeding all those people will require increasing food production by 70%, according to the UN's Food and Agriculture Organization.[1] The conventional model of keeping cities and agriculture distinct and separate cannot continue for long. In fact, if we look closely, we realize that agriculture has always been practiced in and around cities in different forms (see Howard's Garden City). The problem has been that agriculture in cities is generally treated as a marginal or fringe activity and not systematically integrated within city planning and decision making until now.

In the context of urban sustainability, we need to ask a different set of questions regarding the relation between cities and agriculture: In your vision of a sustainable city, how would the food system be designed to meet the diverse food needs of city residents? Does it make sense to bring sources of food production closer to the consumers? If so, to what extent is agriculture an appropriate use of city space and other scarce resources, such as water? Thinking beyond food provision, what other services (or disservices) does agriculture provide within cities? How can we better incorporate the beneficial services that agriculture provides within urban development? Addressing these questions requires us to fundamentally rethink what sustainable agriculture means in an urban context and how we can transition toward it. This is an exciting new area of research and action, where we have more questions than ready-made answers.

The rest of this chapter is organized as follows. We begin by discussing how sustainable agriculture has generally been defined. Then we describe three different agricultural systems that currently provide for the food needs of cities. Each system has its own unique characteristics, and we critically examine the sustainability implications of each of these systems. Then we broaden the discussion to think about agriculture as not only providing food but also other kinds of services and disservices. Lastly, given this broader understanding, we discuss how we might integrate agriculture into urban planning and development to better design cities of the future.

# What Is Sustainable Agriculture?

Many definitions of the term sustainable agriculture exist today. One particularly useful and overarching definition was established in the 1990 Farm Bill[2] and represents the legal definition of Sustainable Agriculture in the United States today: *an integrated system of plant and animal production practices having a site-specific application that will, over the long term*:

- *Satisfy human food and fiber needs*
- *Enhance environmental quality and the natural resource base upon which the agricultural economy depends*
- *Make the most efficient use of nonrenewable resources and on-farm resources and integrate, where appropriate, natural biological cycles and controls*
- *Sustain the economic viability of farm operations*
- *Enhance the quality of life for farmers and society as a whole.*

Embedded within this definition we can clearly see the core elements of sustainability: meeting social, environmental, and economic needs over the long term. Achieving agricultural sustainability, however, is much easier said than done and may involve making difficult tradeoffs. For example, providing low-income populations with affordable fruits and vegetables may come in direct conflict with maintaining economic viability of farms. In the next section, we discuss the sustainability of the different agricultural systems that provide food for cities.

# Agricultural Systems for Feeding Cities

Much of our food takes a very complex path from farm to plate. Examining the **food supply chain** from a **lifecycle approach**, we understand that the process begins with production on a farm. From there, food is processed, packaged, and distributed either directly to consumers, or to retailers. Consumers purchase the food and then prepare and consume it, disposing of the wastes. This process sounds simple enough,

**Food supply chain** - a network of business related to food moving from production to consumption.

**Lifecycle approach** - making decisions on food purchasing and intake based on convictions, philosophies, the "want of something better," and the intangible attributes it adds to one's life.

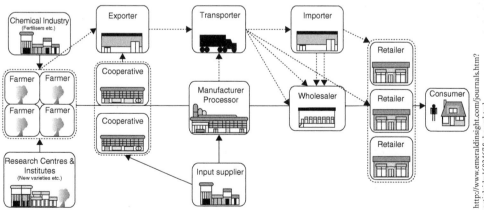

http://www.emeraldinsight.com/journals.htm?articleid=1603467&show=html

**The food supply chain. The food system is defined as the chain of activities connecting food production, processing, distribution, consumption and waste management, as well as the associated actors and the regulatory and institutional environment.**

but at each step along the way, there are different stakeholders, decision-makers, and regulations involved.

Next, we discuss the sustainability implications of three different kinds of food systems that provide food for the cities: the **industrial food system**, the **organic** food system, and the local food system. These three systems compare in terms of the sustainability criteria we outlined above.

## The Industrial Food System

Today, most of us participate in what we call the industrial food system. This is the system we all know and love (or hate). But, let's take a moment and un-package it. How much do we really know about all the things we put in our grocery cart?

Over the past century, the food system has undergone a dramatic shift. Development of high-yielding hybrid crops, widespread irrigation, application of synthetic fertilizers and pesticides, and the increasing use of machinery to replace human and animal labor all contributed to an increase in agricultural yields. Farms focused on efficiency, with each specializing in producing a limited set of crops to streamline their efforts and maximize yield. These practices spread throughout the globe in what is now known as the "**Green Revolution**."

Four-fifths of the world's food production now comes from **industrial agriculture**.[3] This industrial system was initially heralded as widely successful. The new "industrial" techniques doubled the yields of many staple grains and increased the amount of food available for the developing world's growing population, from below 2,000 calories per person in the early 1960s to more than 2,500 calories per person by the mid-1980s.[4] Would feeding the world be possible without industrial agriculture? From a perspective of sustainability, what are the broader impacts of the industrial food system—environmentally, socially, and economically? What are the advantages of this system? What are the disadvantages?

### Economic Impacts—Rise of Large Farms and Agribusiness

Green Revolution technologies were expensive and required substantial capital investment up-front. Despite widespread government subsidies for agricultural inputs such as fertilizers, pesticides, and water, the additional costs were too much for many small farmers. In the 1950s and 1960s, the number of farms in the United States was reduced by half. Meanwhile, large farms thrived and consolidated, and the average U.S. farm size nearly doubled.[5, 6] These trends have continued. Since 1982, there has been a 40% decrease in the number of small and mid-sized farms.[7] As large farms increased in size and market share, they outgrew the regional and local markets and began integrating

Image © Studio 1a Photography, 2012. Used under license from Shutterstock, Inc.

**Rows of young plants growing in a greenhouse.**

**Industrial food system** - the way we eat and how the food is created in mass quantities to supply that demand.

**Organic** - foods produced not using synthetic pesticides or chemical fertilizers, additives or solvents.

**Green Revolution** - occurring between 1940 and the late 1970s, development and technology innovations that increased agriculture production.

**Industrial agriculture** - innovation in technology, farming methods, production, consumption markets, and global trade that effects the production of crops, animals and fish.

horizontally (i.e., with other farms) or vertically (i.e., with processors, distributors, retailers) so they could operate at national or international scales. Over time, this integration has led to the rise in **agribusiness**—large multinational corporations that now control much of the food system worldwide.

## Environmental Impacts and the Ecological Footprint

With the expansion and **globalization of the food system**, its ecological footprint has also increased significantly. The conventional food system requires extensive use of nonrenewable fossil fuel resources for use in agricultural chemical production, on-farm machinery, processing, packaging, and transportation. In the United States, agriculture is estimated to account for approximately 17% of the country's fossil fuel consumption. Recent studies suggest that in the United States, food travels approximately 1,500 miles from "farm to plate," and the average American meal contains ingredients from at least five different countries. [8, 9] Ultimately, the large **food mile** system is highly inefficient—producing 1 unit of food energy for every 7.3 units of fossil fuel energy input.[10] Global estimates of total agricultural greenhouse gas emissions (GHG) range from 20–22% of all anthropogenic GHG emissions.[11] Agriculture also accounts for over two-thirds of water extracted from lakes, rivers, and aquifers worldwide.[12]

The increased application of synthetic fertilizers and pesticides has also had significant impacts on ecosystem health and integrity.

From 1960 to 2000, the use of synthetic nitrogen fertilizers increased 800% in the United States. However, it is estimated that approximately 30–80% of the nitrogen applied to crops is never taken up by the plants themselves. Much of this ends up in streams and lakes, where it can lead to **eutrophication**. Eutrophication is a process in which algae bloom due to the sudden influx of nutrients. When the algae die, the bacteria that decompose them consume oxygen in the region, triggering a chain reaction of dieoffs that can ripple across the aquatic ecosystem. Fertilizer runoff from farms along the Mississippi River flows into the Gulf of Mexico, generating a "Dead Zone" of approximately 5,000 square miles.[13, 14] Excessive and improper use of agricultural chemicals has led to loss in **biodiversity** and severe impacts on human and animal health.

Image © B Brown, 2012. Used under license from Shutterstock, Inc.

**An aerial view of a crop duster spraying, while flying low over farm fields.**

## Food Security, Nutrition and Health

Despite a 25% increase in the amount of food available per person worldwide, and a doubling in food production in the United States, many go without adequate food. In 2008, nearly 15% of the U.S. households were **food insecure** – meaning that they did not have access to enough food for an active, healthy lifestyle at all times throughout

**Agribusiness** - all of the business and the range of activities involved in food production including farming, seed supply, farm machinery, transportation, processing, distribution, and retail sales.

**Globalization of the food system** - acceleration of urbanization creating a strain on agriculture and how food is produced.

**Food mile** - distance food travels from production to consumer.

**Eutrophication** - the reaction of an ecosystem to an addition of natural and/or artificial nutrients or substances.

**Biodiversity** - the variety of life forms within an environment, region, or ecosystem first used referencing wildlife but now widely adopted.

**Food insecure** - access to adequate food varies throughout the year.

the year.[15] The urban poor and minorities feel the worst of the effects. While the Green Revolution was able to increase the total amount of food available worldwide, it could not address people's inability to afford or otherwise access that food.[16, 17, 18]

Many Americans now live in what are known as "**food deserts**"—socially distressed neighborhoods with low average household incomes and an inadequate accessibility of healthy food.

Post World War II, the spread of the automobile led to a steady exodus of those having upper and middle incomes from city centers. As people migrated to the suburbs, supermarkets followed, leaving many urban areas without grocery stores. Approximately 5.7 million people in the United States now live more than a mile from a supermarket and have no access to a vehicle. Low-income and minority neighborhoods have significantly lower access to supermarkets and higher access to convenience stores than do white and middle-to-upper income neighborhoods.[19, 20] The widespread availability of cheap, calorie-rich, and nutrient-low food contributes to unhealthy diets and high rates of obesity in poor and minority neighborhoods.[21, 22]

## Long Term Resilience

Reliance on distant food sources can undermine local resilience—increasing regional vulnerability to shocks from fluctuating markets, mass-scale food contamination, rising fuel costs, breakdowns in the global transportation system, while decreasing communities' capacity to respond to such stresses.[23] Global food prices rose by 80% between 2006 and 2008, significantly affecting the household budgets of urban dwellers.[24] Due in part to the large separation between consumers and producers, people are often unaware of the impacts of their purchasing decisions, making change difficult. However, there have been some attempts at agricultural reform. Next, we look at the organic food system, which seeks to address some of the negative effects associated with the industrial food system.

## Organic Food

The organic food movement began as a much more holistic and transformative endeavor than is sanctioned by the official organic certification processes we see today. Sir Albert Howard (1873–1947) is generally regarded as the founder of the modern organic movement. Howard's philosophy of agriculture was much broader than the organic-inorganic debate he has become known for today. He advocated proactive measures to prevent soil erosion, raising mixed crops (polyculture), integrating livestock farming with crop farming, recycling plant and animal waste back to the soil in the form of compost, and rainwater harvesting. Despite his call for a more holistic view of agriculture, and his followers' later advocacy toward understanding the farm as an "organic whole," the debate over chemical applications was what was galvanized the organic movement.[25] We cannot discount the importance of Barry Commoner's and Rachel Carson's books, which suggested the long-term hazards of pesticide applications for humans.

So, what exactly does "being organic" mean? According to the U.S. Department of Agriculture's National Organic Program (NOP) regulations, organic crops are grown and processed without most conventional pesticides, petroleum-based fertilizers, or sewage-sludge-based fertilizers. Animals raised organically must be fed only organic feed, receive no antibiotics or growth hormones, and have access to the outdoors. In terms of processing and handling, the regulations further prohibit the use of ionizing radiation and genetic engineering.[26]

For several decades, organic agriculture has served as the poster child of the broader sustainable food movement. In fact, many consumers equate "organic" with sustainability as far as food is concerned. In recent years, organic food has increased dramatically in popularity. In 1992, the United States was home to fewer than 1 million organic acres, but by 2008, it contained over 4.8 million acres of certified organic farmland.[27] Consumers have been found to purchase organic products primarily for the following reasons: health, taste, environmental benefits, food safety concerns, animal welfare concerns, support for small and local farms, wholesomeness, agricultural heritage, and trendiness. So how well do our desires match up with reality? How sustainable is organic? Let's take a look at some of its key impacts to the environment, the society, and the economy.

## How Sustainable Is Organic Food?

### Reduction in Synthetic Chemicals— Pros, Cons, and Gray Areas

The core purpose of the organic certification process is to minimize the amount of harmful synthetic chemicals that are used in the production and processing of our food. Here is where organics truly meet sustainability goals. The rejection of synthetic fertilizers forces farmers to re-think the way they interact with soil. Soil health may be improved using organic fertilizers and **nitrogen-fixing cover crops**, as well as innovative techniques such as low-tillage, crop rotation, and **inter-cropped polyculture**. Many organic farmers employ a combination of these procedures to maintain soil health, but proper management of nutrients still remains a challenge. For instance, recent research suggests that organic inputs tend to have adequate nitrogen but too little phosphorus and potassium, leading to a slow depletion of these key nutrients over time on organic farms.[28]

**Young plants growing in a hothouse.**

Image © Malican_India, 2012. Used under license from Shutterstock, Inc.

Lower chemical pesticide use translates to fewer non-target plant and animal species being killed off by potent chemicals. Studies show that biodiversity, and in particular, species abundance and richness tends to be significantly higher on organic farms.[29] Fewer pesticide applications on farms also means less pesticide exposure for farmers and consumers. In the United States, an estimated 300,000 **acute pesticide poisonings** occur each year, and worldwide, this figure may be as high as 26 million.[30] Past studies have found that chemicals present in pesticides are known or suspect carcinogens, endocrine disruptors, and neurotoxins. Intuitively, these seem like good things to keep away from something so intimate to us as our food. Complicating the matter, however, is the fact that many organic products are grown in close proximity

**Nitrogen-fixing cover crops** - crops planted, also known as catch crops, to retain soil nitrogen that is then released back into the soil and absorbed by other nitrogen needing crops.

**Inter-cropped polyculture** - growing several different crops in one area creating individual growing patterns and higher return.

**Acute pesticide poisonings** -extensive use and exposure of pesticides and agrochemicals in local agriculture and food production primarily in low- to middle-class communities due to the commercialization and globalization of agriculture.

to nonorganic ones. This can result in pesticide-drift and contamination of otherwise organic products. It is also important to keep in mind that although under NOP organic regulations, most synthetic substances are banned, there is a long list of allowed synthetic substances.

### Organics—Energy Reduction?

Studies suggest that organically grown crops tend to use less energy than their conventionally grown counterparts. How much less is a matter of debate. Organic farms don't use fossil fuel intensive pesticides and fertilizers, but depending on the crop and the level of mechanization on the farm, fewer pesticides can mean more mechanical weeding—hence, some of the savings are lost. A **lifecycle assessment** of the U.S. food system as a whole indicates that only about 8% of the energy use of the entire system is embodied in the production of chemical fertilizers and pesticides. Some suggest that because organics avoid these chemicals, energy inputs per acre can be 30%–50% lower for organic crops.[31, 32, 33]

### Organics—More Nutritious?

Many perceive organic foods to be more nutritious. Is this really the case? Currently, the research is inconclusive. Studies tend to indicate that vitamin C concentrations are significantly higher in organic produce. However, a recent review of 39 studies comparing organic and conventional produce found that results can vary widely depending on the types of nutrients and the specific crop. For example, vitamin C concentrations were higher in organic tomatoes than conventional ones, but for carrots and potatoes, the reverse was true. Studies reveal no consistent, significant differences between conventional and organic products in terms of many other nutrients, such as vitamin B, vitamin A or beta-carotene.[34, 35]

### Organics—Lower Yield?

One critique levied against organic agriculture is that organic agriculture results in lower yields. A 22-year study performed at the Rodale Institute indicated that fields grown organically can see up to 20% *lower yields* than fields grown conventionally, and other studies have found organic yields to be up to 50% lower.[36, 37, 38] In part, the lower yields are compensated by saving in expenses on chemical fertilizers and pesticides, but potentially higher costs for seeds, labor, and machinery. Thus, price premiums are a key factor in ensuring that farms profit from their organic venture. Some research suggests that a premium of 10% above conventional products may be necessary to ensure comparable farm profits. This has not been a problem in the past because some consumers appear to be willing to pay up to 180% more for their organic products.[39, 40, 41]

More problematic is the following lingering question: with lower yields, could organic agriculture ever feed the world? Critics argue that with 20% lower yields, up to 25% more land would need to be cultivated to supply the same amount of food. Environmental arguments for curbing the expansion of agricultural land aside (deforestation, biodiversity loss), some argue that as populations rise, there will simply not be enough land nor enough organic fertilizer available to feed the world organically.[42, 43] Additional research needs to be done to determine how much yields could be improved by changing on-farm management practices. Could a shift to organic agriculture increase agricultural land use and heighten food insecurity worldwide? It's possible,

**Lifecycle assessment -** environmental impacts associated with a particular crop or agriculture.

but it is also important to realize that food insecurity isn't just about availability of food—it's about the lack of stable access to healthy, usable food. This brings us to the next critique of organic agriculture, its inaccessibility due to cost.

### Organic Food's High Price Tag: Are Industrial Organics a Solution?

People who try to fill their shopping cart with organic products soon realize that these products are much more expensive than their conventional counterparts. The higher cost and relative unavailability of organics significantly diminishes the movement's potential to meet the dietary needs of mid-to-low income populations. But, whereas organics used to be found only at farm stands and small grocers, many organic products have begun to infiltrate our mainstream supermarkets, at increasingly affordable prices. Much of this is due to the entry of large-scale farms into the organic market. These farms are able to achieve **economies of scale** and levels of efficiency that many small farms are incapable of, and as a result, can pass on the savings to their customers.

**Economies of scale** - factors that affect the cost per unit to drop based on increased output.

However, these large organic farms don't come without a cost. For many of us, the term "organic agriculture" conjures up images of small, pristine, family farms, where farmhands work the good soil with nothing between them and the earth but their own bare hands, or perhaps a shovel. However, for much of the food labeled USDA Organic, this is far from the truth. Organic farms that are 500 or more acres control over 60% of the organic farmland in the United States. Furthermore, the size of organic farms is trending upward. In 1997, organic farms averaged 268 acres; by 2005, this figure was 477.[44]

Many would argue that the creation of the label "organic" has done little to transform the industrial food system. This could be seen as both a blessing and a curse. Proponents of large-scale organic farming argue that by working within the industrial system, it is easier to convince farmers to adopt the practice. Critics argue that large-scale agribusiness has simply created a new forum in which business-as-usual agricultural practices may occur, with may be a little less pollution and a lot more profit—a world of **industrial organics**. In 2008, approximately half of all organic purchases were made in mainstream supermarkets and big-box stores.[45] These stores require large volumes of consistent product, and the small-scale organic farms quickly get outcompeted.

**Industrial organics** - organically fed non-antibiotic animals or crops that are raised or grown indoors.

To summarize, organic regulations restrict chemical use, and this means reductions in fossil fuel use and **embodied energy**. Overall, lower chemical use seems to translate to greater energy efficiency of organic crop production, better soil health, improved biodiversity, less risk of human exposure to pesticides. However, there are tradeoffs. Yields appear to be lower in organic fields than conventional ones, which could mean we need more land to produce the same amount of food, which is a sustainability problem since bioproductive land is decreasing at the global scale. For a variety of reasons, organic products are typically far more expensive than conventional ones, limiting their capacity to serve low-income populations. Finally, organic agriculture, for better or for worse, does little to challenge the mainstream, globalized system of industrial agriculture where small-scale farms lose out.

**Embodied energy** - energy used to produce/create a product during its entire lifecycle.

We need to ask ourselves: is this all we want from a sustainable agricultural system? What about other environmental issues such as water use, greenhouse gas emissions, soil erosion, nutrient runoff, deforestation, and biodiversity loss? What about farm livelihoods, the loss of small-scale farms across the United States, and the domination of the industry by large corporate agribusiness? What about the inequities in our food system, rising obesity, rising costs of nutritious food, and the many hungry and food insecure in our midst? On all these issues, the organic movement as we see it today is silent. These are the principle questions of sustainable agriculture and cities for which we need answers.

## Local Food

There is a growing argument that both the industrial and organic models of agriculture fail to address the bulk of the world's food system problems. Both models operate primarily within a structure of an intensely globalized agricultural system in which producers and consumers are distanced, and local regions remain highly vulnerable to global shocks. **Local food systems**, on the other hand, seek to minimize the distance from farm-to-plate and often use direct marketing approaches, where farmers sell directly to consumers. When talking about cities, local agriculture is often called **urban and peri-urban agriculture (UPA)**, which takes place inside the city itself or in the periphery. UPA includes horticulture, aquaculture, arboriculture, and poultry and animal husbandry. It can be found in the form of greenbelts around cities, community gardens, farming at the city's edge and in vacant inner city lots, fish farms, farm animals at public housing sites, municipal compost facilities, schoolyard greenhouses, restaurant-supported salad gardens, backyard orchards, rooftop gardens and beehives, window box gardens, and much more.

In the United States, agriculture in metropolitan regions accounts for about 33% of total crop sales, and 61% of the production of fruits and vegetables by acreage.[46] The **local food** trend is growing. Today, the United States is home to more than 5,200 farmers' markets, and at least 2,500 Community Supported Agriculture programs. Direct sales of farm products have increased from $812 million in 2002 to $1.2 billion in 2007.[47]

**Local food systems** - how food is being produced and delivered to consumers within a community to increase food security.

**Urban and Peri-urban Agriculture (UPA)** - growing, harvesting, producing, and consuming food in an urban area of a city, town, or metropolis.

**Local food** - food being produced and delivered to consumers within a geographical area.

Image © Nick Hawkes, 2012. Used under license from Shutterstock, Inc.

**Rooftop garden, Westminster, London, England.**

## What Is Local Food?

Defining this term is more complex than one might guess at first glance. Unlike organic or fair trade, there is no formal, overarching certification system that defines what makes a product *local*. The definition of local, therefore, varies from region to region and person to person. Geographical or political boundaries such as "state" or "county" are often used by academics, because datasets are readily available at this level. These types of definitions may also tend to be employed by retailers for marketing purposes.[48] However, many consumers tend to conceive the term "local" in narrower terms expressed in "food miles" from their home—for example, a 50- or 100-mile radius. [49, 50] Consumers also often inherently associate particular values with the term *local*. Often implicated in people's definition of local are attributes associated with *who* produced the food, *how* they produced it, or perhaps *where* the food was *purchased*. According to these definitions, large corporations and agribusinesses, or farms without environmentally sound practices, may be excluded from consideration as truly local. The definition of local may be even further constrained to include only products that are bought directly from producers, or those purchased from particular outlets branded as local.[51]

## Why Go Local?

Consumers buy local food for many reasons. Some of the most commonly cited reasons include: improved quality, freshness and taste, environmental concerns, nutritional benefits, a desire to support local farms and economies, direct purchasing from farmers, obtaining organic products, and gaining a sense of knowing where their food came from.[52, 53, 54, 55] So, again, we must ask, how well do these expectations match up with reality? How sustainable is local food? Without clearly defined standards, the answer is often "*it depends*." It depends on the specific practices of the particular farm or local food outlet in question, and on whom you are asking. So, let's take a look.

## Is Local Food Sustainable?

Urban demand for local produce can provide profitable avenues for metropolitan area farms to maintain a sustainable livelihood. But, direct-marketing isn't for everyone. Only 6.2% of farms in the United States participate in direct-marketing.[56] So, why don't more farmers participate in local food systems? Research suggests a variety of reasons, most of which have to do with our mass conversion to industrialized, specialized agriculture. For many large farms, selling products exclusively at a local level is no longer feasible. They produce in quantities beyond what the local markets could consume, and their use of machinery, fertilizers, and pesticides allows them to produce with great efficiency. Working on a small-scale farm can be extremely hard work, and there is a great deal of physical labor involved. In addition, marketing directly to consumers is time-consuming, and many farmers describe feelings of "burnout" associated with producing and marketing their products locally.

Competition with the 24–7, one-stop-shopping, highly subsidized, supermarket experience is difficult. Americans are used to getting what they want, when they want it, and many don't want to be restricted to the seasonal produce that local farms have to offer. Because of this, local farmers have to spend extra time and effort educating the public and seeking out niche markets for their products. Why is it that small-scale farms do not sell their products at regional supermarkets? Supermarket chains—as

**Local foods effect the local economy greater and more quickly than supermarket purchases.**

well as large-scale foodservice, restaurants, and catering companies—typically only buy from large farms that can supply consistent and substantial quantities of product to all their stores.[57, 58] Typically, they purchase products from regional food distribution farms because of market security and diversity of products.

Many people buy local to support their local economy. Does buying local improve the local economy? Unlike supermarket purchases, where much of the profits "leak" to distant corporate headquarters, money spent on local food is more likely to go to a local farmer or retailer, who in turn, is more likely to spend it in the local region. It is estimated that for each dollar spent on local food, more than double this amount is then able to re-circulate in the local economy.[59]

Local food outlets such as farmers' markets may create new job and volunteer opportunities, both directly and indirectly. One study calculated that for every person employed at an Oklahoma farmers' market, an additional 2.44 jobs were created throughout the state.[60]

Noncommercial forms of urban agriculture, such as household and community gardens, can play a particularly significant role in contributing to health and nutrition, especially in food-insecure communities. In developing countries, where poor, urban residents are estimated to spend 60–80% of their meager incomes on food, a few homegrown crops can go a long way to meeting nutritional needs while freeing up financial resources for other investments.[61, 62] Household gardens can also be vehicles of empowerment for women living in regions of the world that still discourage them from seeking a job or participating in economic activities. So, it would seem that for some farmers, and in terms of the local economy, a local food system can contribute a lot. But, what about the rest of the world? What happens when we choose to buy locally rather than import our products from somewhere else?

### Defensive Localism—A Cautionary Tale

Buying something produced locally sounds like a simple idea. But, as you start unpacking what it really means in terms of sustainability, things can get complicated. What if a better, more sustainable, product could have been sourced non-locally? *Buying local for local's sake is at best lazy sustainability, and at worst, irresponsible.* Thus, scholars argue, we need to be careful not to fall into the "local trap"—assuming that local is better without looking more closely at the issues. Assuming that local is better can lead to a sort of **defensive localism**, in which nonlocal products are shunned without a second glance. Along with this can come an array of cascading effects, some potentially positive, others negative. As we have seen, there are *local* economic benefits to buying local. But, this may be at the expense of a job in another community elsewhere. Furthermore, the local scale may be just as susceptible to power imbalances, injustices,

**Defensive localism** - aversion to agriculture products not produced within the community.

and irresponsible practices. In this sense, the *local* label can run the risk of appearing to embody a set of sustainability principles and values that inherently have, in fact, very little to do with the local scale.[63, 64, 65] Let's take a deeper look at some of the other factors that need to be considered when thinking about sustainability.

Lemons are loaded onto trailers at a California processing plant for transportation.

## Local Food—Better for the Environment?

Is eating local better for the environment? One widely used argument for local food is that it travels less distance from "farm to plate." Many argue that fewer *food miles* entails less fossil fuel use and lower greenhouse gas (GHG) emissions. While this seems to make sense intuitively, reality is much less straightforward. What *is* well established is that in the conventional system, food travels a long way to get to our dinner plate. Most studies peg this number at an average of 1,500–2,000 miles for U.S. consumers.[66]

Things get complicated, however, when you start to factor in the *type* of transportation used to deliver food from farm to plate. Personal vehicles and small trucks used by farmers and consumers to transport food on a local scale have lower capacity, and therefore, they transport fewer pounds of food per gallon of gas consumed, despite the fact that these vehicles have relatively good fuel efficiency. It comes down to economies of scale. When carrying substantial amounts of food, large refrigerated trucks can actually be more fuel efficient *on* a per-pound basis.

Moreover, when considering the energy impact of local food, transportation isn't the whole story. In fact, the energy used in food miles to transport a food from farm to plate only accounts for a tiny 14% of the overall energy consumption of the food system.[67, 68] If we truly care about reducing the fossil fuel use and greenhouse gas emissions of our food purchases, we have to think about the big picture and perform a life cycle assessment.

Different regions and different farms may produce food with far less fuel used and far fewer GHGs emitted per unit of product than others—giving them a comparative advantage over local regions. This may be due to a variety of factors, such as soil type, climate, farm-management practices, and the nature of processing and packaging. The question becomes, how much energy is embodied in the product as a whole by the time it hits your refrigerator? For example, one study revealed that tomatoes purchased locally in the United Kingdom in the wintertime came from heated greenhouses and used more energy than would have been used to ship them to the United Kingdom from Spain.[69] Therefore, it is important to consider seasonality, crop yield, regional geography, and on-farm management practices before universally labeling local food as having lower energy use and a smaller carbon footprint. It must be stressed here that it is important to calculate energy use per unit of farm product produced. Some farms may be more productive than others, and therefore, though their energy consumption overall may be greater, they yield more crop per unit energy input.

It's also important to remember that energy use is just one of many indicators that we could use to assess the impact of a local food product on the environment as compared to another, non-local option. But, there are many other aspects to consider. We must compare local and nonlocal options in terms of their use of other nonrenewable and scarce resources such as water and phosphorus-based fertilizers. We must compare them in terms of their impact on air, water, and soil quality, as well as overall biodiversity and ecosystem health. We must do all of this in terms of assessing not only the farm, but also the entire processing, packaging, and distribution **phases of the food system** as well.

**Phases of the food system** - production, processing, distribution, consumption and post consumption.

### Local Food—Better for People?

Today, one of the key reasons that people in the United States turn to local food systems is that, through them, they have a better sense of where their food comes from. Local food systems reconnect producers and consumers and heighten "agricultural literacy" in urban dwellers. They begin to understand what goes into their food, how it's grown, the seasonality of production, and the local environmental characteristics of their region. Because of this increased knowledge, consumers feel that they can make more informed choices when they buy or grow. Furthermore, direct contact with customers and the increased visibility of farms and their practices have been shown to be related to increases in on-farm biodiversity, and environmental and ethical farm management.[70, 71, 72]

An image of a variety of fruits and vegetables at an outdoor farmer's market.

Image © Elena Aliaga, 2012. Used under license from Shutterstock, Inc.

### Local Inequities—Who Gets a Seat at the Local Table?

Who buys local food? Participation in local food outlets is very limited. A growing body of research suggests that local food systems primarily serve the urban elite and that low-income or minority customers are less well served.[73, 74] If local food is ever to be the answer to our food sustainability problems, its inequities must be addressed. The reasons behind low-income and minority consumers' lack of participation in local food markets are complex and not well understood. Much research is yet to be done in this field. One lens that can increase understanding of the issue is that of **food security**. The Food and Agriculture Association of the United Nations states that for food security

**Food security** - access and availability of food to an individual to live a healthy lifestyle.

to be achieved, food must be available, accessible, usable, and stable.[75, 76] The United States has more than enough quality food available, but what about the other factors? We'll address each in turn.

How accessible is local food to consumers? **Food accessibility** encompasses a number of factors—typically aspects of affordability, physical accessibility, and cultural acceptability. Many consumers cite the high cost of local foods as a major barrier to purchasing it. Providing food subsidies to low-income and other vulnerable groups, through food stamps and food vouchers, and making these redeemable at local food outlets such as farmers' markets is one way of addressing the affordability issue. But, affordability is not enough to ensure food security.

Local food outlets such as farms, farm stands, farmers' markets, or Community Supported Agriculture drop-off locations are not always physically accessible for consumers, or that access may be unstable, varying from season to season. A given market must also provide culturally acceptable food. In terms of food, the culture with which we identify can unwittingly play a significant role in what we come to regard as acceptable food and how we utilize it.[77, 78, 79]

Thus, to conclude, it would appear that local food, just like organic options, is not a miracle cure. On a regional scale, local food can bring many benefits. It stimulates the local economy, provides a profitable avenue for many small farmers, and can contribute to increasing resilience and food security. But, we have also seen that local food tends to be unaffordable and inaccessible for many city residents. We have also discussed that although local food may reduce fossil fuel use, this is not *always* the case. Similarly, depending on the region, sourcing non-locally could mean savings in water inputs, fertilizer applications, pesticide use, or even improvements regarding issues of social justice, fair wages, or humane treatment of animals. In this light, it's not *local* in and of itself that is so important as what's actually happening in the process from seedling to dinner plate. However, one could argue that it is much easier to know what's happening on the farm and in the distribution process when the farm is local—and of course this is one of the major reasons people buy from local farms.

**Food accessibility** - access and availability of food to an individual.

# Beyond Food: Ecosystem Services (and Disservices) of Urban Agriculture

Farms can offer urban regions much more than just food. Scholars increasingly recognize the many **ecosystem services** that agricultural lands can provide. Essentially, ecosystem services are the benefits people obtain from a given ecosystem, and agriculture can be thought of as a managed ecosystem. In the case of agriculture, these include food provisioning, waste and nutrient cycling, water runoff management and groundwater recharge, maintenance of soil fertility, provision of educational, recreational and economic opportunities, increased wildlife habitat and biodiversity, reduction in the urban heat island effect, and other microclimate and aesthetic improvements.[80, 81, 82] We'll explore some of these concepts below, as well as some of the potential *disservices* of urban and peri-urban agriculture.

**Ecosystem services** - benefits and resources a human receives from its surroundings or ecosystem.

## City Metabolism—Rethinking "Waste"

Currently, our cities operate in a linear manner. We bring in vast quantities of food and other resources, and emit vast quantities of waste—much of which is processed through our wastewater treatment plants, eventually ending up polluting our waterways or being trapped in our landfills. There is very little active recycling of any kind, and as a result, we see a slow, but persistent removal of nutrients—especially phosphorous—from our agricultural lands.[83] Phosphorus is a nutrient that is absolutely essential to plant growth. It is also a nonrenewable resource, harvested primarily in the form of rock phosphate. Farmers apply it to their fields as fertilizer to maintain soil fertility. Some of this is lost to runoff before the crops can take it in. The part that plants do uptake is shipped off to cities, embedded in our food. Nearly 100% of the phosphorus humans eat is excreted—mostly in urine. Eventually it ends up in our waterways or sewage sludge in landfills. Only 10% of this is estimated to recirculate back to agricultural lands—a serious problem when you recall that global phosphate rock resources will likely be depleted within the next few hundred years.[84, 85]  .

Because of this, many increasingly argue that it is crucial that we begin to think of the **metabolism** (inputs and outputs) of our cities as circular rather than linear.[86] Here, the development of closely integrated urban-agriculture systems could help. Sewage water, if properly treated, could be used to fertilize agricultural lands. In fact, many regions in China have had long-standing traditions of successfully recycling waste back onto cropland near urban areas using **aquaculture ponds**. Of course, recycling human waste into a form that can be applied to edible crops does not come without its own challenges. Improperly treated wastewater can increase exposure to diseases such as cholera, typhoid, giardia, dysentery, and more. Furthermore, urban soils may be contaminated with heavy metals from automobile exhaust and industry.[87] However, there are many examples of such ecological sanitation systems worldwide, and this is promising for a move toward more closed-loop, regenerative urban-agriculture systems.[88, 89]

**Metabolism** - inputs and outputs of ourselves and our ecosystem.

**Aquaculture ponds** - ponds installed and modified to produce grow and harvest fish, other animals, and irrigation of plants.

Image © Calvin Chan, 2012. Used under license from Shutterstock, Inc.

Image © Frontpage, 2012. Used under license from Shutterstock, Inc.

**Photos of urban deforestation.**

## Wildlife Habitat & Biodiversity

Urban areas have become notorious for their destruction of ecosystems. As cities have grown, they have literally paved over much of the world's prime agricultural land and biodiverse habitat.[90, 91]

In the United States, much of this land now lies vacant. Urban agriculture provides an opportunity to provide cities not only with food, but also with much needed green space. Many studies show that due to their high plant diversity, backyard and rooftop gardens can provide key urban habitats for native pollinators, birds, and other wildlife.[92] However, urban agriculture doesn't *always* provide vibrant wildlife habitat. Chemical monocultures, heavy tillage, or farms producing vast amounts of nutrient runoff, for example, don't improve soil and ecosystem health or wildlife habitat; they degrade it. So again, we see that local, urban agriculture isn't *necessarily* a good thing, but that when practiced properly, it could be.

## Microclimate Improvements

There are a number of ways in which urban agriculture can lead to microclimate improvements. Plants help minimize the movement of dust and resulting air pollution. As plants respire, the water they've taken in evaporates, cooling the surrounding region. In desert climates, this urban heat island mitigation can play a critical role in making the city livable and reducing the amount of air conditioning required. Of course, the tradeoff here is water. For evaporative cooling to work, water is needed, and this can be problematic for areas in which water is scarce.[93]

# Integrating Agriculture in Cities: Innovative Urban Design, Policy, and Community Efforts

In the above section, we discussed the various ecosystem services and disservices that agriculture potentially provides in cities. Given this discussion, a central urban design and policy question is whether and to what extent agriculture is an appropriate use of city space and scarce resources such as water. In most places, it has been observed that as a city grows and land prices rise, land held in agricultural production is out-competed by other uses. This is because the market values only the agricultural products (food and fiber); other forms of ecosystem services that we discussed above—such as microclimate regulation, green spaces, biodiversity, and cultural services—are provided free. As a society, we may value these other services for a healthy and resilient city. But, if these services do not earn a market return, then we

Image © leungchopan, 2012. Used under license from Shutterstock, Inc.

Image © Raywoo, 2012. Used under license from Shutterstock, Inc.

**Urban Growth and Agriculture Production are key to land protection and continued agricultural success within cities.**

either need some sort of policy support or we need to think about alternative models of urban design and architecture, together with community efforts, so that we can make urban agriculture viable.

A wide range of policy instruments have been designed to manage urban growth and protect or promote agricultural production.

Agricultural zoning has been used widely by cities across the world to protect land use in agriculture. Land use plans often indicate the areas within the city in which urban agriculture is allowed. Sometimes these plans may also include guidelines from planners on the types of urban agriculture that are permissible. In Botswana, for example, the City of Gaborone has set up poultry zones on land considered of low potential for development for other land uses.[94]

In addition, in the United States, legally recognized geographic areas called *agricultural districts*, or *agricultural preserves*, are designed to keep land in agricultural use. The agricultural preserves differ from exclusive agricultural zoning areas because enrollment in them is voluntary.[95] Farmers who join an agricultural district may receive a variety of benefits, such as differential tax assessment, which implies that they are taxed at a lower agricultural value rather than the higher values associated with developed uses.[96] Another popular approach, widely used not only by government agencies but also a large number of private land trusts, for protecting agricultural land is the *purchase of development rights* (PDR). Under PDR, the landowner retains title to the land but voluntarily sells the development rights that prohibit future subdivision and development.[97] Conservation easements are also being increasingly used to delineate environmentally vulnerable lands that then can be used for agriculture. Several municipalities are also exploring the option of promoting *multifunctional land use*, wherein, through encouraging community participation in the management of open spaces, food can be grown in combination with other urban functions such as recreation and city greening.

Another innovative policy option gaining ground in recent years is the use of vacant public and private land for urban agriculture. With the growing "sprawl" into the suburbs, the last couple of decades have seen a common pattern of inner-city neglect in most cities across North America. For example, it is estimated that Chicago now has 70,000 vacant parcels of land. The economic recession of the past few years has led to depopulation and rise in abandoned properties in several cities across the United States. Urban agriculture can play a regenerative role by transforming these vacant lands, which are often neglected, to vegetable gardens that meet the food needs of the city.

Image © Laura Stone, 2012. Used under license from Shutterstock, Inc.

**This vacant lot in an inner-city neighborhood has been transformed into a community garden.**

The challenge here is negotiating a deal between the owners and potential users of these properties. Without a title or three- to five-year leases, the users risk losing their investment when the land is taken away for other purposes. The temporary nature of use may also make it difficult to secure other resources, such as water.

All these policy options and challenges are leading to a great deal of creative thinking around the question of how food production can be incorporated into the built environment. Architects are finding ways to fit food production into buildings, for instance, through rooftop gardens (which also provide cooling). Unused spaces such as riverbanks, median strips, schoolyards, and hospital lawns are being incorporated into a broader vision of creating green infrastructure within cities. New citywide coalitions are emerging to advance the goal of food security, both at the household and community level. Health and nutrition advocates are joining with community gardeners, university extension services, emergency food distributors, and city planners to design these new food systems. It is through these collaborations that the potential of urban agriculture in providing different types of ecosystem services can be realized.

# Conclusions and Further Thoughts

In this chapter, we have reviewed several of the key food systems utilized in urban areas and discussed their sustainability implications. We have seen that much of the food that passes through U.S. cities today comes not from the local region, but from farmlands and pastures hundreds or even thousands of miles away. In terms of sustainability, there may be some sound economic, social, and environmental reasons for sourcing food from far away—perhaps rain-fed agriculture is possible there, the land is more fertile, or the farm is large enough to achieve greater on-farm efficiency. But, there are costs as well. Buying into the globalized, industrial system may mean that more fossil fuels and chemicals were used to produce the food that arrives on our plates. Furthermore, relying solely on distant sources of food may make urban dwellers more vulnerable to shocks in the global system. Climate change, economic crises, food contamination, and increasing fuel costs could all result in price hikes, dramatically reducing the affordability and availability of food within a city.

One increasingly popular response to the many problems with the mainstream, industrial food system is to source more food *locally*—either within or very close to cities themselves. Urban and near-urban agriculture can take on many forms, including commercial farms and markets, or community and household gardens. Urban agriculture brings consumers back into close contact with the source of their food and can allow them to make more informed decisions about what they are buying into. It can enhance urban resilience by maintaining a city's capacity to feed itself, and furthermore, by providing a number of ecosystem services such as waste recycling, wildlife habitat, economic opportunities, and microclimate improvements.

## ◼ LESSONS LEARNED FOR ACHIEVING SUSTAINABILITY

To achieve sustainability, we must think critically about the type of food system that we foster within cities. It is important to consider whether it provides sustainable livelihoods to the farmers and farm workers who participate in it, and whether it offers affordable food for low-income populations. Moreover, we must consider whether it is environmentally sustainable in terms of energy, water, and other resources. These considerations should be used to inform policy and decision-making to shape our food system and our urban environments in a way that truly embodies the principles of sustainability.

## Supplemental Readings

Arnould, E. J., & Thompson, C. J. (2005). Consumer culture theory (CCT): Twenty years of research. *Journal of Consumer Research, 31.*

Barrett, C. B. (2010). Measuring food insecurity. *Science, 327*, 825–828.

Born, B., & Purcell, M. (2006). Avoiding the local trap: Scale and food systems in planning research. *Journal of Planning Education and Research, 26*, 195–207.

# DISCUSSION QUESTIONS

**1.** What are the three basic principles of sustainable agriculture?

**2.** What are some problems associated with pesticides, and how can they be solved or avoided?

**3.** What are the benefits of local food?

**4.** What are the limitations to implementing local food systems?

# Urban Ecology and Green Networks

*Edward Cook*

## ▨ WHY THIS CHAPTER IS IMPORTANT FOR UNDERSTANDING SUSTAINABILITY

This chapter examines how the scientific field of urban ecology and the emerging planning concept of green networks can contribute to making cities more sustainable. The scientific basis and relevance of urban ecology for sustainable cities is reviewed and an overview of green networks is provided with a discussion of particular challenges and opportunities of working with this concept in urban settings. The importance of hierarchy in ecology and planning for green networks is illustrated through exploration of multi-scalar plans that range from continental to individual sites. A series of examples from these two fields demonstrate how particular planning or design projects are implemented to achieve urban sustainability. Finally, a discussion clarifies how linking science, policy, planning, and design can ultimately lead to making green networks in cities a reality that provides a foundation for urban sustainability.

## ▨ KEY CONCEPTS AND TERMS

*After reading this chapter, you should be able to understand and discuss the following:*

adapt; biodiversity; biodiversity value; deep structure; continental scale conservation strategy; ecological functions; ecological integrity; ecological resilience; ecosystem services; green networks; human-dominated ecosystems; interim revegetation; natural regeneration; postindustrial brownfield sites; re-naturalized systems; urban ecology; and urban ecosystems.

# Urban and Landscape Ecology

The scientific field of ecology focuses on the study of interactions between organisms and their environment. Historically, ecologists have largely tended to study organisms within more natural ecosystems and have undertaken less research in **human-dominated ecosystems**, such as cities. With global shifts toward increasing urbanization and the understanding that impacts on the environment are seldom contained locally, in recent decades, urban and landscape ecology have emerged as important topics of increasing interest to ecologists, urban and regional planners and designers, landscape architects, social scientists, and others. Cities impact **ecological functions** in many ways. Urbanization "fragments, isolates and degrades natural habitat; simplifies homogeneous species composition; disrupts hydrological systems; and modifies energy flow and nutrient cycling."[1] **Urban ecosystems** and natural ecosystems have similar interactions. Urban ecosystems, however, are a blend of natural and human-created elements and, as such, the interactions are significantly affected by human intervention, as well as natural processes.

Integrating ecology into cities should be an important sustainability goal because it: 1) may help ameliorate human impacts on ecosystems, 2) enhances **ecosystem services**, 3) adds **biodiversity value** to cities, 4) ensures equitable access to nature

**Human-dominated ecosystems** - human-dominated ecosystems in which the human species is a central agent.

**Ecological functions** - the building blocks of specific habitat types on which species depend; a disruption to the ecological functions including physical habitat has proven to result in a change or loss in the habitat type.

and resources, and 5) maintains a healthy, functioning planet for future generations. Urban and landscape ecology are interdisciplinary sciences dealing substantially with the interaction of natural and human processes.[2, 3] Landscape ecology addresses how spatial variation in the landscape affects ecological processes. Theories and applications provide a rigorous scientific methodology that can be integrated into urban planning, design processes, and urban sustainability policies, providing the bases for urban planning and design decisions that affect the sustainability of cities.

The goal of **green networks** is to preserve or restore the **ecological integrity** of critical natural systems while allowing for compatible human activities within the network and continued productive use of adjacent lands. Some modification to adjacent land would enhance, in most cases, the network's viability. Ecological integrity is a concept that refers to the health of an ecosystem or a landscape. It can be considered to be the level at which the system is functionally viable. To achieve ecological integrity, near-natural levels of production, **biodiversity**, soil, and water characteristics must be present.[4] Ecological integrity can be characterized as an "umbrella concept," embracing all that is good and right in ecosystems. As a measure for sustainable development, the challenge becomes the quantification of the idea of "near-natural." It is quite simple to assess many areas and determine that they are not near-natural because of the evidence of excessive deterioration. But, because too many natural attributes are often difficult to quantify, determining that areas are near-natural may be a major challenge.

Ecological integrity can be characterized as an "umbrella concept," embracing all that is good and right in ecosystems.[5] It encompasses other conservation values, including biodiversity, **ecological resilience**, and naturalness. Although urban areas will never have the biodiversity, naturalness, and ecological resilience of pristine wilderness areas, reasonable standards can be met. Such considerations include composition, structure, and function of the urban ecosystem. These effectively align with the three basic tenets of landscape ecology: structure, function, and change. Utilizing these and other concepts from landscape ecology, planning and design strategies can be developed within a nested hierarchy that relates to various levels of ecological functioning and correlated levels of human activity and management.

Landscape structure refers to the spatial and structural characteristics of the landscape. Vegetation, soils, hydrology (rivers, streams, lakes, etc.), and topographic conditions, including slope and land form, are all integral to understanding landscape structure. Landscape function refers to the interactions that occur between organisms and the environment. Landscape change occurs constantly. As living dynamic systems, landscapes are in a constant state of flux. These three concepts (landscape structure, function, and change) are interrelated and fundamental to understanding and working with urban ecosystems.

Landscape structure includes patches, corridors, edges, and the matrix. (See conceptual diagram of the various components of a green network.) These are useful terms for describing and understanding the physical nature of landscape patterns. As was noted previously, landscape structure and function are interrelated, and by understanding how landscape structure affects ecological functions, we can plan for spatial arrangements to facilitate ecological functions and restore or strengthen sustainable urban ecosystems. Patches are the irregularly shaped elements in the landscape mosaic, whether it is developed or not, that differ from their surroundings. Corridors are linear elements that traverse the landscape mosaic and facilitate flows and connectivity between landscape elements. Connectivity, in ecological terms, refers to the interactions that occur between species and landscape structure across landscape elements.[6]

Edges are those areas that bound patches or corridors and are zones of critical interaction with adjacent ecosystems. There are a variety of types of patches and corridors and a range of different ways that edges accommodate interaction between ecosystems. By understanding landscape structure and the relative inherent ecological value of different types of patches

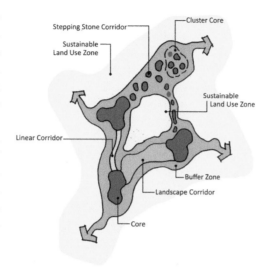

**Conceptual Diagram of a Green Network.**

and corridors, a process can be developed to structure spatial arrangements on the landscape that facilitate high levels of ecological functioning and create opportunities for efficient, but ecologically friendly, land-use activities. Resilient urban ecosystems require effective balances of coupled socio-ecological systems.

Ecological functioning occurs at many scales and is linked between scales. Many of the global environmental challenges we face today are a result of the aggregation of many actions that have occurred on small scales, but taken together, have a global impact. It is also true that organisms function at numerous scales ranging from microbiotic activity to interactions of meta-populations at broad scales. This hierarchy of systems does not always correlate between levels of ecological functioning and levels of government or other organizational structures that may be intended to manage land use and environmental objectives. However, it is important to find ways to allow organizations at various scales to collaborate in order to facilitate the range of levels of ecological functioning that must occur to sustain ecosystems and continue to provide ecosystem services to the population. Unfortunately, this approach often does not work. One goal in sustainability is to develop new institutional arrangements for governance specifically for socio-ecological systems.

The concept of green networks is specifically intended to help mitigate several deleterious effects of human habitation on the landscape, including problems resulting from fragmentation, isolation, and edge effects. Fragmentation of landscapes is a pervasive and significant problem. Prior to human occupation, natural systems were connected and sustained by the flows that occurred within and between various ecosystems. Examples of these flows are the movement of water through rivers, streams, and drainage corridors; the movement of air in and around various landscape elements; the migration of various organisms; and the associated movement of nutrients, energy, and genetic material. For example, a river system does not just move water from one location to another through gravity flow. Along the way, drops of water moving to lower elevations carry particles of soil and other organic material. This sediment that the river accumulates is deposited along the way in various locations changing landscape structure, but also providing nutrient-rich soil for the germination of new plants that then become food and habitat for other organisms in different locations. Fish and other aquatic species move up and down rivers to lakes and seas, sometimes becoming food for other animals, and spawn to create new populations while adding nutrients to the ecosystem.

Many other types of flows are just as critical, but may not be so obvious. The movement of cold air from higher elevations to low-lying areas creates microclimatic variations in the landscape. Since cold air is denser than warm air, it naturally flows to lower elevations. The movement of this cold air creates cooler zones in which more cold hardy plant communities that differ from the surrounding areas can become established. This variation creates the opportunity for increased diversity and, as a result, a broader range of species and potential ecological value. Human interventions such as building roads across valleys, drainage corridors, and other low-lying areas can introduce blockages of cold air drainage changing the microclimate. This change may lead to the extinction of some species in these areas that require certain climatic conditions, ultimately increasing the level of fragmentation of ecosystems. Fragmentation leads to the isolation[7] of various landscape elements and populations that inhabit them. Over time, isolated areas that are no longer connected to a larger supporting structure will decline in richness and diversity. Often, the decline is not immediately observable because the landscape structure changes slowly and the organisms that inhabit these areas are not always easy to observe and document. Because these areas are no longer connected to a larger system, the opportunity for introduction of new genetic material to renew populations becomes less likely.

The subsequent decline in populations and the reduced level of ecological functioning causes a decline in the ecological viability and resiliency of the ecosystem. Biodiversity is declining through the loss of species, as well as a loss of the ecosystems they inhabit. Essential habitats are lost, in part, due to urbanization, pest invasion, disease, and overharvesting. The loss of biodiversity has a direct effect on a system's capacity to be resilient, which is the ability to respond and bounce back from disturbances and retain the same function and structure.[8]

Edge effects occur where natural or near-natural landscape elements are adjacent to other types of ecosystems. Interactions between ecosystems occur naturally, but when human activities are introduced adjacent to natural areas, new stresses can be placed on ecosystems that are not always able to **adapt** to the changing conditions. As a result, even though some areas may still remain designated as natural areas or as important green areas, they may become less viable from an ecological perspective because of the incompatibility of adjacent land uses. It is important, therefore, to maintain and facilitate connections in the landscape or accommodate the flows that are vital to maintaining healthy, functioning ecosystems.

From an ecological perspective, it is also important to understand the landscape morphology (the form and structure of animals and plants) and the history of the evolution of ecosystems with which we interact. Because landscapes are dynamic and constantly evolving, it is helpful to understand how landscapes and ecosystems have come to be in their present form. Although we cannot predict how landscapes will change or evolve, it is possible to identify tendencies that impart knowledge that can be used to make informed decisions about how to best interact with them. Ecological systems

**Adapt** - the ability to evolve or maintain based on changing circumstances, including environmental conditions.

often have what is called a **deep structure**; they have remnant or latent characteristics and long-term tendencies that often reemerge. Within developed areas, such as cities, it is useful to understand what these characteristics are so that plans can accommodate and take advantage of the rhythms and changes that occur naturally in these ecological systems.

One important dimension of urban sustainability is to allow nature to continue to thrive and manage itself without the infusion of energy and resources to keep urban ecological systems functioning. The problems associated with maintaining viable ecosystems in urban areas are significant. Specific challenges often surface, such as the development, conservation, landscape restoration, edge effects, and site-scale ecological design.[9] These can be addressed through the planning and design processes of urban sustainability. Urban landscapes are a finely structured mosaic of property owners and land uses where competing interests for undeveloped land are intense. Over time, cities have largely been formed as a result of many political, economic, cultural, and physical determinants. Resulting urban forms are an amalgamation of the most resilient human creations and ecological processes. However, nature's deep structure is ever-present in our cities and continues to provide evidence that when ecological processes are ignored in city design, nature's response is to recapture parts of the city either through catastrophic natural events or through incremental change. Often, valuable resources are used in an attempt to hold back the forces of nature or to rebuild urban infrastructure after recurring natural disruptions such as floods, soil movement, or weathering. A main goal of **urban ecology** is to understand these forces and work together with natural processes to achieve a sustainable future for cities.

After the December 2004 Indian Ocean tsunami, which killed hundreds of thousands of people, and Hurricane Katrina in August 2005, many scientists observed that the removal of many natural ecosystems (such as mangroves, swamps, and coral reefs) directly contributed to the level of destruction both events caused. These ecosystems had been destroyed and replaced with

Image © Rufous, 2012. Used under license from Shutterstock, Inc.

**The worst flooding in decades occurred on November 5, 2011, in Bangkok, Thailand, resulting in mandatory evacuations.**

Image © Joenne Sindo, 2012. Used under license from Shutterstock, Inc.

**Flooding of the Ipswich River in northeastern Massachusetts engulfs surrounding local buildings. The 2006 New England Flood was the worst flooding to hit the area in almost a century.**

residential, tourist, or commercial development, or through the intentional alteration of natural of water flows and sedimentation processes. Many suggest that if these natural buffers had still existed, the level of destruction, including the loss of life and property, would have been significantly less.[10]

# Green Networks

The concept of green networks embraces urban ecology as an essential determinant of city form that provides a guiding philosophy for sustainable new urban development and opportunities to retrofit existing urban structure to the ecological patterns that nature has shaped over time. A green network is a system of interconnected or related patches and corridors that provide and sustain ecological values within a human-dominated landscape mosaic. The concept of green networks is a human interpretation of relationships that have occurred in nature since the beginning of time. Related terms or concepts include ecological networks[11, 12] (green infrastructure,[13] greenways, green or ecological structure,[14] and habitat networks and dispersal networks).[15] The concept grew out of Dutch planning. It is an emerging planning idea that when applied effectively can create an "ecological infrastructure" for cities and contribute to long-term urban sustainability.

Green networks are also a response to deleterious effects of fragmentation and ecological degradation. If a green network is designed as a coherent system of natural or semi-natural landscape elements configured and managed with the objective of maintaining or restoring ecological functions as a means of conserving biodiversity, it will provide opportunities for the sustainable use of natural resources and ecosystem services. A principal benefit is that this concept allows nature to thrive and essentially manage itself without the infusion of energy and resources to keep urban ecological systems functioning.

The elements indicated as core areas represent relatively large natural or semi-natural open space or landscape elements that provide secure habitats for a variety of species and a range of ecological functions. These areas are often critical as prime habitat for diverse organisms that are not tolerant of significant levels of human activity or deterioration in ecological value. The core area labeled as a clustered core illustrates how it may be possible to organize a collection of smaller natural or semi-natural open space elements into a larger core. This approach may be necessary when working in developed landscapes such as cities where ecosystems are already fragmented and the only way to achieve ecological functioning at a higher level is to attempt to adapt through retrofitting.

Each of the core areas are linked by corridors. Three different types of corridors are highlighted in this diagram—landscape corridors, linear corridors, and stepping stone corridors. Landscape corridors link the core areas with wide continuous landscape elements that allow the zones to be used in similar ways as core areas and would also facilitate flows and migration between cores. Linear corridors are narrower and function primarily as connections from one core area to the next and do not provide sufficient area to be used as prime habitat zones. Stepping-stone corridors allow for connectivity between core areas in different ways that may require migration across less hospitable zones in the landscape with stepping stones operating as points of refuge and temporary habitat as organisms move along the corridor.

Surrounding all of these areas is a buffer zone. The buffer zone plays a critical role in filtering contaminants, invasive species, unnatural predators, and other negative impacts that may be introduced by human activity, such as noise and toxic materials. It provides protection for core areas and corridors, minimizes edge effects, and allows for the effective area of the core or corridor to function at its maximum potential.

The arrows that indicate connectivity to other green network elements illustrate that the system carries on throughout a larger region as an interconnected system of core areas (patches), corridors, buffer zones, and other landscape elements. Surrounding the green network elements are sustainable use areas. These are zones that are dominated by human activity that could be agricultural areas, heavily urbanized zones, suburban development, or dispersed types of human settlement. In each site where the green networks concept is applied, varying sizes and numbers of core areas, corridors, and buffer zones will be depending upon the inherent characteristics of the landscape and the opportunities available for implementation and acquisition of various landscape elements. In some locations, it may be possible to design green networks based largely on the remaining natural ecosystems and habitats; however, in urban settings, ecological restoration will have to be achieved by designing "synthetic" corridors that mimic natural systems to establish linkages where no natural connections are possible. The concept of green networks is also applicable at multiple scales: continental, national, city, or local. In fact, it is important that this concept be linked between these various scales to ensure the long-term resiliency of green networks.

## Ecosystem Services and Cultural Benefits

The principal reason the concept of green networks has gained acceptance as a planning strategy is that a variety of ecosystem services and cultural benefits can result. Ecosystem services are the result of the function of ecosystems that provide many benefits that we often take for granted. They are derived from nature and are used extensively to maintain our society. We depend on ecosystem services to provide breathable air, clean and plentiful water, food, pharmaceuticals, clothing, fuel, climate, waste disposal, pollination of plants, carbon sequestration, and much more. In addition, green infrastructure provides many cultural benefits including increased property value, recreational opportunities, sense of community, and identity. A recent report quantifies economic benefits of green infrastructure for cities.[16] These are things that we have historically relied upon for basic human existence. However, as ecosystems become more stressed both locally and globally, a decline in ecosystem services and cultural benefits has resulted. The following is a brief description of a variety of ecosystem services and cultural benefits that are often associated with the establishment of green networks and infrastructure.

*Increased biodiversity*—The diversity of life on the planet is immense, and it is difficult to fully comprehend and document the variety of species that exist. Both habitat and conduits for species migration are among the most important ecological functions that can be accommodated. In an urban context, some elements of a green network may only be suitable as primary habitat for a few species; however, as islands for refuge or places to forage, they may be quite suitable for many species if connected to node or primary source areas. Plants and animals are dispersed through corridors and patches of natural systems. These zones serve as conduits for nutrient, energy, and gene flow.

*Hydrologic processes*—The functions of hydrologic processes are among the most critical to preserve and restore. Green networks are well-suited to serve as the foundation of a network because they are often left undeveloped because of flood danger. They are also among the most environmentally rich and sensitive areas. When in a viable state, drainage corridors serve as filters for surface runoff, helping to purify water before it returns to water supply sources. They also serve as sinks for groundwater recharge. Flood containment and protection against soil erosion is also important.[17] Groundwater is another important resource that many cities rely upon for municipal water supplies. However, in many locations, groundwater is being extracted more rapidly than it is being naturally replenished. Ecosystems located in areas where groundwater recharge is most viable can be incorporated into green networks, and surface water can be filtered and allowed to percolate to replenish groundwater resources.

*Climate amelioration*—Specifically in urbanized areas, climate modification can be achieved by increasing vegetative cover in appropriate locations. In many metropolitan areas, and particularly in hot arid climates, an "urban-heat island effect" has increased average temperatures significantly, reducing human comfort and causing increased energy consumption.[18] Urban street trees and other green spaces help to mitigate increased temperatures through shading and evapotranspiration. Significant energy savings can be achieved with urban tree plantings.[19] Negative effects of wind can also be mitigated through increased plantings.

*Recreation*—The most common human activity that occurs in natural areas is recreation. Suitable activities are passive, such as hiking, cycling, horseback riding, nature observation, picnicking, and low-impact camping. As concern mounts over the lack of physical fitness, increased obesity, and rising associated health costs, opportunities for urban recreation become increasingly important.

*Carbon sequestration*— As noted in other chapters, the emission of carbon into the atmosphere is creating significant environmental problems. In addition to poor air quality in urban centers, the aggregation of carbon in the global atmosphere is known to be causing changes in climate that may have serious implications for future generations. Many scientists and engineers are exploring ways to artificially sequester carbon to help offset these anticipated climate changes. Natural ecosystems, particularly wet ecosystems, can sequester carbon from the atmosphere. Maintaining viable, functioning ecosystems can help to preserve natural carbon sequestration processes.

*Reduced management and maintenance costs and aesthetics*—Elements of green networks that are predominantly comprised of more-natural ecosystems can be self-sustaining and thus provide areas in which a range of other activities can occur without having to be maintained and managed using public resources. Although it is difficult to place specific monetary values on beautiful scenery, it is generally understood that aesthetic qualities are important. Research has demonstrated that properties adjacent to nature areas have increased economic value. The spiritual or emotional value of beautiful natural areas should also be recognized.

*Education and human psychology*—Education and human psychological ties with nature can be reinforced by having accessible nature areas within cities. As society becomes more urbanized, the danger of losing touch with nature becomes real. Functioning nature areas within an urban setting provide firsthand opportunities for city-dwellers to learn more about natural processes and green spaces, and can provide sanctuary from the strains of urban life. In the long term, this will likely promote a stronger environmental ethic in society.

In his 2011 book, *Biophilic Cities: Integrating Nature Into Urban Design and Planning*," Timothy Beatley describes a biophilic city as one that is abundant with nature and ripe with opportunities to restore and include nature throughout its boundaries, based on humans' innate desire to connect with other living things. Ample evidence suggests that exposure to nature has numerous benefits, including stress reduction, mood enhancement, an improvement in cognitive skills and academic performance, and the moderation of childhood illnesses. In addition, biophilic design and planning incorporates green urban features, such as trees and green rooftops, which lessen the urban-heat island effect and in turn significantly reduces heat-related stress and illnesses in cities.

There are other important functions of green networks; however, these are examples of some of the most relevant in urban areas. All of these ecosystem services or functions would likely not occur simultaneously throughout a green network. However, there may be several compatible functions with varying levels of priority in certain segments.

# The Nested Hierarchy of Green Networks

To be most effective, green networks should be linked at multiple scales. Although the scales or levels may vary depending on the situation, in most cases, four principle scales can be established at this nested hierarchy. At the broadest scale or "mega"-scale, the focus is on linking green network elements of significant size that may have relevance at the continental level. The next level is the "macro"-scale, which consists of national and regional levels. Cities typically occur at the following level or "meso"-scale. Finally, the "micro"-scale is where individual projects and sites become relevant. Linking all of these scales together creates possibilities for connectivity and flows between the levels that are essential for their long-term sustainability.

Several initiatives are focusing on the implementation of green networks from the continental scale down to individual sites or projects. In North America, a proposal entitled the "Yellowstone to Yukon Conservation Initiative" aims to establish a conservation corridor extending from Yellowstone National Park following the Rocky Mountains up through Canada to the Northern Territory of the Yukon.[20] This conservation initiative is intended to protect critical habitat for bears and other large mammals that need vast undisturbed areas to maintain their long-term viability. More than 100 organizations are partnered in this conservation initiative that links major national parks and wilderness areas and other critical habitat as a part of a **continental scale conservation strategy**.

In Europe, after 20 years of planning, the first complete version of the Pan European Ecological Network has begun to be implemented.[21] This network was

**Continental scale conservation strategy** - an approach to ensure the ecological integrity and connectivity of vital habitats across entire landscapes or regions, and establish strategic partnerships involving mixed land uses to promote ecological restoration in the reconnection of large ecosystems.

undertaken in three distinct pieces: one plan for Western Europe; another for Central Europe; and a third for South Eastern Europe, including Turkey. This extensive effort required the generation of national plans that were then integrated into a continental scale initiative. Important European bird migration routes and habitats, as well as varying levels of conservation for a variety of other species and critical ecological sites, were protected and conserved through this planning effort.

In Central America, the Mesoamerica Biological Corridor (MBC) project[22] ranges from the Yucatán Peninsula of Mexico through all of Central America to the southern reaches of Panama. This plan was started at the initiative of a number of international nonprofit conservation organizations. They worked with national governments in a cooperative effort to identify important habitat and ecological zones throughout the region. The plan was originated as a conservation strategy entitled "Paseo Pantera" (Path of the Panther), which was intended to protect biodiversity by providing protected corridors and patches that extend from Mexico to Panama.[23] Over the following five years, the plan was broadened to incorporate many other areas of ecological importance. Each of the participating countries developed a plan and coordinated their efforts with neighboring national governments. The national governments also developed strategies and incentives for the formulation and implementation of local-level plans.

An example of how a multiple scale strategy has been implemented is Hacienda Baru in Costa Rica.[24] Costa Rica participated in the cooperative international planning effort of the MBC and also has a strong national-level plan identifying national parks and other conservation areas that have significant ecological importance. Over 25 percent of the total land area of the country is a National Park or otherwise protected. Part of Costa Rica's economic development strategy is to embrace the idea of ecologically based tourism to preserve their critical natural resources and the ecological integrity of the landscape. As a part of the national strategy, initiatives were launched in the form of tax incentives, preservation easements, education, decentralized administration, partnerships with international organizations, and land purchased to secure the most important ecological zones and encourage more sustainable land use activities.[25]

Hacienda Baru went through the process of converting an 820-acre parcel of land from an active cattle ranch to an eco-lodge, helping to reestablish critical wildlife habitat and support sustainable tourism. The landscape transformations that occurred on the land occupied by the Hacienda Baru Ranch in 1971, 1997, and 2007 was vast. In 1971, it was a working cattle ranch owned by a U.S. meat packing company. The land was completely deforested and open for cattle grazing. Several years later, the company sold the land to ranch employees. The new owners created a series of pastures separated by fence lines. Something that is common in this region is to create fences using cuttings from live trees as stakes in the ground, and then take root and leaf out become living trees while still serving as fence posts. This protects the fence posts from rot and insect infestations and provides a lasting fence system. As the fence lines became established, monkeys, kinkajous, opossums, iguanas, and olingos from the upland forested areas started to use them as migration corridors to travel down to lowlands near the water's edge. The new landowners created a site-scale green network that facilitated the migration of certain of the species in the area.

Subsequently, the landowners embraced the opportunity to convert this series of pastures into an eco-lodge complete with nature trails, rustic lodging, environmental education opportunities, and guided tours. Over time, the pasture naturally regenerated and the former barren landscape of Hacienda Baru is now completely reforested and is home to a wide range of plants and animals that coexist with visitors and eco-lodge owners and employees.

Courtesy of Jack Ewing.

**Hacienda Baru, Costa Rica in 2007.**

# Planning and Design Strategies for Sustainable Cities

This section provides a series of examples that illustrate how the concept of green networks can be applied in urban settings to contribute to the long-term sustainability of cities. The five examples focus on different aspects of cities to illustrate how these various component parts can contribute to a larger plan for urban sustainability. They include:

1. Lifelines: Rivers, Streams, and Riparian Areas
2. Sources and Core Areas: Urban Nature Preserves
3. Cultural Sites: Public Good and Ecological Health
4. Gray to Green Infrastructure: Transportation and Utility Corridors
5. Forgotten Space: Vacant Land, Underutilized Sites, and Brownfields

## Lifelines: Rivers, Streams, and Riparian Zones

Rivers, streams, and other riparian zones are among the most biologically diverse and rich areas in most landscapes. They are also critical lifelines because they are essential for providing connectivity that facilitates flows and many other ecological functions. Where these rivers and streams are in a natural or near natural condition, it is important to preserve or conserve these critical corridors. In many places, however, humans have settled near rivers and streams, primarily for water supply and disposal of waste. In most cities, rivers and streams and their drainage basins are usually significantly modified from their original condition, and the corridors are sometimes channelized or straightened in an attempt to manage flooding and maximize adjacent land for urban development. While this sometimes remedies short-term problems in the zone immediately surrounding the watercourse, many unintended complications often arise. Channelization and straightening of rivers increases the speed of water flow, which in turn increases the force causing erosion of stream banks and further instability downstream. As the water moves more rapidly, it also carries more sediment, reducing water quality. Additional problems occur downstream when the river is no longer channelized. The sediment load that is carried by the rapidly moving water drops once the river returns to its normal meander cycle and over time the channel fills with the sediment, reducing its capacity to carry water, resulting in flooding beyond historical flood zones. Many rivers and streams that have been modified are now being restored and **re-naturalized** by reintroducing the meander and reestablishing streambank vegetation.

An example of a river that was formerly channelized and has been re-naturalized is the Enz River in Pforzheim, Germany. Pforzheim is a city of approximately 120,000 people and is located at the edge of Germany's Black Forest. The Enz River runs through the center of the city and was channelized and straightened in the early 1900s. The land area adjacent to the river in the city has been developed through the decades for urban housing, industrial complexes, shops, and other forms of intense urban development. The river restoration project is part of a larger scheme to create a new urban park following the course of the river for nearly 15 kilometers through the city. The design was undertaken in the late 1980s and construction was completed in 1992.

The re-naturalization process reintroduced the normal meander cycle based on historical analysis of the river form, prior to channelizing and straightening. Trees and shrubs were replanted in locations where they would typically be found in a natural river channel structure. The landscape architects who designed the project followed ecological design principles, using lessons from nature to inform their design strategies. This is also known as bio-mimicry, which encompasses learning from and emulating natural forms, processes, and ecosystems to create more sustainable designs. Some 20 years later, the river corridor is now well reestablished in its natural regime, vegetation has matured providing habitat for many species, and the river corridor now looks much as it did in its original natural condition. Most importantly, it has reestablished many of the ecological functions that were lost when the river was channelized and straightened, and it has now once again become an important ecological corridor linking the Black Forest to other important ecological zones.

## Sources and Core Areas: Urban Nature Preserves

Source and core areas are large areas of natural or near natural landscape, although they do not need to be natural or near natural if high levels of ecological functioning are occurring. Many examples of landscapes have been restored after some significant disturbance or deterioration that provide many of the same benefits as natural or near natural source or core areas. They are important elements in a green network to provide stability because they are generally somewhat resistant to external influences. These areas normally function as prime habitat for various species and may contribute to shaping climate, hydrological, and other biological functions within the larger context of the urban area. The term source area simply refers to the fact that these large areas are places where there are significant populations from which genetic material may spread to other zones and the green network. Because these areas are usually covered by vegetation, they supply oxygen and absorb carbon helping to improve air quality. The presence of vegetation also can help to mitigate urban heat island effects by keeping the surface cooler and through the process of evapotranspiration returning moisture to the air. Depending on the specific characteristics of the core or source area, they may perform important hydrological functions such as water retention, groundwater recharge, and filtration of surface water. From a biological perspective,

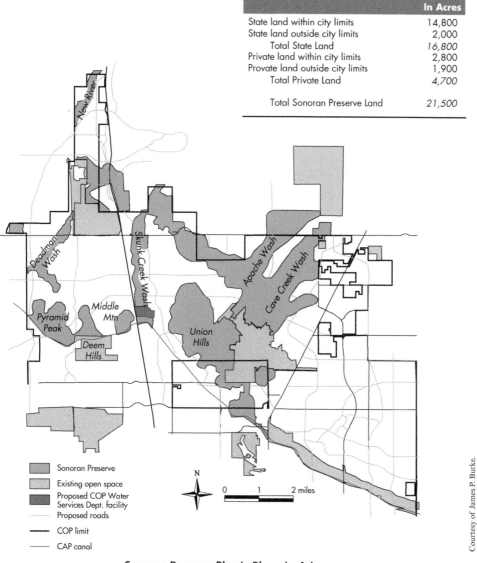

Sonoran Preserve Land Ownership and Location

| | In Acres |
|---|---|
| State land within city limits | 14,800 |
| State land outside city limits | 2,000 |
| Total State Land | 16,800 |
| Private land within city limits | 2,800 |
| Provate land outside city limits | 1,900 |
| Total Private Land | 4,700 |
| Total Sonoran Preserve Land | 21,500 |

Legend:
- Sonoran Preserve
- Existing open space
- Proposed COP Water Services Dept. facility
- Proposed roads
- COP limit
- CAP canal

N
0    1    2 miles

Courtesy of James P. Burke.

**Sonoran Preserve Plan in Phoenix, Arizona.**

these areas usually occupy sufficient terrain to provide habitat and range for migration for many species that may not be tolerant of frequent interaction with, or influence from, humans.

The Phoenix Mountain preserves in Phoenix, Arizona, are an example of a series of open-space elements in an urban area that function as multiple core or source areas. The accompanying figure shows the location of several major open-space preserves that are all part of the city of Phoenix Park system, but are all-natural or near-natural condition. The first of these preserves, South Mountain Park, was established in 1924 and occupies 16,500 acres. It is the largest city park in the United States. An additional 10,500 acres were added to the preserve system in 1972 with the establishment of the

North Mountain range. The most recent addition to the preserve system came with the establishment of the Sonoran preserve master plan, which identifies approximately 21,500 acres in North Phoenix to be added to the system.

## Cultural Sites: Public Good and Ecological Health

The Musee du Quai Branly, a museum of anthropology in Paris, illustrates how a public site can contribute to the betterment of life. The building's exterior living-green wall is 650 feet long and 40 feet high and attracts the attention of nearby visitors to the Eiffel Tower and many passing by the building. In addition to being a spectacle and adding to the cultural interest and discourse, this site provides ecological benefits such as improved air quality, lower energy consumption, and urban habitat, and contributes to reducing the urban heat gain. In addition to the green wall, the gardens located on the site are well-developed and serve as a green oasis in a heavily developed part of the city. This site establishes an example that can be used as a precedent for other public works, as well as private projects.

## Gray to Green Infrastructure: Transportation and Utility Corridors

Most roads, rail lines, utility corridors, and other infrastructure elements form barriers, interrupt flows, and accelerate fragmentation and isolation. Strategies such as ecological bridges and eco-ducts are being utilized to overcome these barriers. It is most effective, however, to research natural systems and understand how alternative road alignments or making infrastructure corridors more compatible with ecological functions can be accomplished. In addition to mitigating barrier effects, designing or retrofitting infrastructure systems as ecological corridors creates opportunities for establishing linkages within urban areas in places where no natural connections occur. Most roads, rail lines, and utility corridors travel through rights of ways that are much wider than the actual infrastructure element. The residual space, either beside the road or rail line, underneath overhead utility lines, or above underground utility lines, can become an ecological corridor by simulating natural corridors through ecological design. These areas can also become useful as recreational corridors for hiking, running, cycling, and horseback riding.

An ecological bridge and an eco-duct can help to mitigate the barrier effects of major transportation elements. An ecological bridge should be situated at the location of a known migration corridor for animals that inhabit the landscape of that region. Initially, the cost may seem prohibitive to accommodate the movement of animals. However, in addition to ecological benefits, these bridges provide greater safety for motorists because they minimize the potential for accidents involving wildlife. Similarly, an eco-duct is a simple and inexpensive way to facilitate the movement of small animals underneath roadways, rather than limiting migration possibilities to crossing roadways.

## Forgotten Space: Vacant Land, Underutilized Sites, and Brownfields

**Postindustrial brownfield sites** - underused or vacant land frequently located in urban settings that were previously used for industrial or commercial purposes, often containing hazardous substances and contamination; cleaning up and redeveloping these properties protects the environment and reduces urban blight.

Vacant and underutilized land and derelict or **postindustrial brownfield sites** represent a viable resource in many cities. Upon examination of 70 cities in the United States, an average of 15% of the land area was vacant.[26] Oftentimes, these vacant parcels remain fallow for decades. Because they are privately owned, it is sometimes difficult to establish programs for temporary use. However, many cities are now exploring ways to use these parcels until they are transformed to a more permanent land-use activity. Vacant parcels can play important roles in green networks as stepping stones within the more developed urban structure, providing linkages between other more stable ecological zones. Strategies such as **interim revegetation**, temporary urban agriculture, and in some cases, **natural regeneration**, can return some ecological value to these sites.

**Interim revegetation** - plant species used to stabilize the soil and nutrients of an idle site in an effort to provide barren land with a new vegetative cover.

**Natural regeneration** - a dynamic process by which life recolonizes land when the vegetation has been partially or totally destroyed.

Brownfields are sites that have been previously occupied, often in some industrial capacity, that are now abandoned and may have significant site contamination issues. Typically, brownfields require intensive research and site investigation to determine appropriate strategies for site restoration and to remove contaminants before developing suitable strategies for reuse. Ecological approaches to site remediation, including phytoremediation,[27] bioremediation,[28] and in-situ oxidation[29] can provide many ecological benefits beyond just cleaning up hazardous waste or other contaminants.

An example of such reuse is BP Park, located on the Waverton Peninsula in Sydney, Australia. The former British Petroleum storage depot held 31 oil tanks and associated facilities that were carved into the sandstone bedrock. The tanks have been removed, but soil contamination at the site was initially significant. Onsite bioremediation was undertaken to decontaminate the topsoil, and then it was mixed with organic compost. After about a year of treatment, the soil was distributed throughout the site and used as a planting medium. Storm-water detention wetlands were designed into the site to remove any remaining contamination before the water returns to Sydney Harbor. The transformed industrial site has become an integral park space that includes frog habitat ponds and native revegetation.[30]

## ■ LESSONS LEARNED FOR ACHIEVING SUSTAINABILITY

While it is clear that a need exists for maintaining the viability of critical ecological systems in urban areas, it is uncertain whether this goal can be achieved over the long term given the current strategies many cities employ in urban planning. Ecological and urban theories have evolved in different directions and are only now starting to meet at a point in time when many urban areas have deteriorated ecosystem values that require substantial efforts to restore. Numerous perspectives exist on how to conserve existing viable systems and restore those with degraded quality. The concept of green networks shows promise in less-populated areas, and indications are that, in proper conditions, urban landscapes will also benefit. Linking science, policy, planning, and design is the most promising way to integrate ecology into cities and help provide a foundation for a more sustainable future.

Landscape metrics can be used to assess the viability of urban ecological networks and facilitate the evaluation of alternative planning strategies.[31, 32, 33] Landscape metrics are tools used to analyze landscape structure, inherent characteristics of the landscape elements, and the interrelationships between landscape elements and external factors affecting the functioning of landscapes. Interrelationships between individual landscape elements and the urban-landscape mosaic can be assessed through several indicators. The use of metrics provides the opportunity to have more objective conversations about ecological outcomes of urban-planning decisions. The most important issue is generating public awareness and support for sound concepts such as green networks. If the public is knowledgeable about the potential contribution toward actually realizing a sustainable future for cities, then the urban development community, government agencies, and politicians will likely follow.

## Supplemental Readings

Cook, E. A. (2002). Landscape structure indices for assessing urban ecological networks. *Landscape and Urban Planning, 58*(2), 269–280.

Ramalho, C. E., & Hobbs, R. J. (2012). Time for a change: Dynamic urban ecology. *Trends in Ecology & Evolution, 27*(3), 179–188.

Reza, M. I. H., & Abdullah, S. A. (2011). Regional index of ecological integrity: A need for sustainable management of natural resources. *Ecological Indicators, 11*(2), 220–229.

# DISCUSSION QUESTIONS

1.  Why is integrating ecology into cities an important sustainability goal?

2.  What is the goal of green networks?

3.  Explain fragmentation of landscapes.

4.  What are the benefits of post-industrial brownfield sites?

# Examining Sustainability through Urban Models

*Subhrajit Guhathakurta*

## ▰▰ WHY THIS CHAPTER IS IMPORTANT FOR UNDERSTANDING SUSTAINABILITY

It is widely accepted that the sustainability of human existence requires the protection of earth's life-support systems, as well as the efficient stewardship of natural resources so that they continue to be available for future generations. Sustainability thinking is about imagining a sustainable future. It is critically dependent upon understanding how the decisions we make today help to shape the future of our societies and settlements. Models are among the most important tools that help us anticipate that future. We use models to analyze how current trends play out over time, to ask "What if?" questions about particular interventions in social and ecological processes, test our hypotheses about social trends, and provide guidance for planning. In other words, models are indispensable for sustainability thinking.

Urban areas are the primary hubs of human settlements and the most challenging places for advancing sustainability. Since 2007, the world population has become predominantly urban and the urbanization trend continues unabated. Cities are the centers of concentrated consumption of resources and the major sources of pollutants, which include climate changing greenhouse gases. Therefore, the future sustainability of the planet will be determined by our ability to transform urban living along sustainable principles. Urban models help us to find sustainable alternatives to our current (often unsustainable) urban lifestyles. This chapter shows how urban models have evolved from basic concerns about land use and transportation to providing important metrics for advancing sustainability in our cities.

## ▰▰ KEY CONCEPTS AND TERMS

*After reading this chapter, you should understand and be able to discuss the following:*

agent-based model; cellular automata; discrete choice models; formalized models; land classification; Land Evaluation/Site Assessment; mental models; negative feedback; positive feedback; spatial interaction; suitability score; system dynamics; urban-environmental models; urban dynamics; and urban models.

# Understanding Models and Modeling

Models are the microcosms of real world phenomena that cannot be experienced or examined in their actual spatial and/or temporal contexts. We use different models for different purposes. Yes, some are indeed human models used by the fashion design and media industries to promote overpriced products. When Georgiou Armani or Calvin Klein want to convey how you might look and feel when you buy their newly designed outfits, they will find a human model to demonstrate these outfits. Of course, what is being modeled is far from our reality given that many of us would probably look uncomfortable or unseemly in the same outfit. In this case, the reality that is being modeled may only exist in peoples' imaginations.

Most models are not meant to cater to the imaginary world, but are designed to bring our imaginations to conform to reality. They are usually quite distinct from the objectified humans described above. Scientists, innovators, and researchers often use physical models to test critical properties of a designed or engineered product before the product is actually used. For example, scaled-down airplane models are tested in a wind tunnel to examine how the shape and structure of the model perform under different wind conditions. Similarly, structural engineers use miniaturized models of buildings designed with different materials and technologies on a vibrating platform to test how these structures perform for different intensities and types of earthquakes. In both cases, models allow us to test, under laboratory conditions, the robustness of our critical infrastructure. They also offer researchers the ability to improve on the existing designs.

Models can be concepts, ideas, or plans. These nonphysical models are expressed through words or symbols—or sometimes not expressed at all. When I leave my home in the morning to go to work, I use a mental map, or a model, that I use to choose my mode and route of travel to my destination. This model mostly remains in my unconscious since I have used it hundreds of times (until I am asked to describe the journey). We use such informal "**mental models**" to accomplish most of our tasks. Without a mental model, we are unable to act deliberately.

Our mental models are often inadequate when we face novel or complex situations. In such cases, we tend to formalize them so that they can be examined and perfected. Take, for example, traveling to various destinations in a new country. Most travelers in new situations will study maps and make copious notes of places to halt for conveniences or sightseeing and alternative routes in the case of road closures. These maps and notes together form a formal model of travel in a relatively strange land.

Complex processes and organizations require **formalized models**. It would be difficult, for example, to have a clear understanding of how a city functions with only mental models. Our mental models may provide bits and pieces of the total picture—we may know that population growth and an auto-oriented culture will lead to high levels of traffic congestion. We could also intuit that high levels of congestion may induce some people to seek homes closer to work—or, in the long run, seek out options in other cities that offer a better quality of life. Each of these processes triggers other changes in individual and social behavior that can either reinforce congestion levels or counteract them. Reinforcing processes are known as **positive feedback** loops, while the counteracting processes offer **negative feedback**. When individuals try to leave the pollution and noise of congested roads by fleeing to the suburbs, they may actually be reinforcing congestion levels by increasing commute distances. On the other hand, when enough commuters decide to give up on driving (because it is no fun to drive at five miles an hour and be abused by other irate drivers) and choose to travel by public transit, congestion levels may ease. This would be a negative feedback of congestion. Our mental models are inadequate to tease out the interactions among all the direct, indirect, and induced feedback loops of individual and social behavior in a city. In such complex situations, we use formal models with specific syntax and notations. These formalized models can both illustrate the interactions among the different

**Mental models** - an image we hold in our minds about how processes and events are related to each other.

**Formalized models** - a specific set of procedures or mathematical formulae that show how different processes result in a particular outcome or a set of outcomes.

**Positive feedback** - a connected causal chain of events in a closed loop where the intensity or scale of the initial driving force increases with each cycle.

**Negative feedback** - a connected causal chain of events in a closed loop where the intensity or scale of the initial driving force decreases with each cycle.

parts of the system (such as individual and social decisions) and communicate how the system can change under different scenarios.

One such model of a city was developed by Jay Forrester, who became interested in questions about urban policies and how they affect the quality of life of urban populations in the long run. He wrote a book called ***Urban Dynamics*** based on his findings from this modeling exercise (1969). This model incorporated specific kinds of syntax, notations, and mathematics; known as ***system dynamics*** that Forrester himself developed to examine logistical aspects of firm growth and decline. Through his system dynamic model of the city, Forrester demonstrated that policies meant to alleviate urban problems like housing shortages, unemployment, or neighborhood decline in fact exacerbate those problems. These models show that our intuitive "mental models" are often wrong when situated in a complex dynamic context.

As you can guess, there is a reason why I am using models of urban areas as prime examples of formalized models. Formalized models with complex mathematical expressions are used in numerous domains—from power systems to meteorology to economics. But urban areas pose a specific challenge given that the dynamics of urban processes include complex interactions among human, social, and natural systems. **Urban models** can never capture the richness of all interacting processes within an urban region. However, they can be useful in predicting future location and intensity of activities based on prior trends and show how different decisions we make today might play out in the future. Also, importantly, this chapter is about modeling urban sustainability. In the next few pages, I will demonstrate how to examine future sustainability impacts with the help of **urban-environmental models**. Before I delve into the questions of sustainability, a brief background on urban modeling is warranted.

## The First Generation of Urban Models

While Forrester was developing his system dynamic framework, another form of urban model was already transforming land use and transportation planning in large urban regions across the United States. This type of model was based on the concept of "**spatial interaction**," which assumed that activities that were closer together had a higher intensity of interaction than those further away. This premise was an analogue to the Newtonian law of gravitation, which stated that every mass in the universe attracts every other mass by a force equal to the product of their masses and inversely proportional to the square of the distance between them. In mathematical terms, this translates to:

$$F \propto \frac{m_1 m_2}{d^2}$$

Where: $F$ = Force of attraction between two masses; $m_1$ and $m_2$ = masses of the two bodies; and $d$ = distance between $m_1$ and $m_2$.

If you are wondering whether the inverse relationship with distance is always to the second power for all situations, your suspicion is not without merit. In fact, a more generalized version of the above equation is:

$$F = K \frac{m_1^\alpha m_2^\beta}{d^\lambda}$$

**Urban dynamics** - changes in the total connected urban system induced by changes in one component of this system. It is also the title of a book on examining a systems model of an urban region by Jay Forrester.

**System dynamics** - a methodological approach for characterizing a connected system of processes and events and examining how changes in one component of this system affect all other parts of the system.

**Urban models** - mathematically derived expressions for connecting aspects of urban processes, most commonly the relationship between land use and transportation.

**Urban-environmental models** - connecting urban models with environmental processes such as determining air quality from land use and transportation attributes.

**Spatial interaction** - a term used to characterize movement across spatial domains based on distance and other factors that impede such movement.

In this case, $\alpha$, $\beta$, $\lambda$, *and* $K$ are constants to be determined. Note that both the numerator and the denominator have power values that are not fixed but determined through empirical observations for each context of their use. If you now consider that $m_1$ and $m_2$ can also represent intensity of activities (e.g., number of people working, living, or shopping, in an area), it is not difficult to see how the interactions among these activities can be modeled as an extension of the general spatial interaction model shown above. Consider, for example, that you want to allocate future population growth to three neighborhoods in a small city (which has only three neighborhoods). Also, you expect that the attractiveness of these neighborhoods to be based on the amount of space available in them for accommodating new housing units (a proxy for price of entry) and how close the neighborhoods are to employment locations relative to the number of jobs in these locations. In other words, the *accessibility* ($A_j$) of a neighborhood $j$ to employment locations is proportional to the sum of the number of jobs in these employment locations ($E_1$, $E_2$, and $E_3$), each weighted by the inverse of distance to the neighborhood $j$ ($d_{ij}$). That is:

$$A_j = K \sum_{i=1}^{3} \frac{E_i}{d_{ij}^{\lambda}} \qquad \text{Where } K \text{ } and \text{ } \lambda \text{ are constants estimated empirically.}$$

Once the accessibility of each neighborhood is known, the allocation of growth to these neighborhoods can be apportioned according to the ratio of the product of land availability and accessibility of each neighborhood, in relation to the total of similar products of all neighborhoods. Again, in mathematical terms this would be:

$$G_j = G_T \left( \frac{L_j A_j}{\sum_{i=1}^{n} L_j A_j} \right)$$

Where $L_j$ is the indicator of amount of space available; $G_j$ = Growth allocated to $j$; and $G_T$ = Total growth in the city

## The Lowry Model

In 1964, Ira Lowry of the Rand Corporation unveiled a land use and transportation model that became the precursor to the first generation of such models. These first-generation models allocated activities spatially using some form of the generic spatial interaction model described above.

The Lowry model included jobs and housing, and their location relative to each other as in the example above. There were, however, several key innovations. First, Lowry distinguished between two types of jobs—*basic* and *non-basic*. The basic jobs were jobs employed in the export-oriented sectors. That is, the product of this sector was mostly consumed outside the region, such as the output of manufacturing, mining, agriculture, tourism, and other similar economic activities. All other jobs were considered non-basic, which indicated that they were mostly serving the local population. The number of basic jobs and their locations, current and future, are provided as *exogenous* inputs to the model (i.e., decided outside the model). The model then figures out where the non-basic jobs and households will be located *endogenously* (i.e., estimated by the model).

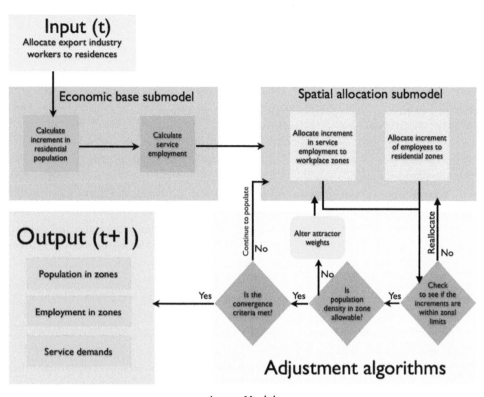

**Lowry Model**

The Lowry model consists of two sub-models. The first, known as the *economic base sub-model*, jointly determines the additional service-related jobs and the increment in households and population because of new basic employment. The second sub-model is the *spatial allocation sub-model* that allocates the new households, population, and service employment to zones using the familiar spatial interaction format. As you can tell, there is positive feedback between new households and new service-related jobs. As we add households of basic employees, more service-related jobs are needed, which in turn generates more households (families of those service employees), and subsequently, more service jobs in a chain effect. This iterative process is stopped when additional increments are too small to account for. A simple schematic of this process in provided in the Lowry model.

The Lowry model inspired a surge of successors that improved upon its basic framework. Within a period of about six years from Lowry's publication of "A Model of Metropolis,"[1] about a dozen such models were formulated both in the United States and in Europe. These included 1) Time-Oriented Metropolitan Model (TOMM 1964); 2) Bay Area Simulation Study (BASS I 1965); 3) The Cornell Land Use Game (CLUG 1966); 4) A Dynamic Model for Urban Structure (TOMM II 1968); 5) Projective Land Use Model (PLUM 1968); and 6) a portfolio of eight models developed by various individuals for different regions in the United Kingdom. (See Goldner 1971 for detailed review.) Even today, over 50 years past the initial Lowry formulation, aspects of his approach continue to be applied in urban land use and transportation models (such as in DRAM, EMPAL, and METROPILUS models by Putnam 1983, and Putnam and Chen 2001).

The subsequent developments in urban land use change models included several innovations that extended the theoretical and empirical scope of the Lowry model. Most of these models included a more disaggregated set of households and jobs. Many broke away from the rigid square grid and adopted census tracts for zones. Several later models also experimented with different forms of land use constraints and limitations on household behavior and budgets. In addition, new techniques for calibration and evaluation were also introduced to make the models better "fit" the data available for specific places.

Despite the relatively rapid pace of development of the first generation of urban models, these models were perceived as being too large, too expensive, too reliant on extensive data, and therefore, inadequate in offering critical and reliable information planners needed in formulating long range plans. A seminal article written by Douglas Lee in 1973 called "Requiem for Large Scale Models" was significant in substantially slowing down research and application of urban models. Lee noted "seven sins of large scale models" that together rendered the first generation of models irrelevant to the new directions in which planning was headed.[2,3] Regardless, urban models continued to progress and mature, while computers became more powerful and data management, less onerous with the advent of Geographic Information System (GIS) technologies. A second generation of models began to take shape, albeit more self-consciously and with more humble objectives.

# The Second Generation of Urban Models

The second-generation urban models followed two general approaches. The first is rule-based **land classification** that would assign all land parcels a "suitability" score for various forms of development. The second approach follows from the well-known **discrete choice models** developed by Daniel McFadden, which won him the Nobel Prize in economics. Both these approaches were enabled by rapid advances in computing and geographic information systems technologies, together with the proliferation of the Internet, which brought high performance computing to individual desktops.

The **suitability score** approach originated from landscape analysis, particularly through Ian McHarg's most celebrated book called "Design with Nature" (1969). McHarg popularized the "overlay method" in which transparent map layers, each containing information about one particular aspect of land (slope, soil type, land use, vegetation, floodplain, drainage, etc.), are overlaid to identify suitable areas that can be developed with minimum disruption to the natural environment. This approach became one of the primary functions of Geographic Information Systems (GIS), especially in the formative years of Arc/Info (ESRI). The overlay approach was also the foundation for the **Land Evaluation/Site Assessment** (LESA) technique adopted by the U.S. Department of Agriculture (USDA) in evaluating the suitability of land parcels for agriculture, conservation or development. This technique essentially assigned scores to a set of land attributes (land evaluation, or LE) and site characteristics (site assessment, or SA), which were individually weighted according to their importance

**Land classification** - a system for categorizing land according to the use and the physical attributes of that piece of land. Several such schemes are now used; the most common being the USGS Anderson Land Classification Scheme.

**Discrete choice models** - models examining choices between two or more alternatives such as choosing between different modes of transport or between different residential locations.

**Suitability score** - a score assigned to different plots of land according to its suitability for development.

**Land Evaluation/Site Assessment (LESA)** - a point-based approach for rating the relative importance of agricultural land resources based upon specific measurable features. The land evaluation component measures soil quality, while the site assessment component evaluates the site's importance for agricultural activities in relation to conservation or development potential.

for a particular use. These scores were then aggregated to determine which parcels were most suitable for that use.

The basic tenets of the land-suitability approach (adopted for the urban context) is implemented in an urban model called "What If?" developed by Richard Klosterman of What If?, Inc.[4,5] The approach incorporated development capability of different predetermined spatial units of land reflected in a suitability score. While the technique relies on significant amount of user input, the process is primarily based on assumptions about growth, public policies, and decision rules supplied by the users, mostly as weights for physical and locational characteristics of parcels that are suitable for particular developments or for conservation. Klosterman emphasizes that the "What if" method is not a forecasting tool but a planning support tool that shows *What* would happen *If*: a) particular development policies are enacted; b) growth assumptions prove to be true; and 3) the user supplied suitability scores are appropriate and reasonable.

A variation of the suitability approach was implemented in California Urban Futures (CUF 1) model developed by John Landis and his team at Berkeley.[6,7] Suitability for development in this model was based on "profitability" rather than physical and environmental constraints assumed by the user. In CUF 1, as in What If?, the units of land were synthetically created from land attributes; hence, they have no legal existence. These parcels are constructs generated from spatial intersection and /or union of various land attributes such as zoning, slopes, density, distance from transport infrastructure, and others. Landis called them developable land units or DLUs. These DLUs ranged in size from one to several hundred acres.

In CUF 1, each DLU was assigned a profitability score based on estimated costs of development in that land unit. Only residential developments were considered in this first version. The future residential growth in the region (calculated separately for counties and cities) was then allocated according to profitability rankings of the DLUs. A subsequent process examined the growing DLUs adjacent to the urban areas to determine if they should be incorporated within the city boundaries. The process stopped when all residential growth was allocated to the cities and unincorporated areas in the county. Although CUF1 adopted a market-based approach, it assumed that profitability is independent of demand characteristics and purely a function of costs of residential development. In other words, the initial estimate of growth was not affected by demand parameters, which would presumably impact congestion levels and cost of living and thereby moderate growth.[8] Also, given that no other types of land uses were considered, other types of development (commercial, retail, industrial, etc.) could not compete for land parcels (DLUs). Therefore, CUF 1 was quite limited in its scope and ability to capture land-market dynamics.

The second generation of California Urban Futures model, CUF 2, made several improvements over its predecessor, CUF-1, described above. First, it incorporated and predicted different land use types, including commercial, single- and multi-family residential, industrial, and so on. This version of the model predicted land use transitions from vacant to each of the above-mentioned land use types and also redevelopment from one use to another. Second, the spatial unit of analysis was now 100m × 100m (1 hectare) grid cells instead of the DLUs of CUF-1. Third, it generated job forecasts for each of the three-digit NAICS industry sectors through separate econometric models to determine employment growth. The employment growth parameters are then used to drive the demand in commercial and industrial land uses.

Finally and importantly, CUF-2 was among the first land use models to implement a statistical framework based on a theory called the "random utility theory," which allowed estimation of probabilities of discrete events. Discrete events are unique and exclusive activities within a set of possible activities that can occur. For example, a commuter can choose among a set of unique mode choices such as self-driven auto, carpool, or transit. Only one option (a discrete event), say, self-driven auto, is finally chosen, at which point the others, carpool and transit, are rejected (exclusive). Land use change is also a similar discrete event since each type of land use is unique and exclusive. Once a group of parcels is designated as "residential," we would (at least in theory) eliminate all other uses. CUF-2 implemented a statistical technique known as "multinomial logit" to estimate the probabilities of land use change to any one of the discrete land use types or between them. This form of modeling based on "random utility" theory using "multinomial logit" techniques is now pervasive in the current generation of urban and transportation models.

## The New Era of Urban Environmental Models

The evolution of urban and environmental models has accelerated since the new millennium. Advances in computation can now allow complex dynamic simulations at a fine spatial and temporal scale. So, we can now look closely at how neighboring land uses and activities are influencing a specific parcel and how this influence is changing at regular temporal intervals (yearly, quarterly, etc.). Also, as discussed previously, the random utility theory has been instrumental in expanding the range of competing activities we can model. A good example of such a highly disaggregated and spatially as well as temporally dynamic model that is becoming a "gold standard" in metropolitan planning organizations is *UrbanSim*.[9,10] UrbanSim has been in active development since the late-1990s, first at the University of Washington and now at the University of California at Berkeley. In 2005, UrbanSim was completely re-engineered to adopt a more extensible and modular platform called OPUS based on the Python code. As of this writing, OPUS is already in version 4.4 (http://urbansim.org).

### UrbanSim

UrbanSim introduced several innovations in the field of urban environmental models. First, it is a highly disaggregated model with each household, business, and developer behaving as a "decision-making agent." The interplay of these individual decisions leads to the final outcome of their location in space. This form of modeling from the bottom-up is also known as "agent-based" modeling. UrbanSim explicitly models each household's decision to locate in or relocate to a neighborhood in the metropolitan area. Similarly, every business is identified and location and relocation decisions estimated.

Second, new developments in the real estate sector are predicted by modeling the change in land prices. Previously, few urban models included real estate prices in their estimation. Third, the changes in travel behavior and its impact on locational and development decisions are explicitly incorporated in the modeling platform by

**UrbanSim San Fransisco Buildout**

interfacing UrbanSim with a travel demand model. Therefore, UrbanSim is usually run in tandem with a separate travel demand model given that this feature is not included in the current platform.

Finally, UrbanSim and OPUS are under active development with new features being added in relatively quick succession. UrbanSim now includes a graphical user interface (GUI) that shows all the models and datasets in one place, provides drop-down, user selectable commands to run the models, and shows geographic information systems based maps of the output. The most recent version also includes a module to "evolve" the households as they age over the period of the simulation. That is, households are no longer static entities throughout 20- or 30-year horizons, but grow and or split up due to marriage, educational choices, dissolution of marriages, new births, and deaths. Very soon, a 3-D platform will also be included with the UrbanSim portfolio of tools for immersive visualization and scenario development.

Several other models are also being developed and tested at different parts of the world. Some, such as TLUMIP2 (Oregon) and IRPUD (Dortmund, Germany), are similar to UrbanSim in their approach in terms of their level of spatial disaggregation and the explicit modeling of individual agent behavior. Other modeling approaches include **cellular automata** (such as CLUE and SLEUTH) and system dynamics (similar to Forrester's model described earlier). Many previous studies have categorized and evaluated urban land use/transport/environmental models based on attributes such as the level of disaggregation, the ability to incorporate dynamics, methodological approach, and whether they are region specific or generic. Readers are especially directed to the reviews by Haase and Schwarz,[11] Aggarwal[12] et al., and Wegener[13] for more in-depth examination of the different model characteristics.

**Cellular automata -** a collection of "cells" on a grid where each cell is affected by the condition of its neighboring cells according to a set of predetermined rules.

## Modeling with Cellular Automata

Cellular automata consists of an array of similar "cells" that are arranged in a two-dimensional lattice where each cell is affected by changes in the state of its neighbors. Cells in the automata have different discrete states (e.g., dead or alive; residential, commercial, industrial, or vacant). Also, the state of a cell changes based on the aggregate changes in adjacent cell states according to a predetermined rule. Imagine, for example, a neighborhood with a group of identical houses and one of the houses in the middle of this neighborhood is abandoned and falls into disrepair. Very soon, the households in the houses immediately adjacent to it will begin to resent this eyesore and move out of the neighborhood by underpricing their houses (since buyers will demand a discount to have the abandoned property next door). This in turn affects other houses adjacent to the first wave of home sales, and they drop in value as well. This devaluation will continue until the values are low enough for an investor to buy up several of the properties and redevelop them to the latest standards, which triggers a virtuous cycle in home values. Cellular automata models can capture this process of decline and redevelopment of housing.

One of the most celebrated examples of a land use model based on cellular automata is SLEUTH. The acronym is based on the six attributes that the model uses to drive urban growth—slope, land use, exclusion, urban extent, transportation, and hillshade. These six types of data are provided as input tables for a gridded map, where each grid represents a "cell." Based on several years of information on these parameters, five rules of transition for each cell are determined. These transition rules are based on: a) diffusion (controlling overall scatter of growth); b) breed (like-lihood of new settlements being generated); c) spread (growth outward and inward from an existing cluster); slope (a resistance parameter and threshold beyond which development does not happen); and roads (an attraction parameter). The process of figuring out the appropriate parameters for the five transition rules is called *calibra-tion*. The calibration process actually proceeds in three sequential stages where at each stage, 13 different goodness-of-fit measures are evaluated and the best values for the transition rules extracted. The final calibration parameters are used for simulating future changes in land use.

## Advancing Sustainability through Urban Models

How do urban models help us in making decisions about urban sustainability? In the early years of urban modeling, sustainability was not a term that was part of an urban planner's lexicon. Regardless, the objective of urban models was to illus-trate, in visual and tabular form, how the future of urban regions will evolve based on past trends and an assumed set of social and individual decisions over the simula-tion period. This orientation toward a future that is deliberately planned to provide adequate resources for meeting the needs of future populations makes the process of urban modeling also appropriate for discussing issues of sustainability. A substan-tial component of sustainability falls within the narrow concerns of land use and transportation, which has been the bedrock of all urban models. The distribution of human activities within urban space as reflected in land use patterns impact a range of core issues of sustainability including energy use, open space preservation, protection of ecological resources, pollution, and social equity, among others. Travel behavior is substantially influenced by land use patterns; hence land use and transportation are modeled together. The transportation sector consumes 28% of carbon-based energy in the United States and responsible for commensurate amount of greenhouse gas emissions. Transportation is therefore among the most important components of urban sustainability.

Most metropolitan planning organizations (MPOs) in the United States have invested in developing urban modeling capacity in-house to coordinate regional planning efforts. One principle impetus for using urban models at this level of metropolitan governance is to meet air quality standards as mandated by the Environmental Protection Agency (USEPA). Failure to meet the air quality standards triggers a series of actions that could result in withholding federal highway dollars for the region. Urban land use and transportation models are used to demonstrate how a non-complying region will improve air quality through a coordinated set of actions such as increasing carpooling and transit use and reducing self-driven automobiles. MPOs also use urban models for engaging the community in making long-range decisions by showing how the decisions they make result in urban growth scenarios and the implications of such growth for the environment and quality of life.

The new generation of urban models is bringing ecological, urban, and social dynamics closer together. Critical challenges of integrating the different modeling domains remain since each developed under different theoretical and methodological traditions. For example, ecological models examine competition among species to predict abundance, distribution, and other characteristics of organisms co-located in a habitat. These models reflect nonlinear dynamics and critical thresholds through time. In contrast, socio-behavioral models are often based on economic theories of static equilibrium, such as equating demand and supply of goods and services. Recent advances in **agent-based models** have brought the two traditions closer together.

Agent-based models mimic the goal-seeking behavior of autonomous agents who interact with each other to maximize their utility while generating higher-level patterns and rules. Therefore, these models are highly disaggregated and built from the bottom up. The process of building such models involves assigning each agent with a set of rules based on the specific attributes of its environment (which includes other agents). For example, one rule might be "if another agent or an obstacle is sensed directly in front on the path of motion, move to the right." Yet another could be "if more than two agents or a large obstacle is sensed in front on the path of motion, turn around and head back." Highly complex agent-based models will have a large set of such "if—then" rules for each type of agent—and there could be many different types of agents. The larger objective of building such models is to determine if simple rules of behavior of different agents lead to more complex "emergent" properties that we may or may not have expected.

A simple example of an agent-based model can illustrate its basic principles. Consider a metropolitan region comprising two types of agents—city households and suburban households. Both these types of households tend to remain in their present location unless they realize that they are better off moving. City households move to the suburbs if they find that the taxes they are paying compared to the investments in city infrastructure is higher in the city than in the suburbs. In other words, city households move to the suburbs if, for example, more and more people end up moving to the suburbs (with far fewer jobs moving in that direction) or the transportation infrastructure gets congested and commutes get longer. At some point, many suburban households will move to the city to get relief from long and stressful commutes. Equilibrium will be reached when the number of households coming from the city matches the number moving back to the city from the suburbs. At this point, the size

**Agent-based model** - a class of computational models that simulate the behavior of autonomous agents in relation to each other and observe the patterns that emerge from such interaction.

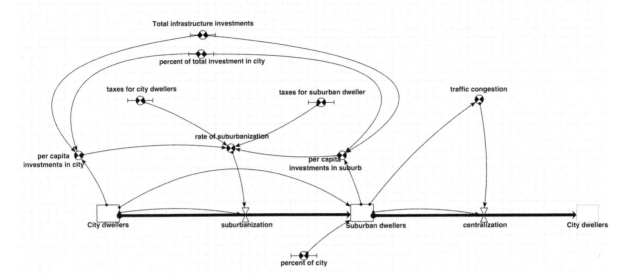

Total infrastructure investments

percent of total investment in city

taxes for city dwellers

taxes for suburban dweller

traffic congestion

rate of suburbanization

per capita investments in city

per capita investments in suburb

City dwellers

suburbanization

Suburban dwellers

centralization

City dwellers

percent of city

**City-suburb dynamics and subsequent equilibrium**

of the city and suburb will stabilize until taxes and investments are changed again. For simplicity, no increase in population through natural growth or migration from other regions is considered in this model.

This phenomenon of city-suburb dynamics and subsequent equilibrium can be represented by the model shown here. The figure depicts a very specific form of graphic representation of stocks, flows, and influences, pioneered by Jay Forrester mentioned earlier. City households and suburban households are represented by boxes or stocks since they "contain" households that flow in or out of them based on the rules suggested above. All other variables, such as taxes, investments, congestion levels, and other derived variables, influence the rate of suburbanization and centralization. We begin exploring this model by setting up some reasonable parameters such as:

Starting number of city households: 100,000

Suburban households: 10% of the city (so 10,000)

Total infrastructure investments (annual): $10,000,000

Percent of total investments for city: 60% (the rest goes to the suburbs)

Taxes for city dwellers (annual): 1000/household

Taxes for suburban dwellers (annual): 500/household

Using the values above to drive the model in image on next page, we find that the trend to suburbanize at low levels of congestion is strong, but increasing the congestion levels leads to an equilibrium condition where the flows out of the city to the suburbs equals the flows in the reverse direction. Suburbs gain population at the expense of the city under most circumstances. However, in one scenario, city gains population when it receives 90% of the total investments, but imposes a tax that is only 50% of what suburban households pay.

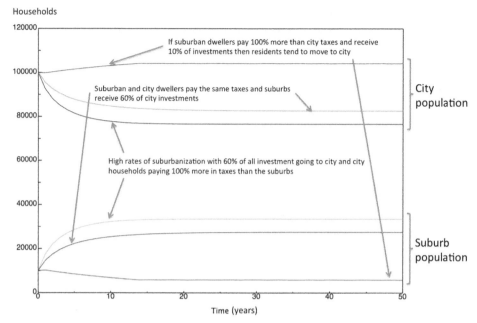

Households

| | | |
|---|---|---|

*Graph Y-axis labels (Households):* 120000, 100000, 80000, 60000, 40000, 20000, 0

*Annotations on graph:*

If suburban dwellers pay 100% more than city taxes and receive 10% of investments then residents tend to move to city

Suburban and city dwellers pay the same taxes and suburbs receive 60% of city investments

High rates of suburbanization with 60% of all investment going to city and city households paying 100% more in taxes than the suburbs

City population

Suburb population

Time (years)

**Change in household distribution between city and suburb over 50 years for different tax and investment scenarios.**

Once the model is set up and offering logically consistent results, it can be used to address questions through experimental (trial-and-error) methods. For example, one obvious question that arises from the model runs above is: *What level of taxation and investment would make the relative movement of people between the city and suburb negligible?* By making small adjustments to the parameters and checking the results, one can incrementally arrive at the answer to the question. It turns out that if the city residents were paying about 11% lower taxes per household than suburban residents but receiving 90% of the total investments (remember, they are 90% of total metropolitan population), then the city population (and concomitantly, the suburban population) remains more or less unchanged.

Understanding where people are choosing to live and why provides a critical input for estimating sustainability parameters of the region. One obvious implication of how the population and employment are distributed in a region is the resulting impact on travel behavior. If housing is dispersed and jobs are concentrated in the center, a significant number of people may be experiencing long commutes. Assuming that these commuters drive to work (which is more than 85% of all trips), the resulting implications for energy demands, fossil fuel use, air pollution, and climate-changing carbon emissions would make the region less sustainable. However, if alternative forms of mobility, such as transit systems, were available, the adverse impact on the environment would be lower.

Besides impacting travel, the location and distribution of jobs and housing also influence several other aspects of sustainability. As a city sprawls and develops low-density suburbs, it encroaches upon agricultural land and compromises biodiversity by destroying some habitats. The low-density form of development with its concomitant long commutes reduces social contacts and increases isolation of social groups. Large private yards also require more water for maintenance and upkeep. On the other hand, high-density developments in central areas can also have adverse effects on sustainability if the high concentration of heat-absorbing materials, such as concrete and asphalt, leads to urban-heat island effects. These materials absorb the radiant energy of the sun during the day and release that in the night thereby keeping the nighttime temperatures higher than surrounding areas. The high nighttime temperatures lead to higher levels of air pollution, higher energy demands for cooling, more water, and more heat related illnesses. Therefore, determining the optimum levels of density and dispersal of different land uses to achieve urban sustainability requires the use of sophisticated urban models that can balance the multiple positive and negative influences and offer guidance for planning.

# Where Are We Headed?

We are now witnessing the confluence of several technological and social trends that is revolutionizing the way we interact with our physical surroundings and with each other. High-speed communication networks, mostly in the urban locations, have integrated many of the city functions such as transport, service delivery, and emergency management. Devices that sense locations, see objects, and measure the ambient environment (temperature, noise, air quality, and other activities) are everywhere. You are probably holding one such device in your hand, which is also known as a smartphone. It is now possible to track the flow of people and crowds through different parts of the city with the help of cellphone records. This could be complemented with information about the most significant events that are happening by capturing the data from social media like Twitter feeds.

## ▰ LESSONS LEARNED FOR ACHIEVING SUSTAINABILITY

Urban models are designed to portray the future state of a region by showing how their essential functions are going to change and how these functions may be accommodated in space. Where people live and work, how they travel, what buildings they use, and how they spend their leisure are important questions for determining the sustainability of that region. By projecting social behavior and conditions of urban life into the future, urban models also allow us to estimate the amount of energy, water, and open space that will be needed. In addition, they can inform us about the quality of air, water, and land we will inherit in that future. However, urban models are not omniscient; that is, they only project what we can imagine. It is only our imagination and our ability to form mental models that ultimately allow us to contemplate and envision urban sustainability. Urban models are the tools to make our mental models correspond to reality.

## Supplemental Readings

Batty, M. (2005). *Cities and complexity: Understanding cities through cellular automata, agent-based models, and fractals.* Cambridge, MA: MIT Press.

Miller, E. J. (2009). Integrated urban models: theoretical prospects. the expanding sphere of travel behaviour research. In Ryuichi Kitamura, Toshio Yoshii and Toshiyuki Yamamoto (Eds.), *Selected Papers from the 11th International*

*Conference on Travel Behaviour Research*. Chapter 14, pp. 351–384, Bingley, U.K.: Emerald Group Publishing Limited.

Santé, I., García, A. M., Miranda, D., & Crecente, R. (2010). Cellular automata models for the simulation of real-world urban processes: A review and analysis. *Landscape and Urban Planning*, *96*(2), 108–122. doi:10.1016/j.landurbplan.2010.03.001

Schwarz, N., Haase, D., & Seppelt, R. (2010). Omnipresent sprawl? A review of urban simulation models with respect to urban shrinkage. *Environment and Planning B-Planning and Design*, *37*(2), 265–283.

# DISCUSSION QUESTIONS

1. How do land use and transportation models inform future environmental conditions in an urban area? Draw a schematic diagram showing the linkages between various aspects of land use and transportation, together with their effects on air quality, energy use, and open space.

2. Discuss how the proliferation of electric mobility (electric vehicles and electrified transit) will change our current notions of sustainability of sprawling urban regions.

3. The example shown in the figures assume that residential choice is principally determined by the variation in taxes and investments in infrastructure in cities and suburbs together with congestion levels during commute. Are there other important factors that drive residential location choice?

# Course Assignments: Learning Outcomes in Sustainability Education

*K. David Pijawka*
*Martin A. Gromulat*

## Introduction

In this chapter, we have provided the assignments given in the *Sustainable Cities* class at Arizona State University. *Sustainable Cities* is an undergraduate course that introduces students to the concepts of sustainability and sustainable development of cities at the global, regional, and local scales. The course covers some of the most pressing environmental, socio-economic, and structural problems facing cities today, and their consequences on the natural and built environments. Topics covered in the course include the urban heat island effect, resource consumption, land use change, transportation, energy, waste management, and environmental justice and quality of life, as well as attendant current and possible future negative effects of these externalities on cities and how such impacts can be mitigated or prevented in terms of sustainable solutions.

This chapter specifically looks at one important method for meeting the objectives of sustainability competencies—the assignments given to the students. We selected the following assignments, which were given to students over a six-year period in the course, and explain why we developed these and what we hoped the students would gain from them. Each assignment includes a preface centered on learning outcomes and objectives, and is connected to at least one of the content chapters in the text.

The framework for this textbook is to incorporate sustainability learning from the perspective of cities; integrate sustainability within an urban context to see the connections between sustainability concepts, cases, and illustrations of these concepts; and suggest solutions to urban sustainability problems. The assignments implore students to recognize the inherent connectivity between theoretical ideas in sustainability and real-world problem solving by encouraging critical thinking outside of the classroom and, furthermore, by encouraging exploration or re-exploration of their own neighborhood or city in an attempt to gain real-world knowledge.

By way of background, the course roughly follows this sequence: after an introduction to the history and philosophy of sustainability and the evolution of cities, students learn about sustainable alternatives and mechanisms in current and future urban structures and dynamics. Technological, social, and cultural innovations for sustainable cities throughout the globe are addressed during the course. The class also presents state-of-the-art theory and practice of urban sustainability, including topics such as the ecological footprint, green buildings, regenerative design, life-cycle assessment, urban sustainability indicators, energy alternatives, urban vulnerability, resilience, and environmental justice, among other areas from local to global scales.

The goals of the course are for students to develop an appreciation of interdisciplinary learning through a focus on sustainability and an understanding of the concepts, theories, and practices of urban sustainability on a local, regional, and global scale. The assignments aim to provide students with practical experience and foster the ability to think critically about real-world problems, planning, and design, and to learn how to connect the key concepts and theories to the practice of urban sustainability.

The *Sustainable Cities* class was also selected as one of only a few university-wide courses that was granted approval to provide extra credit for Honors students. We have weekly meetings with our undergraduate students from Barrett, The Honors College at Arizona State University, outside of lectures in small group conference settings, and we will discuss some successful learning outcomes they achieved below. We also required these students to take on an additional assignment.

The class assignments were developed to provide the following important competencies and learning outcomes as identified recently in sustainability education scholarship:

1. Develop a working vocabulary in sustainability and build exposure to interdisciplinary vocabularies and foundational skill sets;

2. Encourage "out of the classroom" learning to increase chances of experiencing firsthand, real-world sustainability situations and applications;

3. Increase communication-building and leadership skills through collaborative group assignments with student teams and assignments that call for interaction with the local community;

4. Foster critical thinking skills, the importance of questioning assumptions, authority, and scientific findings, and the consideration of the vital role of values and ethics;

5. Increase student knowledge in analytical and planning skills to better prepare students for confronting community-related sustainability issues;

6. Gain an understanding of the importance of participatory fieldwork and experiential learning experiences;

7. Develop experience with community visioning processes and the role of sustainability in city futures;

8. Provide exposure to diverse styles and methods (pedagogies) of educational learning experiences to increase chances of increased personal growth; and,

9. Gain an appreciation of the connections between physical and social dimensions in deep, personal learning experiences.

Based on the class structure, I have developed and given the following assignments for several years. These assignments have been refined over time, and I offer them here as examples that have successfully achieved the desired learning outcomes described before each assignment. Furthermore, the assignments are appropriate for undergraduate students new or fairly new to sustainability, and help accomplish the objectives of sustainability education. Importantly, the assignments have proven to be effective, as evidenced by positive student feedback both personally and in the high ratings given by students in course evaluation surveys.

Additionally, the assignments encourage students to critically think about and apply the theories and concepts of sustainability in their own surroundings. This example of student work-product is from a compilation of independent research conducted by Honors students at Arizona State University in the *Sustainable Cities* course. The goal of the project was to measure the sustainability of the City of Phoenix in various sectors, spanning from food to infrastructure. One aspect of the assignment focused on the sustainability of Phoenix as measured by the existence of LEED (Leadership in Energy and Environmental Design Program) certified buildings. One recent student team's paper, *Exploring Urban Sustainability in Metropolitan Phoenix, AZ* "concluded that the city of Phoenix and the state of Arizona have made clear strides toward becoming leaders in sustainability. However, there are other major cities and states that have shown to have made even further strides and advances toward becoming more environmentally responsible and are the true leaders of sustainability. There are ways in which they can become more prevalent national leaders in environmental sustainability, such as mandating new construction to meet a minimum LEED-Silver certification level, providing incentives to meet those new standards or go beyond them, spreading the word on how feasible becoming more sustainable is and why it matters, and increasing the population density of the urban and state landscapes."

These assignments or derivations of these assignments can be useful in other broad-based entry-level sustainability courses. For faculty teaching such a course as *Sustainable Cities*, these assignments can be modified to your own courses and used as a means of both enlightening students and assessing their development of key learning competencies. For students, we suggest advancing your knowledge of sustainability by completing these exercises on your own and thinking of them as an educational resource.

## Supplemental Readings

Barth, M., Godemann, J., Rieckmann, M., & Stoltenberg, U. (2007). "Developing key Competencies for sustainable development in higher education". *International Journal of Sustainability in Higher Education, 8*(4), 416–430.

Blewitt, J., & Cullinford, C., (Eds.), (2004). *The Sustainability Curriculum: The Challenge for Higher Education*. London: Earthscan.

Dale, A., (2005). "Sustainable development education and literacy". *International Journal of Sustainability in Higher Education, 7*(1), 34–56.

Sibbel, A., 2009. "Pathways toward sustainability through higher education". *International Journal of Sustainability in Higher education. 10*(1), 68–82.

# Assignment Number 1: *Envision the Sustainable City*

## LEARNING OUTCOMES

This assignment is the first one given in the Sustainable Cities class at the beginning of the semester, after students have read about sustainability and we have discussed it in class. This assignment follows a few weeks of immersion into a new framework we call Sustainability Thinking. Although this class is generally very large (approximately 450 students), students are divided into teams of four to discuss the various dimensions of sustainability, as well as the geographical scales in which it operates—from households, to neighborhoods, places, cities, and regions. Issues of values and ethics that influence sustainability are addressed in readings and lectures, and students are asked to discuss value assessments in the context of sustainability within their teams.

The assignment reflects some of the recent literature in sustainability education. The importance of self-reflection of living in a place, to understand the various dimensions of a neighborhood—social, physical space, economic, and environmental (both the natural and built environment) is recognized as a learning outcome. Moreover, this method of education builds on personal views on what makes places sustainable, especially going beyond just the traditional Brundtland definition, and seeing real-world connections and thinking within a transdisciplinary context. This assignment also asks students to think about the importance of values and visioning in sustainability, two issues identified in the Melbourne Principles.

## ASSIGNMENT

The environment that you grew up in and the experiences in your life up to this point have shaped and molded your view of sustainability as it relates to cities and the built environment. Use this assignment to explore how you view and perceive neighborhoods, cities, and regions. As you ponder and answer the questions below, ask yourself what role do your values play in perceiving sustainability, and what factors, if any, motivate you to develop or continue a green lifestyle?

### PART 1. Briefly describe one of the places where you grew up.

Answering the questions below, write at least 250 words about the place where you grew up.

1. Where did you grow up and what was it like?

2. What elements in the human or natural environment were important to your daily life?

3. With whom did you interact on a daily basis?

4. Where did you go and how did you get around?

5. What, if anything, about your life was sustainable?

## PART 2. Describe your vision of a sustainable city or neighborhood.

Write at least 250 words describing the sustainable neighborhood or city that you would like to see in the future. Imagine the ideal community—a place you would especially like to live in, and that is sustainable (in whatever way you want to define that term).

1. How is this place laid out in terms of streets, buildings, public spaces, parks, homes, workplaces, and shopping areas?

2. How do people get around?

3. What types of people live there, and how do they interact?

4. How does the built environment relate to the natural landscape?

5. What makes this place sustainable, and do you think it is possible to achieve?

## PART 3. Sustainability Theory (500–700 words)

1. How does your unique past affect your vision of the future and the way you choose to live your life today?

2. How do human values come into play when people think about sustainability?

# Assignment Number 2: *Sustainability Indicators*

## LEARNING OUTCOMES

Prior to completing this assignment, students were provided with course materials including coverage of sustainability measures and indicators. Of particular importance is to have students gain knowledge of how urban areas apply principles of sustainability and measure progress from municipal efforts in planning, environmental management, and policy. In this assignment, our goal is for students to understand the tangible differences between measures of conventional urban objectives, and those of sustainability and its attendant complexity. Moreover, it is important for students to comprehend the connections between theory and its practical application in communities because over 200 communities have various sustainability indicator programs. During lectures, the instructor should point out differences among various indicator programs and ask students why these differences occur, the characteristics of the differences, and the implications of these differences to sustainability solutions. The basis for these types of questions is to get students to think critically, be able to communicate about issues of urban sustainability policy and definitions, and understand the process of evaluation. In this exercise, the focus of the evaluation is on one indicator program. Another version of this assignment is to have students examine three indicator programs, and then critically evaluate any differences and draw conclusions about the varied possible outcomes between the three programs. This type of assignment is one that the students generally want more of; their expressed interest is on how to evaluate sustainability plans, programs, and policies. This type of assignment broadens the students' scope of study, enabling them to think critically about the policy/governance domain, which is very important in sustainability, and is an area in which students new to the field have likely had none to very little exposure.

## ASSIGNMENT

This assignment asks you to use what you have learned about sustainability indicators in course readings and lectures to analyze a municipal (city) government's sustainability indicator program.

### PART 1. Find and review a sustainability indicator program for a municipal government:

As an example, the website for Minneapolis, Minnesota's Sustainability Indicators can be found here (do not use this one for the assignment):

http://www.ci.minneapolis.mn.us/sustainability/indicators/ sustainability_indicators.

**PART 2. Answer the following questions in 750–1000 words, using at least three properly cited sources:**

1. What is the definition of a sustainability indicator, and how is it different from a typical urban indicator?

2. Describe the sustainability indicator program you chose.

3. What are the indicators that were used, and why do you think the municipality chose those particular ones?

4. How would you evaluate the effectiveness of the chosen indicators?

5. What changes could be made to improve the program, and why do you think they would help?

# Assignment Number 3: *Urban Sustainability Rating Systems (Ranking Greenness)*

## LEARNING OUTCOMES

The literature on education for sustainable development highlights the importance of providing knowledge on communities and places in terms of their sustainability or level of sustainability. The idea of measuring sustainability is debatable in terms of the philosophy behind sustainable places or the concept of sustainability itself, but the idea of developing criteria for measuring how sustainable a city is or how far it has to go to improve its sustainability is an important learning topic and is essential for students to know.

SustainLane.com is an online community where people who are interested in sustainability and green practices can connect with each other. The 2008 SustainLane U.S. City Rankings is a leading national survey that ranks the 50 most populous U.S. cities (according to 2004 Census data) in terms of their sustainability practices in 16 areas including, air quality, energy and climate change, local food and agriculture, planning and land use, and water supply. While the weight established for each criterion is unsettled, knowing why a city received the rating that it did is helpful as a learning device. Accordingly, it serves as an excellent educational tool and is used as the central element of this assignment.

The learning outcome of this assignment is not so much focused on the ranking mechanism, but on gaining knowledge of the various and divergent criteria that need to be incorporated into sustainable solutions. Like the various domains in sustainability—equity, economic well-being, social well-being, ecology/environment, health, and place-making, the criteria in SustainLane are multidimensional. Student will learn how to operationalize imprecise concepts and definitions into practical programs and plans—a transition from theory to practical application. To do this, students will interact with the SustainLane website, examine and evaluate what has been achieved in other cities, and should be encouraged to ask themselves questions such as "Can my city successfully adopt what was done elsewhere? Can we adapt from other models? Can new criteria that are more appropriate for my city be added?" Outcomes include gaining experience using an interdisciplinary approach, testing of the strengths of the approach, linking theory to practice, and critically examining why cities are ranked differently. It is important to let students know that there are no right or wrong answers. The assignment encourages discussion among students, innovation and creativity, and deep learning. This assignment also introduces students to the concept of interacting with local government officials, specifically when we ask students to draft a report to communicate their analysis to a city mayor in a similar assignment at the graduate school level.

This assignment can be given in two ways: 1) the instructor can choose one city and have all of the students complete the assignment for that city, or 2) students can be allowed to pick the city of their choice.

## ASSIGNMENT

SustainLane.com ranks the status of sustainability programs, policies, and practices for the nation's 50 largest cities. It covers 16 categories that include metro street congestion, air quality, tap water quality, city innovation, planning and land use, green economy, and energy and climate change. First, go to SustainLane.com (http://www.sustainlane.com/us-city-rankings/overall-rankings) and choose a city that is not in the top ten. The mayor of that city wants to be in the top ten and has asked you to draft a report with your analysis of how this can be achieved. This assignment asks you to identify those areas where your city needs to change to make it into the top ten.

Take a look at the list of cities both by Overall Rankings and by Study Categories.

Next, click on your city and read more about its strengths and weaknesses.

As you browse the website, pick a few areas where your city could improve and go to the Study Categories to learn more about how each topic is measured and considered.

Write 750 to 1000 words describing what you think your city could do to improve itself in those areas. Be specific and describe not only what you would change, but also how it might be accomplished, what challenges might be faced, and what other cities are doing to become more sustainable. You should draft your analysis into a report for your city's mayor.

# Assignment Number 4: *The Ecological Footprint*

## LEARNING OUTCOMES

The Ecological Footprint concept is fundamental to the understanding of sustainability and is discussed in Chapter 1. Generally, the Ecological Footprint measures humanity's demand on nature. We introduce this concept to the students in the first lecture of the course and illustrate it through a number of examples and exercises found in the literature. In one sense, the "Footprint" can be viewed as part of the definition of sustainability. There is no shortage of material on the topic, its use, and methodology, and it may be valuable to review the original source, *Our Ecological Footprint: Reducing Human Impact on the Earth*, written by Wackernagel and Rees, as well as other good sources and calculation exercises available on the Internet. Using the Ecological Footprint website (http://myfootprint.org), from the Center for Sustainable Economy, students are asked to estimate their own footprint and determine their personal consumption behavior. Specifically, students take the Ecological Footprint Quiz, which estimates the amount of land and ocean required to support their consumption of food, goods, services, housing, and energy, and assimilate their wastes on an annual basis. After answering 27 questions, students can compare their Ecological Footprint to others' and learn how to reduce their impact on the earth.

The goal is for students to understand the consequences of the overconsumption of resources to meet their needs—the reality of their behavior in relation to the earth's resources and resulting global biocapacity deficit. In terms of educational outcomes, knowledge about larger sustainability issues is gained by starting from a personal, value-based level. The material on sustainability competencies calls for ethics based evaluation and critical thinking about changes in behavior, both at the individual and societal levels. To achieve these competencies, the assignment exposes students to the reality of their individual consumption behaviors and resultant costs to the planet. Additionally, we have found that the assignment has inspired students to think about individual ethics, especially when they begin to recognize the importance of their own consumption from local to global transformations, particularly in terms of volume of waste products, life-cycle costs, carbon dioxide emissions, and possible justice issues. The assignment also asks students to evaluate how they can best lower their footprint. According to end-of-the-semester assignment surveys, students were highly motivated by this assignment (relative to the other course assignments), with over 80% indicating that this assignment resulted in personal behavioral changes.

## ASSIGNMENT

Determining your individual Ecological Footprint will help you begin to analyze and determine what personal steps you can take to live greener.

### PART 1. Go to www.myfootprint.org and take the Ecological Footprint Quiz (it may be helpful to take notes about your impact as you progress through the Quiz).

After completing the Quiz, you should save the results. Then retake the Quiz and change the parameters to reflect different resource usage levels. You may answer the questions using your current lifestyle and living conditions if you live on campus, or you may choose to answer as if you were living at home.

### PART 2. Write a report in 750 to 1000 words answering the following questions:

1. What is an Ecological Footprint?

2. What were the results of your test and what, if anything, did you find surprising or noteworthy?

3. What changes can you make in your life to reduce your Ecological Footprint?

4. If everyone lived like you do, how many earths would be needed to sustain the population, and what does that mean? (Why can't we continue consuming resources at the current rate? What would happen if nothing were done?)

5. What changes would you suggest to others to reduce their Footprint?

6. What is the relationship between changes in your consumption level and your Footprint? (What happens to your Footprint as your consumption level changes?) Why is this significant?

7. What are the two most significant categories of your Ecological Footprint and why?

8. What adjustments would you make to these two categories to significantly reduce their environmental impact?

9. What have you learned from working through this process?

# Assignment Number 5: *Local Food Systems*

## LEARNING OUTCOMES

Within sustainability, there is growing interest in looking at local food systems as a means to enhance the sustainability of cities and regions. Chapter 10 explores the various issues of urban agriculture as a topic of sustainability because it has implications for urban economies, social networking, health and "food deserts" (also Chapter 4), land coverage, urban infill, community-building and sense of place, and self-sufficiency. In this assignment, students are asked to view Food Inc., a documentary on the nation's food industry that argues that our food supply is now managed by a few corporations that seemingly put profit before health, and in the process cause hardship for the family farmer, and pollute the environment. The filmmaker advises that although this has resulted in "benefits" such as bigger-breasted chickens and tomatoes that won't spoil, unintended consequences include new strains of E. coli, the toxic bacteria that makes approximately 73,000 people ill each year, higher levels of obesity, and an increased amount of adult diabetes.

This documentary is shown following readings and lectures on local food systems. Utilizing a documentary as a learning tool has merit because the learning outcome literature calls for applying a variety of pedagogies, especially in light of differing learning styles. We sought to attain several learning outcomes through this exercise. First, the film is somewhat provocative, and the assignment asks students to critically think about food production and reflect on its role in sustainability through a reflective essay. Second, several of the questions that students must answer require personal responses to the film and the values it questions. Reflecting on and discussing the role of ethics and values are important aspects of sustainability education. We ask students to take a position and form an argument over the importance of "local" in food systems and how to make food systems more resilient. Answering this requires them to think critically about resiliency from a different perspective than others they have to read in the course such as on renewable energy systems.

## ASSIGNMENT

Watch the documentary Food, Inc., which is about our nation's food industry and can be seen here: http://vimeo.com/34457916. Then, in at least 1,000 words, write a personal reflection essay about the movie by answering the following questions:

1. What were your initial thoughts after watching the documentary?

2. Do you think that the movie provided a fair perspective on the American agricultural system?

3. What are your feelings about where your food comes from? Why is where your food comes from important?

4. Do you feel compelled to change any of your eating and purchasing habits after watching Food, Inc.?

5. Why does food matter to the sustainability of cities or local communities? (Include at least two properly cited references.)

6. What are some of the things that you think could be done to make our food system more resilient?

7. Do you agree or disagree with the following statement and why: "For a restaurant to be sustainable, it should only offer food that is produced within 200 miles of its location."

# Assignment Number 6: *Resilient Cities*

## LEARNING OUTCOMES

The concept of resiliency within a sustainability framework is discussed in Chapter 1. As taught in my *Sustainable Cities* course (and in pertinent literature), resiliency is a key principle in helping define and frame sustainability. The concept of resiliency is woven throughout the course and appears in the course's coverage of social-ecological systems, Global Climate Change, disaster recovery planning, anticipatory governance, community and place making, and in energy alternatives, among other topics. In addition to providing lecture materials and separate readings on resiliency, the students in this class are required to read and discuss *Resilient Cities: Responding to Peak Oil and Climate Change* written by Newman, Beatley, and Boyer in 2009. However, the following assignment can be given without requiring that this book be read.

As a learning outcome, our goal is for students to understand what resiliency means and how it can be applied as a fundamental building block to various urban conditions and varying geographical scales: neighborhoods, cities, and regions. Therefore, we ask students to select a city and examine its characteristics in terms of resiliency. We seek to have students learn how to examine resiliency from a particular perspective, for example, renewable, small-scale energy systems, and translate the underlying logic from that scenario to other areas of resiliency, such as that found in an unfamiliar city. The goal is in developing a skill set in sustainability where knowledge can be transferred. For instance, students are asked to apply their knowledge of resiliency in one system to develop a plan or program for building resiliency in another, potentially unrelated, system. Certainly, such a plan requires knowledge of what resiliency means in urban environments and a holistic view of the issue. This is a necessary approach to teaching students about the transference of knowledge required in sustainability education.

## ASSIGNMENT

Consider the following quote from *Resilient Cities: Responding to Peak Oil and Climate Change*: "Resilience can be applied to cities. They too need to last, to respond to crises and adapt in a way that may cause them to change and grow differently; cities require an inner strength, a resolve, as well as a strong physical infrastructure and built environment" (Newman, Beatley, & Boyer, 2009).

For this assignment, choose a U.S. city that you are familiar with or one you would like to learn more about. After choosing a city, write at least 1,000 words answering the questions below. Before tackling the questions, you may find it helpful to review the Building Resilient Regions website, and specifically its Resilience Capacity Index, which provides data and ranks 361 U.S. metropolitan areas in terms of their resiliency:

http://brr.berkeley.edu/

1. Provide a brief introduction about the city and why you chose it.

2. What, if anything, makes this city vulnerable with regard to climate change and concerns about peak oil?

3. What might happen to this city in the future if it continues "business as usual" and no steps are taken to increase its resiliency?

4. What can be done to the city's built environment to increase its resiliency?

5. What can be done with the city's transportation systems to increase their resiliency?

6. What might be an effective way to implement a resiliency plan for this city, or improve upon an existing plan?

# Assignment Number 7: *Sustainable Plans, Programs, and Design: A Team-Based Approach*

## LEARNING OUTCOMES

There are certain classroom assignments that are difficult to undertake because the class is very large, or the students' skill set in methods and analysis have not yet fully developed in order to do original research. However, the education literature argues for "moving outside of the classroom" into the real-world of interaction with the community such as with "Participatory Action Research" or "Studio–Based Research." Students in an introductory broad-based course in urban sustainability will likely not have developed the necessary skill set or level of maturity to effectively communicate with professionals and the public, or fully appreciate the complexities and intricacies of community issues. However, over the years of teaching this course, collaborative group-based, real-world projects have worked quite successfully even in a class as large as my *Sustainable Cities* course, which routinely averages approximately 450 students each semester.

The learning outcome for this assignment is to identify a problem area within a city or region for which sustainability solutions could be applied to remedy, improve, or repair the problem, and have students "solve" the issue. It is important that the instructor help students view and dissect the problem within a perspective of sustainability—that is, for example, the conundrum of too many environmental resources being used for consumption because of wasteful systems, the overuse of nonrenewables, and other inefficiencies resulting in deleterious effects such as ever-increasing carbon dioxide emissions. Other examples include the minimal use of natural systems in cities, equity problems relating to food distribution and availability resulting in "food deserts" that disproportionally the poor, disadvantaged, and minority residents, and the failure to address neighborhood deterioration issues because of Brownfield locations. Because this assignment was given close to the end of the course, students were encouraged to take their recently acquired knowledge of sustainable cities and urban environmental problems from lectures, class readings, and prior assignments to identify a problem, discern the issues surrounding the problem, and explain how they would go about developing and implementing a remedy or mitigation action plan. Students formed teams, developed a proposal on the issue, and described how they were going to study the problem. This assignment is an applied project directed at improving a building, park, neighborhood, or transit system. The successful completion of the assignment achieves several learning outcomes: commitment to work collaboratively (and independently) as part of a group setting for several weeks, enhancement of communicative skills, allocation and implementation of individual tasks, and dealing with and resolving potential intragroup conflicts and tension.

Another learning outcome evident in this assignment is the development of a methods skill set for sustainability analysis. Students should be encouraged to document the information and data that they use to characterize the baseline or existing conditions and subsequent development of the data or measures to show how their plan or project improves the current conditions and by what magnitude. It may be a challenge to manage such an assignment in a large class, but it is well worth the extra preparatory time because the learning outcomes achieved and knowledge gained are paramount.

## ASSIGNMENT

Form student groups of four to seven students maximum.

Meet with your group and identify a problem area within a city or region for which sustainability solutions could be applied to remedy, improve, or repair the issue. The following are potential problems that are given to help you choose an area to examine:

- The inefficient use of environmental resources that cause or exacerbate deleterious effects such as increased carbon dioxide emissions;

- Equity problems that arise from unequal food distribution and availability resulting in "food deserts" that disproportionally impact the poor, disadvantaged, and minority residents; and

- The failure to address neighborhood deterioration issues because of Brownfield locations.

The written report of your project should follow this format:

- **Introduction:** Clearly state the issue your group will be exploring, why you chose it, and how sustainability offers a solution.

- **Literature Review:** Perform research and locate scholarly articles that have been written about the issue and potential solutions. Summarize and synthesize the literature in this section, addressing how the literature has informed your solution. Each team member should contribute literature on the issue.

- **Plan:** What is the plan or organization for the research/study/design your group is undertaking?

- **Methods Utilized in the Research:** What is your approach? How are you going to analyze the data and what data are you relying on?

- **Objectives:** What are the objectives of your research and plan? Why is it important to solve or mitigate the problem area that you have identified?

- **Baseline Conditions:** Identify the problem you have selected to address. Discuss the existing conditions of the place, building, or problem area.

- **Alternatives Analysis:** Are there alternative solutions to the problem? How does the alternative address the issue?

- **Conclusion:** Include a summary of your research and an analysis of the problem, as well as your group's recommendations on how to solve the problem.

Feel free to use GIS, photos, interviews, or other creative visual images or techniques to illustrate your point.

# Assignment Number 8: *MIST Urban Heat Island*

## LEARNING OUTCOMES

This assignment provides important learning outcomes for students in urban sustainability through the use of the Mitigation Impact Screening Tool (MIST) that can be found at this website: http://www.heatislandmitigationtool.com/Introduction.aspx. MIST provides accurate assessments of the likely impacts of heat island mitigation strategies at the city level. Through lectures and readings, students are introduced to the dynamics of Urban Heat Island (UHI) effects, causes, science, and its manifestation in cities because of building, road, and parking materials, urban vegetation distribution, water features, building design, and the nature of heat generating transportation and cooling systems (see Chapter 9). Understanding sustainability science is one of the objectives of exploring UHI because the impacts are largely anthropogenic and its reduction is a function of mitigation and adaptation strategies and policies. Accordingly, this assignment is an excellent example of sustainability science learning because the student learns about the relationships between ecological systems, material sciences, and urban design—the interactions between socio-ecological and physical systems in cities. The MIST assignment reveals to the student that human plans, programs, and policies can shape and modify deleterious effects that make cities less sustainable.

The MIST tool allows students to select a vegetation, albedo, or combined mitigation strategy, thereby providing them with the opportunity to model urban futures, change expected scenarios, and lessen adverse impacts. Therefore, students gain knowledge in the science of UHI and develop an understanding of the results of urban impacts through human decisions on design, materials, and other factors that can be controlled and modified. Because this assignment provides learning in cause and effect and intervening mechanisms that lead to a changed and improved environment, it is a compelling learning device for students in sustainability. For example, students will see firsthand how planting roof gardens and using alternative surface materials instead of asphalt directly result in a decrease in ambient temperatures. Envisioning urban futures, understanding the importance of sustainability science, learning systems thinking, and seeing how adaptive capacity works in the real world are important competencies in sustainability and the MIST assignment brings these to the foreground.

## ASSIGNMENT

Read about the Urban Heat Island on the U.S. EPA's website at:

http://www.epa.gov/heatisland/about/index.htm.

Then review the information found on the Mitigation Impact Screening Tool (MIST) website, paying particular attention to Mitigation Strategies (Albedo Modification, Vegetation Modification, and Temperature Reduction) and Impacts (Meteorological, Ozone, and Energy):

http://www.heatislandmitigationtool.com/.

Next, click on the MIST tool (http://www.heatislandmitigationtool.com/Inputs.aspx?t=1). Select a city, then the type of mitigation strategies you would like to implement, and run the tool to get the impacts.

Write a minimum of 500 words about why you chose the city, why you chose the specific mitigation strategies you did, and what different types of strategies you think would be most successful (such as to increase albedo you would create a city ordinance requiring homeowners to paint their roofs white). Be specific in the explanation of what strategies you would use. You may also brainstorm new strategies to achieve a reduction in the heat island effect, but anything you brainstorm needs to be backed up by evidence (you may look for examples of reduction methods being used in other places in the world and incorporate them into your paper).

# REFERENCES

## Introduction

1. Kates, R., Clark, W., Corell, R., Hall, J., Jaeger, C., Lowe, I., … Mooney, H. (2001). Sustainability science. *Science, 292*(5517), 641–642.

## Chapter 1

1. Pendall, .R., Foster, K. A., & Cowell, M. (2010). Resilience and regions: Building understanding of the metaphor. *Cambridge Journal of Regions, Economy and Society, 3*(1), 71–84.
2. Timothy, B. (2009). *Planning for coastal resilience: Best practices for calamitous times*. Washington, D.C: Island Press.
3. Building Resilient Regions website. Retrieved from http://brr.berkeley.edu/
4. Walker, B., & Salt, D. (2006). *Resilience thinking: Sustaining ecosystems and people in a changing world*. Washington DC: Island Press.

### Frieberg Case Study

1. Bündnis 90 and Die Grünen, Topics. Retrieved from http://www.gruene.de/themen.html
2. City of Freiburg, Freiburg's City Council. Retrieved from http://www.freiburg.de/servlet/PB/menu/1146382/index.html
3. Newman, P., Beatley, T., & Boyer, H. (2009). Resilient cities: *Responding to peak oil and climate change* Washington, D.C.: Island Press.
4. "Green City Freiburg," Freiburg. Retrieved from http://www.fwtm.freiburg.de/servlet/PB/menu/1182949_l2/index.html
5. Gregory, R. "Germany – Freiburg – Green City," "Germany – Freiburg – Green City," in The EcoTipping Points Project.
6. Newman, P., Beatley, T., & Boyer, H. Resilient Cities.
7. "Vauban.de: Stadtteil Vauban, Freiburg," Vauban. Retrieved from http://www.vauban.de/info/abstract.html

## Chapter 2

1. Our common future, Chapter 2: Towards sustainable development. UN Documents: Gathering a body of global agreements. Retrieved from http://www.un-documents.net/ocf-02.htm
2. Framing Sustainable Development: The Brundtland Report – 20 Years On. (2007). United Nations Commission on Sustainable Development. Retrieved from http://www.un.org/esa/sustdev/csd/csd15/media/backgrounder_brundtland.pdf

3. *Demographia World urban areas* (*World agglomerations*, 8th ed). (2012). Retrieved from http://www.demographia.com/db-worldua.pdf

4. Haiti two years after the earthquake. Humanitarian Response. Retrieved from http://haiti.humanitarianresponse.info/Default.aspx?tabid=208

5. Haiti: Humanitarian snapshot. (2012). Retrieved from http://reliefweb.int/node/499785

6. Diamond, J. (2006). *Collapse: How societies choose to fail or succeed.* New York, NY: Penguin Books.

7. Walker, B., & Salt, D. (2006). *Resilience thinking: Sustaining ecosystems and people in a changing world* (p. 46). Washington, DC: Island Press.

8. Beck, E. C. (1979). The love canal tragedy. United States Environmental Protection Agency. Retrieved from http://www.epa.gov/history/topics/lovecanal/01.html

9. Backgrounder on the three mile island accident. United States Nuclear Regulatory Commission. Retrieved from http://www.nrc.gov/reading-rm/doc-collections/fact-sheets/3mile-isle.html

10. The Second Annual Report of the Council on Environmental Quality. (1971). Retrieved from http://www.slideshare.net/whitehouse/august-1971-the-first-annual-report-of-the-council-on-environmental-quality

11. Levy, J. M. (2011). *Contemporary urban planning.* Boston, MA: Longman.

12. Shrogen, E. *For 30 Years, a political battle over oil and ANWR.* Retrieved from http://www.npr.org/templates/story/story.php?storyId=5007819

13. Keystone XL Pipeline. (2012). *New York Times.* Retrieved from http://topics.nytimes.com/top/reference/timestopics/subjects/k/keystone_pipeline/index.html?inline=nyt-classifier

14. Beatley, T. (2010). *Biophilic cities: Integrating nature into urban design and planning.* Island Press.

15. Global Footprint Network (website). Retrieved from http://www.footprintnetwork.org/en/index.php/GFN/page/basics_introduction/

# Chapter 3

1. Diamond, J. (2005). *Collapse: How societies choose to fail or succeed.* New York, NY: Penguin Group.

# Chapter 4

1. Lester, J. P., Hill, K. M., & Allen, D. W. (2001). *Environmental injustice in the United States: Myths and realities.* Boulder, CO: Westview Press.

2. EPA and Environmental Justice. U.S. Environmental Protection Agency (EPA). Retrieved from http://www.epa.gov/environmentaljustice/basics/index.html

3. Rechtschaffen, C., & Gauna, E. (2002). *Environmental justice: Law, policy, and regulation.* Durham, NC: Carolina Academic Press.

4. Ibid.

5. Ibid.

6. Ibid.

7. Environmental Justice. U.S. Environmental Protection Agency (EPA). Retrieved from http://www.epa.gov/compliance/ej/basics/ejbackground.html

8. Mohai, P., Pellow, D., & Roberts, J. T. (2009). Environmental justice. *Annual Review of Environment and Resources, 34*(1), 405–430.

9. Allen, W. (2012). *The good food revolution*. New York, NY: Gotham Books.

10. *Unlocking brownfields: Keys to community revitalization*. National Association of Local Governments Environmental Professionals. Retrieved from http://www.nalgep.org/ewebeditpro/items/O93F4460.pdf

11. Brownfields and land revitalization. U.S. Environmental Protection Agency (EPA). Retrieved from http://www.epa.gov/brownfields/basic_info.htm

12. Brownfields and land revitalization, Grants & Funding. U.S. Environmental Protection Agency. Retrieved from http://www.epa.gov/brownfields/grant_info/index.htm

13. Warner, K. D., & DeCosse, D. A short course in environmental ethics. Retrieved from http://www.scu.edu/ethics/practicing/focusareas/environmental_ethics/lesson4.html

14. Bullard, R. D. (Ed.). (2007). *Growing smarter: Achieving livable communities, environmental justice, and regional equity*. Cambridge, MA: MIT Press.

15. Smart growth. U.S. Environmental Protection Agency. Retrieved from http://www.epa.gov/smartgrowth/equitable_development_report.htm

# Chapter 5

1. Joint Monitoring Programme for Water Supply and Sanitation. (2012). *Progress on drinking water and sanitation: 2012 update*. New York, NY: World Health Organization and UNICEF.

2. Vorosmarty, C. J., McIntyre, P. B., Gessner, M. O., Dudgeon, D., Prusevich, A., Green, P., … Davies, P. M. (2010). Global threats to human water security and river biodiversity. *Nature, 467*, 555–561.

3. World Bank. (2007). *Cost of pollution in China: Economic estimates of physical damages*. Washington, DC: World Bank.

4. Falkenmark, M., & Molden, D. (2008). Wake up to realities of river basin closure. *Water Resources Development, 24*(2), 201–215.

5. The Worldwatch Institute. (2004). *State of the World 2004*. New York, NY: W. W. Norton.

6. Shiklomanov, I. A. (1993). World fresh water resources. In P. H. Gleick (Ed.), *Water in crisis: A guide to the world's fresh water resources* (Vol. 33, pp. 13–24). New York, NY: Oxford University Press.

7. Diamond, J. M. (2005). *Collapse: How societies choose to fail or succeed*. New York, NY: Penguin Books.

8. Kenny, J. F., Barber, N. L., Hutson, S. S., Linsey, K. S., Lovelace, J. K., & Maupin, M. A. (2009). *Estimated use of water in the United States in 2005* (p. 1344.). U.S. Geological Survey Circular.

9. Swift, B. L. (1984). Status of riparian ecosystems in the United States. *Journal of the American Water Resources Association, 20*, 223–228.

10. Milly, P. C., Betancourt, J., Falkenmark, M., Hirsh, R. M., Kundzewicz, Z. W., Lettenair, D. P., Stouffer, R. J. (2009). Climate change: Stationarity is dead: Whither water management? *Science, 319*(5863), 573–574.

11. Quay, R. (2010). Anticipatory governance—A tool for climate change adaptation. *Journal of the American Planning Association, 76*(4), 496–511.

# Chapter 6

1. Schoenauer, N. (2003). *6,000 Years of Housing, revised and expanded ed.* W. W. Norton & Company.

2. Conservation measures. Las Vegas Valley Water District. Retrieved from htpp://www.lvved.com/conservation/drought.html

# Chapter 7

1. Pisarski, A. E. (2006). *Commuting in America III, Transportation Research Board* (3rd ed.). Washington, DC: Transportation Research Board.

2. Pucher, J., & Dijkstra, L. (2000). Making walking and cycling safer: Lessons from Europe. *Transportation Quarterly, 54*(3), 25–50.

3. Delucchi, J., & McCubbin, D. (2010). External cost of transport in U.S. In A. de Palma, R. Lindsey, E. Quinet, & R. Vickerman (Ed.), *Handbook transport economics*, UK: Edward Elgar Publishing Ltd.

4. Ibid.

5. Ibid.

6. Oak Ridge National Laboratory. (2010).

7. United States Environmental Protection Agency (EPA). (2010). *Our Nation's Air-Status and Trends through 2008*. Research Triangle Park, NC: EPA.

8. United States Environmental Protection Agency (EPA). (2012). *Inventory of U.S. Greenhouse Gas Emissions and Sinks: 1990–2010*. EPA.

9. Freund, P. E. S., & Martin, G. T. (1993). *The Ecology of the Automobile* (p. 18). Montreal, QC: Black Rose Books.

10. Etkin, D. S. (2001). *Analysis of oil spill trends in the United States and worldwide*. Presentation at the International Oil Spill Conference, Tampa, Florida.

11. Ewing, R., Bartholomew, K., Winkelman, S., Walters, J., & Chen, D. (2010). *Growing cooler—the Evidence on Urban Development and Climate Change* (p. 7). Urban Land Institute.

12. Ibid.

13. Ibid, 12.

14. Ardila-Gomez, A. (2004). *Transit planning in curitiba and bogota: Roles in interaction, risk and change* (PhD Thesis). Massachusetts Institute of Technology.

15. Lublow, A. (2007). The road to curitiba. *The New York Times Magazine*. New York, NY: The New York Times.

16. Ewing, R., & Others. (2010). *Growing cooler—the evidence on development*. Urban Land Institute.

17. Mohl, R. A. (2004). Stop the road: Freeway revolts in American cities. *Journal of Urban History, 30*(5), 674–706.

18. Shaheen, S., Cohen, A., & Chung, M. (2009). North American carsharing: A ten-year retrospective. *Journal of the Transportation Research Board, 2110*, 35–44.

19. Ibid.

20. Cervero, R., Golub, A., & Nee, B. (2007). City carshare: Longer-term travel demand and car ownership impacts. *Journal of the Transportation Research Board*, 1992, 70–80. Transportation Research Record.

21. Golub, A., & Henderson, J. (2011). The greening of mobility in San Francisco. In M. Slavin (Ed.), *Sustainability in America's cities: Creating the green metropolis*. Washington, D.C.: Island Press.

22. San Francisco Municipal Transportation Agency (SFMTA). (2009). 2008 San Francisco State of Cycling Report, San Francisco, CA: San Francisco Bicycle Program, Department of Parking and Traffic, Municipal Transportation Agency.

23. United States Department of Transportation (USDOT). (2010). *The National Bicycling and Walking Study: 15-Year Status Report* (22). Washington, DC: USDOT.

24. Harry Wray, J. (2008). *Pedal power: The quiet rise of the bicycle in american public life*. Boulder, CO: Paradigm Publishers.

25. SFMTA, *San Francisco Cycling Report, 2009*, 22 and SFMTA, 2010 *San Francisco State of Cycling Report*, San Francisco: San Francisco Bicycle Program, Department of Parking and Traffic, Municipal Transportation Agency, 2010), 22.SFMTA. (2009). 22.

26. The name was inspired by Return of the Scorcher, an independent documentary film that included a narrative observing hundreds of cyclists bunching at an intersection in China and pushing their way into traffic. Bicyclists would wait until they had "critical mass" to push into the stream of cross-traffic, and the phrase was borrowed by local activists organizing the monthly ride.

27. Switzky, J. (2002). Riding to See. In C. Carlsson (Ed.), *Critical mass: Bicycling's defiant celebration* (pp. 186–192). Oakland, CA: AK Press.

28. Ardila-Gomez, A. Transit planning in Curitiba and Bogota. (PhD Thesis).

# Chapter 8

1. Intergovernmental Panel on Climate Change (IPCC). (2007d). Climate change 2007: Synthesis report. *Contribution of working groups 1, 2 and 3 to the fourth assessment report of the intergovernmental panel on climate change*. Cambridge, UK and New York, NY, USA: Cambridge University Press.

2. Barrie Pittock, A. (2009). *Climate change: The science, impacts and solutions*. London: Earthscan.

3. National Research Council (NRC). (2010). *Committee for the study on the relationships among development patterns, vehicle miles traveled, and energy consumption, advancing the science of climate change.* Washington, DC: The National Academic Press.

4. IPCC. (2007a). Climate change 2007: The physical science basis. *Contribution of working group 1 to the fourth assessment report of the intergovernmental panel on climate change.* Cambridge, UK and New York, NY, USA: Cambridge University Press.

5. IPCC. (2007d). Synthesis Report.

6. IPCC. (2007a). Physical Science Basis.

7. NASA Research Finds Last Decade was Warmest on Record, 2009 One of Warmest Years. National Aeronautics and Space Administration (NASA). Retrieved from www.nasa.gov.

8. IPCC. (2007a). Physical Science Basis.

9. Pittock, A. B. (2009). *Impacts and Solutions.* Collingwood, VIC, Australia: CSIRO Pub.

10. Ibid.

11. IPCC. (2007b). Adaptation and vulnerability. *Contribution of working group 2 to the fourth assessment report of the intergovernmental panel on climate change.* Cambridge, UK and New York, NY, USA: Cambridge University Press.

12. Ibid.

13. Ibid.

14. IPCC. (2007a). Physical Science Basis.

15. IPCC, "Adaptation and Vulnerability," 2007b.

16. IPCC. (2007c). Climate change 2007: Mitigation of climate change. *Contribution of working group 3 to the fourth assessment report of the intergovernmental panel on climate change.* Cambridge, UK and New York, NY, USA: Cambridge University Press.

17. IPCC. (2007d). Synthesis Report.

18. Stern, N. (2006). The economics of climate change: The stern review – executive summary. *Journal of Economic Literature, 7*(4).

19. IPCC. (2007a). Physical Science Basis.

20. Sallenger, A. H., Jr., Doran, K. S., & Howd, P. A. (2012). Hotspot of accelerated sea-level rise on the Atlantic coast of North America. *Nature Climate Change.* http://www.nature.com/nclimate/journal/vaop/ncurrent/full/nclimate1597.html

21. 2012 National Academy of Sciences (NAS). (2012). *Sea-level rise for the coasts of california, oregon, and washington: past, present, and future.* Washington, DC: The National Academy Press.

22. IPCC. (2007b). Adaptation and Vulnerability.

23. Quay, R. (2010). Anticipatory governance: A tool for climate change adaptation. *Journal of the American Planning Association, 76*(4).

24. Fuerth, L. S. (2009). Foresight and anticipatory governance. *Foresight, 11*(4), 29.

25. IPCC. (2007c). Mitigation of Climate Change.

26. National Research Council (NRC). (2009). *Committee for the Study on the Relationships Among Development Patterns, Vehicle Miles Traveled, and Energy Consumption, Driving and the Built Environment: The Effects of Compact Development on Motorized Travel, Energy Use, and $CO_2$ Emissions* (Special Report 298). The National Academies Press.

27. Millard-Ball, A. (2010). Where the action is. *Planning, 76*(7), 16–21.

28. City of Chicago. (2008).

29. Leiserowitz, A., Maibach, E., & Roser-Renouf, C. (2010). *Climate change in the American mind: Americans' global warming beliefs and attitudes in January 2010.* New Haven, CT: Yale University and Mason University.

30. Moser, S. C. (2006). Talk of the city: Engaging urbanities on climate change. *Environmental Research Letters, 1*(1), 1–10.

# Chapter 9

1. Census Bureau (website). (2010). www.census.gov

2. Davis, M. (2006). *Planet of slums*. London: Verso.

3. Landsberg, H. E. (1981). *The urban climate*. New York, NY: Academic Press.

4. Howard, L. (1833). *The Climate of London* (Vol. 1, No. 348, p. 3).

5. Oke, T. R. (1995). The heat island of the urban boundary layer: Characteristics, Causes and Effects. In *Wind climate in cities* (pp. 81–107). Dordrecht, The Netherlands: Kluwer Academic Publishers.

6. Brazel, A. J., Selover, N., Vose, R., & Heisler, G. (2000). The tale of two climates-Baltimore and Phoenix urban LTER sites. *Climate Research, 15*, 123–135.

7. Landsberg, H. E. (1981). *Urban Climate* (1st ed., Vol. 28). Academic Press.

8. Oke, T. R. (1982). The energetic basis of the urban heat island. *Quarterly Journal of the Royal Meteorological Society, 108, 1*–24.

9. Masson, V. (2006). Urban surface modeling and the meso-scale impact of cities. *Theoretical and Applied Climatology, 84*(1–3), 35–45. doi: 10.1007/s00704-005-0142-3.

10. Arnfield, A. J. (2003). Two decades of urban climate research: A review of turbulence, exchanges of energy and water, and the urban heat island. *International Journal of Climatology, 23*, 1–26.

11. Oke, T. R. (1973). City size and the urban heat island. *Atmospheric Environment, 7*, 769–779.

12. Roth, M. (2007). Review of urban climate research in (sub)tropical regions. *International Journal Climatology, 27*, 1859–1873.

13. Runnalls, K. E., & Oke, T. R. (2000). Dynamics and controls of the near-surface heat island of Vancouver, British Columbia. *Physical Geography, 21*(4), 283–304.

14. Kunkel, K. E., Pielke, R. A., Jr., & Changnon, S. A. (1999). Temporal fluctuations in weather and climate extremes that cause economic and human health impacts: A review. *American Meteorological Society, 80*, 1077–1098.

15. Rosenzweig, C., Solecki, W. D., Parshall, L., Chopping, M., Pope, G., & Goldberg, R. (2005). Characterizing the urban heat island in current and future climates in New Jersey. *Global Environmental Change Part B: Environmental Hazards, 6*(1), 51–62. doi: 10.1016/j.hazards.2004.12.001.

16. Centers for Disease Control and Prevention (CDC). (2006). Extreme heat: A prevention guide to promote your health and safety. CDC. Retrieved from http://www.bt.cdc.gov/disasters/extremeheat/heat_guide.asp

17. Kalkstein, A. J., & Sheridan, S. (2007). The social impacts of the heat–health watch/warning system in Phoenix, Arizona: Assessing the perceived risk and response of the public. *International Journal of Biometeorology, 52*, 43–55.

18. Semenza, J. C., McCullough, J. E., Flanders, W. D., McGeehin, M. A., & Lumpkin, J. R. (1999). Excess hospital admissions during the July 1995 heat wave in Chicago. *American Journal of Preventive Medicine, 16*, 269–277.

19. Semenza, J. C., Rubin, C. H., Falter, K. H., Selanikio, J. D., Flanders, W. D., Howe, H. L., & Wilhelm, J. L. (1996). Heat-related deaths during the July 1995 heat wave in Chicago. *American Journal of Preventive Medicine, 16*, 269–277.

20. Klinenberg, E. (2002). *Heat wave: A social autopsy of disaster in Chicago.* Chicago, IL: University of Chicago Press.

21. Larson, J. (2006). *Setting the record straight: more than 52,000 Europeans died from heat in summer 2003. Eco-Economy Update.* Washington, D.C: Earth Policy Institute. Retrieved from http://www.earth- policy.org/Updates/2006/Update56.htm

22. Golden, J. S., Brazel, A. J., Salmond, J., & Laws, D. (2006). Energy and water sustainability – The role of urban climate change from metropolitan infrastructure. *Journal of Green Building, 1*(3), 124–138.

23. Guhathakurta, S., & Gober, P. (2007). The impact of the Phoenix urban heat island on residential water use. *Journal of the American Planning Association, 73*, 317–329.

24. Wentz, E., & Gober, P. (2007). Determinants of small-area water consumption for the city of Phoenix, Arizona. *Water Resources Management, 21*, 1849–1863.

25. Gober, P. (2006). *Metropolitan Phoenix place making and community building in the Desert.* Philadelphia, PA: University of Pennsylvania Press.

26. Shashua-Bar, L., Pearlmutter, D., & Erell, E.(2009). The cooling efficiency of urban landscape strategies in a hot dry climate. *Landscape and Urban Planning, 92*, 179–186.

27. Hu, E., Yang, Y. P., Nishimura, A., Yilmaz, F., & Kouzani, A. (2010). Solar thermal aided power generation. *Applied Energy, 87*, 2881–2885.

28. Parmesan, C., Root, T. L., Willig, M. R. (2000). Impacts of extreme weather and climate on terrestrial biota. *Bulletin of American Meteorological Society; 81*, 443–450.

29. Besser, L. M., & Dannenberg, A. L. (2005). Walking to public transit: steps to help meet physical activity recommendations. *American Journal of Preventive Medicine, 29*, 273–280.

30. West, J. J., Fiore, A. M., Horowitz, L. W., & Mauzerall, D. L. (2006). Global health benefits of mitigating ozone pollution with methane emission controls. *Proceedings of the National Academy of Sciences, 103*, 3988–3993.

31. Nurse, J., Basher, D., Bone, A., & Bird, W. (2010). An ecological approach to promoting population mental health and well-being – a response to the challenge of climate change. *Prospectives in Public Health, 130*, 27–33.

# Chapter 10

1. Food Agriculture Organization (FAO). (2006). Food security: Policy brief, Food and Agriculture Organization of the United Nations no. 2. ftp://ftp.fao.org/es/ESA/policybriefs/pb_02.pdf

2. Food Agricultural Conservation and Trade Act of 1990, no. 101-624,104 Stat. 3359. 28 November 1990.

3. Miller, T. G. (2007). *Living in the environment* (15th ed.). Belmont, CA: Thomson Learning.

4. Conway, G. (1998). *The doubly green revolution: Food for all in the 21st century*. Ithaca, NY: Cornell University Press.

5. Grey, M. A. (2000). The industrial food stream and its alternatives in the United States: An introduction. in *Human Organization, 59*(2), 143–150.

6. Conway, G. 1997. *The doubly green revolution: Food for all in the twenty-first century.* Ithaca, NY: Comstock Publishing Associates.

7. Hoppe, R., MacDonald, J., & Korb, P. (2010). Small farms in the United States; persistence under pressure. United States Department of agriculture, Economic Research Service. Retrieved from http://www.ers.usda.gov/publications/eib63/

8. Pimentel, D., & Pimentel, M. (2003). Sustainability of meat-based and plant-based diets and the environment. *American Journal of Clinical Nutrition, 78*, 660–663.

9. Pirog, R., & Benjamin, A. (2003). Checking the food odometer: Comparing food miles for local versus conventional produce sales to Iowa institutions. Leopold Center for Sustainable Agriculture. Retrieved from http://www.leopold.iastate.edu/pubs/staff/files/food_travel072103.pdf.

10. Heller, M. C., & Keolian, G. A. (2003). Assessing the sustainability of the US food system: A life cycle perspective. *Agricultural Systems, 76*, 1007–1041.

11. McMichael, A., Powles, J., Butler, C., & Uauy, R. (2007). Food, livestock production, energy, climate change, and health. *The Lancet, 370*, 1253–1263.

12. Postel, S. (2000). Entering an era of water scarcity: The challenges ahead. *Ecological Applications, 10*(4), 941–948.

13. Canfield, D. E., Glazer, A. N., & Falkowski, P. G. (2010). The evolution and future of earth's nitrogen cycle. *Science, 330*, 192–196.

14. Pretty, J. (2008). Agricultural sustainability: Concepts, principles and evidence. *Philosophical transactions of the Royal Society, 363*, 447–465.

15. Nord, M., Andrews, M., & Carlson, S. (2009). *Household food security in the United States 2008*. United States Department of Agriculture, Economic Research Service, Economic Research Report no. 83.

16. Pretty, J. Agricultural sustainability.

17. Nord, M., Andrews, M., & Carlson, S. (2003). Household food security in the United States, 2003. Food Assistance and Nutrition Research Report No. 42.

18. Barrett, C. B. (2010). Measuring food insecurity. *Science, 327*(5967), 825–828.

19. Ploeg, M. V., Breneman, V., Farrigan, T., Hamrick, K., Hopkins, D., Kaufman, P., … E. Tuckermanty. (2009). Access to affordable and nutritious food: Measuring and understanding food deserts and their consequences. *Economic Research Service*. Retrieved from http://www.ers.usda.gov/Publications/AP/AP036/AP036.pdf

20. Powell, L. M., Slater, S., Mirtcheva, D., Bao, Y., & Chaloupka, F. (2007). Food store availability and neighborhood characteristics in the United States. *Preventive Medicine, 44*, 189–195.

21. Glanz, K., Sallis, J. F., Salens, B. E., & Frank, L. D. (2007). Nutrition environment measures survey in stores (NEMS-S): Development and evaluation. *American Journal of Preventative Medicine, 32*(4), 282–289.

22. Larson, N. I., Story, M. T., & Nelson, M. C. (2009). Neighborhood environments: Disparities in access to healthy foods in the U.S. *American Journal of Preventative Medicine, 36*(1), 74–81.

23. Peters, C. J., Bills, N. L., Wilkins, J. L., & Fick, G. (2008). Foodshed analysis and its relevance to sustainability. *Renewable Agriculture and Food Systems*, 1–7.

24. Dubbeling (2009).

25. Heckman, J. (2006). A history of organic farming: Transitions from Sir Albert Howard's to war in the soil to USDA national organic program. *Renewable Agriculture and Food Systems, 21*(3), 143–150.

26. National Organic Program (NOP). *National organic program: Background information*. United States Department of Agriculture, NOP, 2008. Retrieved from http://www.ams.usda.gov/AMSv1.0/getfile?dDocName=STELDEV3004443

27. Economic Research Service (ERS). 2008. U.S. certified organic farmland acreage, livestock numbers, and farm operations. *Economic Research Service*.

28. Trevwas, A. (2001). Urban myths of organic farming: Organic agriculture began as an ideology, but can it meet today's needs? *Nature, 410*, 409–410.

29. Hole, D. G., Perkins, A. J., Wilson, J. D., Alexander, I. H., Price, G. V., & Evans, A. D. (2005). Does organic farming benefit biodiversity? *Biological Conservation, 122*, 113–130.

30. Pimentel, D., Hepperly, P., Hanson, J., Douds, D., & Seidel, R. (2005). Environmental, energetic, and economic comparisons of organic and conventional farming systems. *BioScience, 55*(7), 573–582.

31. Heller, M. C., & Keolian, G. A. (2003). Assessing the sustainability of the US food system: a life cycle perspective. *Agricultural Systems, 76*, 1007–1041.

32. Pimentel, D., & Pimentel, M. (2003). Sustainability of meat-based and plant-based diets and the environment. *American Journal of Clinical Nutrition, 78*, 660–663.

33. Topp, C. F. E., Stockdale, E. A., Watson, C. A., & Rees, R. M. (2007). Estimating resource use efficiencies in organic agriculture: A review of budgeting approaches used. *Journal of the Science of Food and Agriculture, 87*, 2782–2790.

34. Williams, C. M. (2002). Nutritional quality of organic food: Shades of grey or shades of green? *Proceedings of the Nutrition Society, 61*, 19–24.

35. Hoefkens, C. (2009). A literature-based comparison of nutrient content and contaminant contents between organic and conventional vegetables and potatoes. *British Food Journal, 111* (10), 1078–1097.

36. Miller, T. G. (2007). *Living in the environment* (15th ed.). Belmont, CA: Thomson Learning.

37. Pimentel, D., et al. (2005). Environmental comparisons. *BioScience, 55*(7).

38. Kirchmann, H., Bergstrom, L., Katterer, T., Andren, O., & Andersson, R. (Springer, 2008). Can organic crop production feed the world? In H. Kirchmann, & L. Bergstrom (Eds.), *Organic crop production – Ambitions and limitations*.

39. Pimentel, D., et al. (2005). Environmental comparisons. *BioScience, 55*(7).

40. Oberholzter, L., Dimitri, C., & Greene, C. (2005). Price premiums hold on as U.S. organic produce market expands. United States Department of Agriculture. Retrieved from http://www.ers.usda.gov/publications/vgs/may05/vgs30801/vgs30801.pdf

41. Lin, B. H., Smith, T. A., & Huang, C. L. (2008). Organic premiums of US fresh produce. *Renewable Agriculture and Food Systems, 23*(3), 208–216.

42. Kirchmann, H., & Others. Price premiums.

43. Connor, D. J. (2008). Organic agriculture cannot feed the world. *Field Crops Research, 106*, 187–190.

44. Dimitri, C., & Oberholtzer, L. (2009). Marketing U.S. organic foods: Recent trends from farms to consumers. *Economic Research Service*. Retrieved from http://www.ers.usda.gov/publications/eib58/eib58.pdf

45. Ibid.

46. Heimlich, R. E., & Anderson, W. D. (2001). *Development at the urban fringe and beyond: Impacts on agriculture and rural land.* United States Department of Agriculture: Economic Research Service, Agricultural Economic Report no. 803. Retrieved from http://www.ers.usda.gov/publications/aer803/aer803.pdf

47. Hoppe, R., MacDonald, J., & Korb, P. Small farms. *Economic Information Bulletin, 63*.

48. Martinez, S., Hand, M., De Pra, M., Pollack, S., Ralston, K., Smith, T., … Newman, C. (2010). *Local food systems: Concepts, impacts and issues.* United States Department of Agriculture, Economic Research Service Report 97.

Retrieved from http://www.ers.usda.gov/publications/err-economic-research-report/err97.aspx

49. Taylor, C., & Aggarwal, R. (2010). Motivations and barriers to stakeholder participation in local food value chains in Phoenix, Arizona. *Urban Agriculture Magazine, 24*, 46–48.

50. Martinez, S. et al. (2010, May). Local food. Economic Research Report Number 97.

51. Hand, M. S., & Martinez, S. (2010). Just what does local mean? *Choices: The Magazine of Food, Farm and Resource Issues, 25*(1).

52. Feagan, R., & Morris, D. (2009). Consumer quest for embeddedness: A case study of Brantford Farmer' Market. *International Journal of Consumer Studies, 33*(3).

53. Goland, C. (2002). Community supported agriculture, food consumption patterns, and member commitment. *Culture & Agriculture, 24*(1), 14–25.

54. Hunt, A. R. (2007). Consumer interactions and influences on farmers' market vendors. *Renewable Agriculture and Food Systems, 22*(1), 54–66.

55. Wolf, M. M., Spittler, A., & Ahern, J. (2005). A profile of farmers' market consumers and the perceived advantages of produce sold at farmers' markets. *Journal of Food Distribution Research, 36*(1), 192–201.

56. United States Department of Agriculture (USDA). (2009). 2007 Census of agriculture: United States summary and state data. *The Geographic Area Series*, vols. 1 part 51. Retrieved from http://www.agcensus.usda.gov/Publications/2007/Full_Report/usv1.pdf

57. Griffin, M. R., & Frongillo, E. A. (2003). Experiences of farmers from Upstate New York farmers' markets. *Agriculture and Human Values, 20*, 189–203.

58. Jarosz, L. (2008). The city in the country: Growing alternative food networks in Metropolitan areas. *The Journal of Rural Studies, 24*, 231–244.

59. Barney and Worth (2008). page 12.

60. Henneberry, S. R., & Agustini, H. N. (2004, 18 February). *An analysis of Oklahoma direct marketing outlets: Case study of produce farmers' markets.* Selected Paper prepared for presentation at the Southern Agricultural Economics Association Annual, Tulsa, Oklahoma.

61. Bryld, E. (2003). Potentials, problems, and policy implications for urban agriculture in developing countries. *Agriculture and Human Values, 20*, 79–86.

62. Cofie, O., van Veenhuizen, R., & Drechsel, P. (2003, March 17). Contribution of urban and peri-urban agriculture to food security in sub-saharan Africa. Presented at the Africa session of 3rd World Wildlife (WWF), Kyoto.

63. Born, B., & Purcell, M. (2006). Avoiding the local trap: Scale and food systems in planning research. *Journal of Planning Education and Research, 26*, 195–207.

64. Kneafsey, M. (2010). The region in food – important or irrelevant? *Cambridge Journal of Regions, Economy and Society, 3*(2), 1–14.

65. Winter, M. (2003). Embeddedness, the new food economy and defensive localism. *Journal of Rural Studies, 19*, 23–32.

66. Hill, H. (2008). Food miles: Background and marketing. ATTRA – National Sustainable Agriculture Information Service. Retrieved from https://attra.ncat.org/attra-pub/PDF/foodmiles.pdf

67. Heller, M. C., & Keolian, G. A. (2003). Assessing the sustainability of the US food system: A life cycle perspective. *Agricultural Systems, 76*, 1007–1041.

68. Mariola, M. (2008). The local industrial complex? Questioning the link between local foods and energy use. *Agriculture and Human Values, 25*, 193–196.

69. Edwards-Jones, G., Mila I Canals, L., Hounsome, N., Truninger, M., Koerber, G., Hounsome, B., … Jones, D. L. (2008). Testing the assertion that 'local food is best': The challenges of an evidence-based approach. *Trends in Food Science and Technology, 19*, 265–274.

70. Lyso, T., & Guptill, A. (2004). Commodity agriculture, civic agriculture and the future of U.S. farming. *Rural Sociology, 69*(3), 370–385.

71. Milestad, R., Westberg, L., Geber, U., & Björklund, J. (2010). Enhancing adaptive capacity in food systems: Learning at farmers' markets in Sweden. *Ecology and Society, 15*(3).

72. Hinrichs, C. C., Gillespie, G. W., & Feenstra, G. W. (2004). Social learning and innovation at retail farmers' markets. *Rural Sociology, 69*(1), 31–58.

73. Allen, P., Guthman, J., & Morris, A. (2006). Research brief #9: Meeting farm and food security needs through community supported agriculture and farmers' markets in California. *Center for Agroecology and Sustainable Food Systems*.

74. Guthman, J. (2008). Bringing good food to others: Investigating the subjects of alternative food practice. *Cultural Geographies, 15*, 431–447.

75. FAO. Food security.

76. Barrett, C. B. (2010). Measuring food insecurity. *Science, 327*(5967), 825–828.

77. Arnould, E. J., & Thompson, C. J. (2005). Consumer culture theory (CCT): Twenty years of research. *Journal of Consumer Research, 31*(4), 868–882.

78. Conner, D. S., Colesanti, K. J. A., & Smalley, S. B. (2010). Understanding barriers to farmers' market patronage in Michigan: Perspectives from marginalized populations. *Journal of Hunger and Environmental Nutrition, 5*, 316–338.

79. Grace, C., Grace, T., Becker, N., & Lyden, J. (2007). Barriers to using urban farmers' markets: An investigation of food stamp clients' perceptions. In *Journal of Hunger & Environmental Nutrition, 2*(1), 55–75.

80. Dale, V. H., & Polansky, S. (2007). Measures of the effects of agricultural practices on ecosystem services. *Ecological Economics, 64*, 286–296.

81. Swinton, S. M., Lupi, F., Robertson, G. P., & Hamilton, S. (2007). Ecosystem services and agriculture: Cultivating agricultural ecosystems for diverse benefits. In *Ecological Economics, 64*, 245–252.

82. Deelstra, T., & Girardet, H. (2000). Urban agriculture and sustainable cities. *Growing Cities, Growing Food*, Retrieved from http://www.trabajopopular.org.ar/material/Theme2.pdf

83. Ibid.

84. Cordell, D., Drangert, J.-O., & White, S. (2009). The story of phosphorus: Global food security and food for thought. *Global Environmental Change, 19,* 292–305.

85. United Nations Environment Progamme (UNEP). (2011). Phosphorus and food production. *UNEP Yearbook 2011,* 35–45. http://www.unep.org/yearbook/2011/pdfs/phosphorus_and_food_productioin.pdf

86. Eaton, R. L., Hammond, G. P., & Laurie, J. (2007). Footprints on the landscape: An environmental appraisal of rural and urban living in the developed world. *Landscape and Urban Planning, 83,* 13–28.

87. Bryld, E. (2003). *Agriculture in developing countries. Agriculture and Human Values, 20*(1), 79-86(8).

88. Cordell, D., Drangert, J.-O., & White, S. (2009, May). The story of phosphorus. *Global Environmental Change, 19*(2), 292–305.Traditional Peoples and Climate Change.

89. Deelstra, T., & Girardet, H. Urban Agriculture.

90. Colding, J. (2007). Ecological land-use complementation for building resilience in urban ecosystems. *Landscape and Urban Planning, 81,* 46–55.

91. Ricketts, T., & Imhoff, M. (2003). Biodiversity, urban areas and agriculture: Locating priority ecoregions for conservation. *Conservation Ecology, 8*(2).

92. Colding, J. Ecological land-use.

93. Bryld, E. Agriculture in developing countries.

94. Ministry of Agriculture Botswana (website). (2006). Retrieved from http://www.moa.gov.bw/?nav=.

95. Bengston et al. (2004). *Landscape and Urban Planning, 69,* 271–286.

96. American Farmland Trust. (1997).

97. Bengston et al. (2004). *Landscape and Urban Planning, 69,* 271–286.

# Chapter 11

1. Alberti, M. (2005). The effects of urban patterns on ecosystem function. *The International Regional Science Review, 28*(2), 169.

2. Forman, R. T. T., & Godron, M. (1986). *Landscape ecology* (p. 619). New York, NY: Wiley.

3. Forman, R. T. T. (1995). *Land mosaics* (p. 499). Boston, MA: Cambridge University Press.

4. Ibid.

5. Noss, R. F. (2004). Can urban areas have ecological integrity? In *Proceedings 4th International Urban Wildlife Symposium.*

6. Tischendorf, L., & Fahrig, L. (2000). On the usage and measurement of landscape connectivity. *Oikos, 90,* 7–19.

7. Soulé, M. E. (1991). *Science New Series, 253*(5021), 744–750.

8.  Walker, B. H., & Salt, D. (2006). *Resilience thinking: Sustaining ecosystems and people in a changing world*. Washington, DC: Island Press.

9.  Van der Ryn, S., & Cowan, S. (1996). *Ecological design*. Washington, DC: Island Press.

10. Walker, B. H., & Salt, D. (2006, August 22) *Resilience thinking*. Washington, DC: Island Press.

11. Cook, E. A., & Van Lier, H. N., (Eds.). (1994). Landscape planning and ecological networks. (p. 354). Amsterdam, The Netherlands: Elsevier.

12. Jongman, R., & Pungetti, G. (Eds.). (2004). *Ecological networks and greenways: Concept, design, implementation* (p. 345). Cambridge: Cambridge University Press.

13. Benedict, M. A., & McMahon, E. T. (2006). *Green infrastructure*. Washington, DC: Island Press.

14. Hellmund, P., & Smith, D. (2006). *Designing greenways: Sustainable landscapes for nature and people*. Washington,DC: Island Press.

15. Smith, D., & Hellmund, P. (Eds.). (1993). *Ecology of greenways: Design and function of linear conservation areas*. Minneapolis, MN: University of Minnesota Press.

16. Werquin, A. C., Duhem, B., Lindholm, G., Oppermann, B., Pauleit, S., & Tjallingii, S. (Eds.). (2005). *Green structure and urban planning: Final report*. Brussels: European Commission.

17. Asbirk, S., & Jensen, S. (1984). An example of applied island theory and dispersal biology. In P. Agger & V. Nielson (Eds.), *Dispersal ecology* (pp. 49–54). Copenhagen: Naturfredningstradet of Fredningsstrylsen.

18. Daily, G. C. (Ed.). (1997). *Nature's services: Societal dependence on natural ecosystems*. Washington DC: Island press.

19. Odefy, J., Detwiler, S., Rousseau, K., Trice, A., Blackwell, R., O'Hara, K., Buckley, M., Souhlas, T., Brown, S., & Raviprakash, P. (2012). *Banking on green*.

20. Cook, (2007).

21. Bowler, D. E., Buyung-Ali, L., Knight, T., & Pullin, A. S. (2010). Urban greening to cool towns and cities: A systematic review of empirical evidence. *Landscape and Urban Planning, 97*, 147–155.

22. Gregory McPherson, E. (1992). Accounting for benefits and costs of urban green space. *Landscape and Urban Planning, 22*(1), 41–51.

23. Love (2010).

24. *Yellowstone to Yukon: Conservation initiative annual report*. (2008). Bozeman, MT.

25. Schultz, F. (Ed.). (2005). *Yellowstone to yukon: Freedom to roam*. Seattle, WA: Mountaineers books.

26. Jongman, R., Bouwma, I., Griffioen, A., Jones-Walters, L., & Doorn, A. M. (2011). The pan European ecological network: PEEN. *Landscape Ecology, 26*(3), 311–326.

27. Miller, K., Chang, E., & Johnson, N. (2001). *Defining common ground for the mesoamerican biological corridor*. World Resources Institute.

28. Carr, M. H., Lambert, D. J., & Zwick, P. D. (1994). Mapping of biological corridor potential in Central America: Final Report. *Conservation Corridors in the Central American Region*, Regional Conference by Paseo Pantera Project (Florida: University of Florida).

29. Ewing, J. (2005). The mesoamerican biological corridor: A bridge across the Americas. *Ecoworld*. Retrieved from www.ecoworld.com/home/articles2.cfm?tid=377.

30. Ibid.

31. Ibid.

32. Pagano, M., & Bowman, A. (2000). *Terra incognita: Vacant land and urban strategies*. The Brooking Institute Survey Series.

33. Suresh, B., & Ravishankar, G. (2004). Phytoremediation – a novel and promising approach for environmental cleanup. *Critical Reviews of Biotechnology, 24*(2–3), 97–124.

34. Diaz, E. (Ed.). (2008). *Microbial biodegradation: Genomics and molecular biology*. Caister: Academic Press.

35. Huling, S., & Pivetz, B. (2006). *In-situ chemical oxidation*. Engineering Issue of EPA.

36. Margolis, L., & Robinson, A. (2007). *Living systems*. Basel: Birkhauser.

37. Botequilha, L., Miller, J., Ahern, J., & McGarigal, K. (2006). *Measuring landscapes* (p. 118). Washington, DC: Island Press.

38. Cook, E. A. (2002). Landscape structure indices for assessing urban ecological networks. *Landscape and Urban Planning, 58*, 269–280.

39. McGarigal, K., & Marks, B. J. (1995). *FRAGSTATS: Spatial pattern analysis program for quantifying landscape structure*, (122). Gen. Tech. Rep. PNW-GTR-351 (Portland, OR: US Department of Agriculture, Forest Service).

40. Dramstadt, W. E., Olson, J. D., & Forman, R. T. T. (1996). *Landscape ecology principles in landscape architecture and land use planning* Boston, MA: Island Press.

# Chapter 12

1. Lowry, I. S. (1964). *A model of metropolis*. Santa Monica, CA: Rand Corporation.

2. Goldner, W. (1971). The lowry model heritage. *Journal of the American Institute of Planners, 37*(2), 100–110.

3. Guhathakurta, S. (1999). Urban modeling and contemporary planning theory: Is there a common ground? *Journal of Planning Education and Research, 18*(4), 281.

4. Wegener, M. (1994). Operational urban models state of the art. *Journal of the American Planning Association, 60*(1), 17–29.

5. Asgary, A., Klosterman, R., & Razani, A. (2007). Sustainable urban growth management using What-if? *The International Journal of Environmental Research, 1*(3), 218–230.

6. Klosterman, R. E. (2008). A new tool for a new planning: The What if?™ planning support system. In R. K. Brail (Ed.), *Planning support systems for cities and regions* (pp. 85–99). Cambridge, MA: Lincoln Institute of Land Policy.

7. Landis, J. D. (1994). The California urban futures model: A new generation of metropolitan simulation models. *Environment and Planning B, 21*, 399–399.

8. Landis, J. D. (1995). Imagining land use futures: Applying the California urban futures model. *Journal of the American Planning Association, 61*(4), 438–457.

9. Landis, J. D., & Zhang, M. (1998). The second generation of the California urban futures model. Part 2: Specification and calibration results of the land-use change submodel. *The Environment and Planning B, 25*, 795–824.

10. Waddell, P. (2002). UrbanSim: Modeling urban development for land use, transportation, and environmental planning. *Journal of the American Planning Association, 68*(3). http://lab.geog.ntu.edu.tw/lab/errml/%E5%A4%A7%E5%B0%88%E9%A1%8C/03021%E5%8E%9F%E6%96%87.pdf

11. Waddell, P. (2000). A behavioral simulation model for metropolitan policy analysis and planning: Residential location and housing market components of UrbanSim. *Environment and Planning B, 27*(2), 247–264.

12. Haase, D., & Schwarz, N. (2009). Simulation models on human—Nature interactions in urban landscapes: A review including spatial economics, system dynamics, cellular automata and agent-based approaches. *Living Reviews in Landscape Research, 3*(2), 1–45.

13. Wegener, M. (2004). Overview of land use transport models. *Handbook of transport geography and spatial systems, 5*, 127–146.

14. USDOE. (2011).

# CONTRIBUTOR BIOGRAPHIES

## Rimjhim Aggarwal

Dr. Aggarwal is Assistant Professor at Arizona State University's School of Sustainability and a Senior Sustainability Scientist in the Global Institute of Sustainability. Dr. Aggarwal's research explores global dimensions of sustainability such as the links between globalization, local ecosystems, and poverty in less-developed countries. She has conducted extensive fieldwork on groundwater-irrigation institutions in India; her recent research examines the emerging tradeoffs between water availability and the growing demands of agriculture in dry-land regions of the world.

## Anthony Brazel

Dr. Brazel is Professor Emeritus at Arizona State University's School of Geographical Sciences and Urban Planning and is a Senior Sustainability Scientist in the Global Institute of Sustainability. His areas of expertise include physical geography and climatology with applications to urban environments, and he is a coauthor of Environmental Sciences: A Student's Companion. He was the Director of the Southwest Center for Environmental Research & Policy (which is supported by the U.S. EPA). He has authored numerous articles on mitigating the urban heat island effect, urban climatology, and vulnerability to climate change.

## Winston Chow

Winston Chow is a post-doctoral research fellow affiliated with the Department of Engineering at Arizona State University, as well as at the Department of Geography at the National University of Singapore. His areas of published research expertise include investigating the urban heat island and in applying sustainable concepts in urban climatology, which include investigating methods and techniques in minimizing detrimental impacts of the heat island in cities. Apart from being the news editor of Urban Climate News, the quarterly magazine of the International Association for Urban Climate, Dr. Chow has also taught lower- and upper-level undergraduate courses on geography and meteorology, which include courses examining sustainability at the human-environment interface.

## Edward Cook

Dr. Edward A. Cook is a Landscape Architecture faculty member in The Design School at Arizona State University where he teaches courses on urban ecological design, landscapes and sustainability, and landscape ecological planning. He has published books and articles focused on his research in urban ecology, green/ecological networks, and sustainable urbanism. He has worked on projects on landscape ecological planning throughout the world, and he was one of the pioneers in developing planning and design strategies for ecological networks in urban landscapes. He has a PhD from Wageningen University in the Netherlands, a Master of Landscape

Architecture degree from Utah State University, and a Bachelor of Science in Landscape Architecture from Washington State University.

## Aaron Golub

Dr. Golub is an Assistant Professor at Arizona State University's School of Geographical Sciences and Urban Planning, as well as the School of Sustainability. Dr. Golub's research and teaching interests fall into three areas: 1. The effects on social equity of current transportation planning practices. This work looks at the distributional impacts of policies like transit fare changes, road pricing, gas price changes, and public transit regulatory policies, while also making normative arguments about the desired outcomes of planning practices. Related work explores the contribution of theories of justice to the emerging field of sustainability science. 2. Planning, policy, and activism in support of alternatives to the automobile. This work includes interests in bus planning, bus rapid transit implementations, car-sharing, cycling, and community-based transit systems in the developing world. 3. The historical roots of automobile dependence in the United States. This work explores the specific planning and policy mechanisms underlying the Fordist (mass production/consumption) demand management process resulting in nationally standardized planning methods, cultural changes, and federal policies in support of automobile consumption and use.

## Subhrajit Guhathakurta

Dr. Guhathakurta joined Georgia Institute of Technology in 2011 as the Director of the Center for Geographic Information Systems and Professor in the School of City and Regional Planning. He was previously Associate Director of the School of Geographical Sciences and Urban Planning at Arizona State University (ASU) and among the founding faculty members of ASU's School of Sustainability. Professor Guhathakurta was instrumental in developing the Urban Modeling and Simulation Lab in ASU's College of Design. He also served as the lead member of several research centers at ASU including the GeoDa Center for Geospatial Analysis and Computation, Decision Center for a Desert City, and the project on Sustainable Urban Systems, Technologies, and Infrastructure (SUSTaIn). He is an author of five books and monographs and over 70 scientific papers. His article on the interface between urban modeling and planning theory was awarded the Chester Rapkin Award for the best paper (1999) in Journal of Planning Education and Research. His editorial contributions include books such as "Integrated Urban and Environmental Models: A Survey of Current Applications and Research" (Springer-Verlag, 2003) and "Visualizing Sustainable Planning" (Springer, 2009). He has held visiting appointments at the Center for Urban Spatial Analysis at University College London, the Indian Institute of Information Technology, Bangalore, and at the Center for Sustainable Urban and Regional Futures at the University of Queensland in Brisbane. More recently, he held the German National Science Foundation (DFG) Mercator Guestprofessorship at Technische Universitat Kaiserslautern, Germany.

## Bjoern Hagen

Bjoern Hagen is a Ph.D. candidate in Environmental Design and Planning at Arizona State University. He received his Master's degree in urban planning from the Technical University Kaiserslautern, Germany, focusing on sustainable urban and transportation planning in low-density environments. He has worked on projects focusing on sustainable urban and regional development with the Development Agency of Rhineland Palatinate (Entwicklungsagentur Rheinland-Pfalz e.V) and the redesign of the UNESCO (United Nations Educational, Scientific, and Cultural Organization) World Heritage site Völklingen Ironworks towards a sustainable future. For the past three years, he has conducted research in the areas of climate change mitigation and adaptation, public risk perception, and risk communication. By studying the nature of public perceptions of global climate change in different countries and over time, his research contributes to improving climate change communication efforts to reduce greenhouse gas emissions and to increase the adaptive capacity and resiliency of urban environments.

## John Meunier

John Meunier came to Arizona State University in 1987 to be Dean of the College of Architecture and Environmental Design, a position he held until 2002 when he returned to the faculty as a Professor of Architecture. Previously, he was Director of the School of Architecture and Interior Design at the University of Cincinnati. He started teaching architecture at Cambridge University in England where he was on the faculty from 1962 to 1976 and was Acting Head from 1973 to 1974. During his career, Professor Meunier has been a Visiting Critic and Lecturer at many schools of architecture, but has spent extended periods as a visitor at McGill, Harvard, Yale, San Luis Obispo, and Charlotte, North Carolina. He is a registered architect in West Germany and Britain and has received reciprocal certification in the United States from the National Council of Architectural Registration Boards. He is a registered architect in the State of Arizona and a member of the AIA. From 2005 to 2006, he was Interim Director of the School of Architecture at Clemson University while on leave from ASU.

At the end of his deanship at ASU, he began the research phase of a project intended to produce a television series for KAET and National Public Television called "Desert Cities: Surviving the 21st Century." This has involved travel to desert cities in many parts of the world, including Iran, Morocco, Tunisia, India, Egypt, Yemen, Australia, Chile, and Peru. The thesis of the series is that there are important lessons to be learned from visiting pre-industrial desert cities that are relevant to the challenge of sustainability as we contemplate the future of rapidly growing desert cities of today.

## Ray Quay

Dr. Quay has been associated with the Decision Center for a Desert City project at Arizona State University since 2004 as a stakeholder, advisor, and researcher. In his former position as an Assistant Director of the Water Services Department for the City of Phoenix, Quay was involved with DCDC in stakeholder outreach, water demand and heat island research, and in the application of climate change science and research to public adaptation policy and programs. Dr. Quay joined the DCDC project in 2010 as an academic professional. His involvement now includes expanding the capabilities and facilitating the use of WaterSIM as a research and public policy tool, expanding

DCDC's stakeholder outreach with water managers and land use planners, facilitating the initiation and development of academic research that is applicable to current and future public policy issues, and participating directly in various DCDC supported research. Quay's research interests include advanced scenario planning, anticipatory governance, climate change impacts and adaptation, water demand analysis and models, regional growth, and visualization of sustainability and uncertainty.

## Charles Redman

Dr. Charles Redman has been committed to interdisciplinary research since, as an archaeology graduate student, he worked closely in the field with botanists, zoologists, geologists, art historians, and ethnographers. Redman received his BA from Harvard University, and his MA and PhD in Anthropology from the University of Chicago. He taught at New York University and at SUNY-Binghamton before coming to Arizona State University in 1983. Since then, he served nine years as Chair of the Department of Anthropology, seven years as Director of the Center for Environmental Studies and, in 2004, was chosen to be the Julie Ann Wrigley Director of the newly formed Global Institute of Sustainability. From 2007–2010, Redman was the founding director of ASU's School of Sustainability. Redman's interests include human impacts on the environment, sustainable landscapes, rapidly urbanizing regions, urban ecology, environmental education, and public outreach. He is the author or co-author of 14 books, including *Explanation in Archaeology*, *The Rise of Civilization*, *People of the Tonto Rim*, *Human Impact on Ancient Environments* and, most recently, co-edited four books: *The Archaeology of Global Change*, *Applied Remote Sensing for Urban Planning, Governance and Sustainability*, *Agrarian Landscapes in Transition*, and *Polities and Power: Archaeological Perspectives on the Landscapes of Early States*. Redman is currently working on building upon the extensive research portfolio of the Global Institute of Sustainability and teaching in the School of Sustainability, which is educating a new generation of leaders through collaborative learning, trans-disciplinary approaches, and problem-oriented training to address the environmental, economic, and social challenges of the twenty-first century.

## Darren Ruddell

Dr. Darren Ruddell is a Lecturer for the Spatial Sciences Institute at the University of Southern California where he teaches Geographic Information Science (GIS) courses as part of an advanced online GIS program. Dr. Ruddell earned his Ph.D. in 2009 from the School of Geographical Sciences and Urban Planning at Arizona State University. The title of his dissertation was: "Scale and Scientific inquiry: An Investigation of Theoretical, Methodological, and Practical Applications." Ruddell served as a post-doctoral researcher from June 2009 to June 2011 where he utilized geospatial technologies to investigate issues of urban sustainability and resiliency. Ruddell's work focuses on Phoenix, AZ where he studies physical and social dimensions of climate change at the regional and sub-regional scales of analysis. Ruddell also served as a Faculty Associate for the School of Sustainability where he co-taught Sustainable Cities in the 2010-2011 academic school year.

# Carissa Taylor

Carissa Taylor is a Ph.D. Student at Arizona State University's School of Sustainability. She received her master's degree from the School of Sustainability in 2009. She co-authored an article with Dr. Aggarwal in 2010, "Motivations and barriers to stakeholder participation in local food value changes in Phoenix, Arizona" in *Urban Horticulture Magazine*.